Research in Principles of Life

Advanced Seminar

TEXTBOOK

Instructor: BILL GOTHARD

Advanced Seminar

TEXTBOOK — WORKBOOK

This book belongs to

B & P DAKE

Character Curriculum Series®

"And they that shall be of thee shall build the old waste places: thou shalt raise up the foundations of many generations; and thou shalt be called, The repairer of the breach, The restorer of paths to dwell in" (Isaiah 58:12).

Advanced Seminar

Ewing Galloway

8 HOW TO APPLY PRINCIPLES TO FRIENDSHIP AND ENGAGEMENT

9 HOW TO PREPARE FOR GOD'S PURPOSE IN MARRIAGE

Ewing Galloway

10 HOW TO BUILD THE SPIRIT OF THE MARRIAGE

11 HOW TO PREPARE FOR EFFECTIVE SPIRITUAL WARFARE

Dover

12 HOW TO TEACH SONS AND DAUGHTERS TO "STAND ALONE"

13 HOW TO APPLY PRINCIPLES OF DISCIPLINE

14 HOW TO CARRY OUT SUCCESSFUL EDUCATION

©Providence Lithograph

15 HOW TO TRANSFORM CRITICISM

NON-OPTIONAL
PRINCIPLES OF LIFE

BASIC LIFE PRINCIPLES	DEFINITIONS
1 DESIGN	God has precise purposes for each person, object, and relationship which He established. Only as we understand and follow these will we find our identity and fulfillment in life.
2 RESPONSIBILITY	God holds us personally responsible for every one of our words, thoughts, actions, attitudes, and motives. Therefore, whenever we sin, there must be confession and proper restitution.
3 AUTHORITY	God has established a structure of authority and a balance of power. He has also ordained that with proper attitudes and wise appeals, those under authority can have far-reaching influence.
4 SUFFERING	God has ordained that we receive grace for personal cleansing, growth, and achievement by learning how to properly respond to those who offend us.
5 OWNERSHIP	God allows us to conquer anger and worry as we acknowledge that all we have is from Him and belongs to Him. Based on this we must yield our personal rights and expectations to God.
6 FREEDOM	Godly freedom is not the right to do what we want but the power to do what we ought. The freedom which God designed in morals and finances is to allow us to serve others in love.
7 IDENTIFICATION	God conquered the world, the flesh, and the devil through the death, burial, and resurrection of Christ. As we engraft Scripture into our soul and renew our mind with these truths day and night, we enter into His power and live above the law of sin.

APPLICATION OF BASIC LIFE PRINCIPLES

GOALS OF THE BASIC SEMINAR	GOALS OF THE ADVANCED SEMINAR
SELF-ACCEPTANCE	**TRACING CONFLICTS TO PRINCIPLES** **REJECTING VIOLATIONS OF GOD'S DESIGN** **UNDERSTANDING GOD'S DESIGN OF THE HOME**
CLEAR CONSCIENCE	**DISCOVERING AND USING SPIRITUAL GIFTS** **ESTABLISHING PROPER PRIORITIES**
PROPER SUBMISSION	**UNDERSTANDING BALANCE OF POWER** **LEARNING HOW TO WISELY APPEAL** **DEFINING RELATIONSHIPS IN DISCIPLINE** **APPLYING PRINCIPLES OF DISCIPLINE**
FULL FORGIVENESS	**LEARNING HOW TO STAND ALONE** **BENEFITING FROM CRITICISM** **OVERCOMING DISCOURAGEMENT**
YIELDING RIGHTS	**GAINING FINANCIAL FREEDOM** **FINDING UNYIELDED RIGHTS** **CONQUERING SLOTHFULNESS** **CHOOSING A GOOD NAME OVER RICHES**
MORAL PURITY	**APPLYING LEVELS OF FRIENDSHIP** **LEARNING PHASES OF GODLY COURTSHIP** **UNDERSTANDING SIX PURPOSES OF MARRIAGE** **BUILDING THE SPIRIT OF A MARRIAGE**
SUCCESS THROUGH MEDITATION	**LEARNING HOW TO HAVE WISDOM SEARCHES** **DEVELOPING GODLY CHARACTER QUALITIES** **KNOWING GOD'S PRINCIPLES OF EDUCATION**

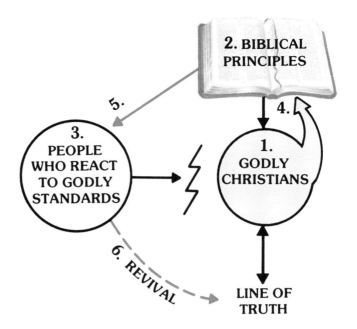

The above diagram depicts a group of dedicated Christians (1) who are committed to building their lives, marriages, families, education, and businesses around the principles of God's Word (2). They are reviled and persecuted by those who have rejected God's truth (3).

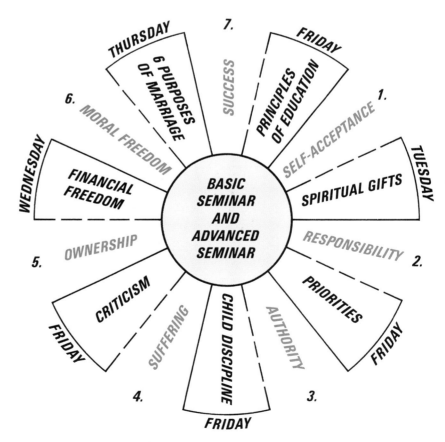

HOW THE BASIC AND ADVANCED SEMINARS RELATE

DISCERNING LEVELS OF CONFLICT

Surface Problem (Visible consequences)	Surface Cause (The Lie)	Root Problem (Strong delusion)	Root Cause (Violation of:)
			DESIGN
			RESPONSIBILITY
			AUTHORITY
			OWNERSHIP
			SUFFERING
			FREEDOM
			IDENTIFICATION

PERSONAL APPLICATION:

NOTES

DIAGRAMS

UNDERSTANDING THE CAUSES

BEHIND HUMANISM

Whenever God's people abandon Scriptural principles, God raises up a heathen power to judge them. (See Judges 2:22; Matthew 5:13.)

What motivates heathen powers today?

- _____
_____
_____

"*. . . They received not the love of the truth, that they might be saved. And for this cause God shall send them strong delusion, that they should believe a [the] lie*" *(II Thessalonians 2:10-11).*

"*Who changed the truth of God into a [the] lie, and worshipped and served the creature more than the Creator, who is blessed for ever. Amen*" *(Romans 1:25).*

How is "the Lie" expressed today?

- _____
_____
_____
_____

How does humanism attack the principles of Scripture?

1 SCRIPTURAL PRINCIPLE:

DESIGN

God created all things for His purposes.

"*For by him were all things created, that are in heaven, and that are in earth, visible and invisible, whether they be thrones, or dominions, or principalities, or powers: all things were created by him, and for him: And he is before all things, and by him all things consist*" *(Colossians 1:16-17).*

Dover, Harper's Home Weekly

HUMANIST MANIFESTO TENETS:

1. "*Religious humanists regard the universe as self-existing and not created.*"
2. "*Humanism believes that man is a part of nature and that he has emerged as the result of a continuous process.*"
3. "*Holding an organic view of life, humanists find that the traditional dualism of mind and body must be rejected.*"

THEIR INROADS AND DESTRUCTION SO FAR -

IN EDUCATION:

Secular Humanism is now the religion in public schools.

11

NOTES

DIAGRAMS

- *Humanism is a religion. (Torcaso v. Watkins 367 US 488 - 1961)*

Is it possible to have neutral education?

- _____
_____
_____
_____

- *John Dewey, founder of progressive education, was a signer of the 1933 manifesto.*

- *Charles Francis Potter, influential in forming modern educational philosophy, stated:*

"Education is thus a most powerful ally of Humanism, and every American public school is a school of Humanism."

Notice the context of his statement.

HUMANISM: A NEW RELIGION

"Education is thus a most powerful ally of Humanism, and every American public school is a school of Humanism. What can the theistic Sunday schools, meeting for an hour once a week, and teaching only a fraction of the children, do to stem the tide of a five-day program of humanistic teaching? . . .

"So very humanistic is modern education that no religion has a future unless it be Humanism. The religion of tomorrow in America and of the day after tomorrow in all the world may not be in all respects identical with the religious Humanism we are advocating in this book, but it will be mightily like it and of the same spirit.

"One American educator, Dr. John Dewey, from whom the new type of modern education received its impetus and much of its method, and who is also best acquainted with the progress of education round the world, has this to say (*Forum*, March 1930) of great interest to all who are studying religious Humanism and the future of religion:

'I would suggest that the future of religion is connected with the possibility of developing a faith in the possibilities of human experience and human relationships that will create a vital sense of the solidarity of human interests and inspire action to make that sense a reality.'

There stands the hope and program of religious Humanism in a single pregnant sentence.

"Not only public school education is an ally of Humanism: science itself is its mother. Said Rev. Edwin H. Wilson (*The New Humanist*, April, 1929):

'The fact is that what we are calling Humanism is a subtle, permeating influence growing organically out of the progress of scientific knowledge wherever that knowledge is effectively related to human life.'

"What needs to be done to science if it is to accomplish its proper service for the growth of Humanism is to correlate all human knowledge and synthesize it that it may adequately serve human ends. This is a tremendous task, but agencies are already at work to that end."

Quotations from "Humanism: a New Religion," pages 128, 129, written fifty-five years ago.

IN THE COURTS:

Humanistic "fairness" laws are being made which are contrary to Biblical laws of justice and mercy.

WHY MUST LAWS BE BASED ON SCRIPTURE?

- _____
_____
- _____
_____
- _____
_____
- _____
_____
- _____
_____
_____
_____
_____

NOTES   **DIAGRAMS**

2 SCRIPTURAL PRINCIPLE:
AUTHORITY

The inspired Word of God is the final authority for our life.

"Heaven and earth shall pass away, but my words shall not pass away" (Matthew 24:35).

HUMANIST MANIFESTO TENETS

4. *"Humanism recognizes that man's religious culture and civilization, as clearly depicted by anthropology and history, are the product of a gradual development due to his interaction with his natural environment and with his social heritage. The individual born into a particular culture is largely molded to that culture."*

5. *"Humanism asserts that the nature of the universe depicted by modern science makes unacceptable any supernatural or cosmic guarantees of human values."*

6. *"We are convinced that the time has passed for theism, deism, modernism, and the several varieties of 'new thought.' "*

Notice how the adherents of religious humanism vigorously attack the supernatural nature and work of God. This is necessary to their religion because they have replaced God with man.

The supernatural working of God in the lives of Christians is the most powerful evidence and argument to refute humanism. For this reason, God wants to show Himself strong through those whose hearts are perfect toward Him. (See II Chronicles 16:9.)

During a period of apostasy in the nation of Israel, God raised up a courageous prophet who said to the people, *". . . How long halt ye between two opinions? if the Lord be God, follow him: but if Baal, then follow him . . ." (I Kings 18:21).*

The people "answered him not a word"; therefore, he set up a demonstration so that the people could see God's supernatural power. The parallels between Elijah's day and our day are striking.

The modern "prophets of Baal" have promised utopias in personal freedom, marriage pleasure, financial security, and perpetual health. The results have been the bondage of destructive habits, the

Bible Art Series, Standard Publishing, Cincinnati

After the prophets of Baal failed to achieve their goal, Elijah demonstrated the supernatural power of God. It became a national turning point.

break-up of millions of marriages, the insecurity of financial bondage, and the spread of baffling new diseases.

The time has come for Christians to let the world know who the true God is by allowing Him to demonstrate His supernatural power through victory over habits, restoring broken marriages, experiencing God's provision through finances, and enjoying health by following Biblical principles.

How have courts based decisions on Humanistic reasoning rather than on Scriptural authority?

* _____

_____

_____

How does humanistic reasoning result in absurd decisions in the courtroom?

* *New York's highest court ruled that their legislature must determine which human beings are actually persons who are entitled to live. (Byrn v. New York City Health and Hospitals Corp., 31 N.Y. 2d 194, 335 NYS 2d 390, 393 - 1972)*

- *California's Supreme Court ruled that a handicapped child can sue for being born. (Tupin v. Sortini, 31 Cal 3 220 - 1982)*

- *Parents sued a Sacramento hospital for not informing them of prenatal tests for brain damage. The courts required the hospital to pay $900,000 in damages. (Tupin v. Sortini)*

- *The Attorney General of Delaware issued an opinion stating that a doctor who had failed to kill two unborn babies with lethal saline injections could be sued for criminal malpractice. (Philadelphia Inquirer, June 9, 1979)*

- *Indiana courts, parents, and hospital allowed an unwanted newborn child to starve to death. (Infant Doe v. Bloomington Indiana Hospital - 1982)*

HUMANIST MANIFESTO TENETS

7. *"Religion consists of those actions, purposes, and experiences which are humanly significant. Nothing human is alien to the religious. . . ."*

8. *"Religious humanism considers the complete realization of human personality to be the end of man's life and seeks its development and fulfillment in the here and now. . . ."*

9. *"In place of the old attitudes involved in worship and prayer the humanist finds his religious emotions expressed in a heightened sense of personal life and in a cooperative effort to promote social well-being."*

10. *"It follows that there will be no uniquely religious emotions and attitudes of the kind hitherto associated with belief in the supernatural."*

When Humanists speak of "fulfillment" they are refering to sensual gratification in all of its perverted forms.

What happens when God's moral standards are rejected?

- _____
_____
_____
_____

- *Humanistic "Values Clarification" courses indoctrinate children to reject the authority of God and of their parents.*

- *All traces of Christianity are being removed from public schools and institutions by the misapplication of the idea of separation of church and state.*

- *Marriages and families are being destroyed by liberalization of divorce laws.*

- *The family is being attacked by "children's rights" laws.*

3 SCRIPTURAL PRINCIPLE:
RESPONSIBILITY

We are accountable to a holy God for every word, thought, and deed which violates His moral standards.

"For the wrath of God is revealed from heaven against all ungodliness and unrighteousness of men, who hold the truth in unrighteousness" (Romans 1:18).

When there is no fear of God and when man tries to decide what is right and wrong, all moral standards become relative and every man ends up doing that which is right in his own eyes. Here are just a few tragic illustrations.

- *A church council in Minnesota published a booklet urging churches to accept "homosexuals" and "lesbians" and to help them "celebrate" their life-style. (Minnesota Council of Churches, "Statement on Ministry to and with Gay and Lesbian Persons" - October 1982)*

- *New York's highest court ruled that a 32-year-old "homosexual" man could adopt a 43-year-old "homosexual" as his son. (Adult Anonymous II, SU NY Sup. Ct. [Asch, J.], July 8, 1982, 452 NYS2d. 198)*

Sodomy is like a raging forest fire, and God warns that devastating destruction will come to any nation that allows it to continue unchecked.

NOTES   **DIAGRAMS**

4 SCRIPTURAL PRINCIPLE:

OWNERSHIP

All that I am and have belongs to God and must be used according to His purposes.

"What? know ye not that your body is the temple of the Holy Ghost which is in you, which ye have of God, and ye are not your own? For ye are bought with a price: therefore glorify God in your body, and in your spirit, which are God's" (I Corinthians 6:19-20).

HUMANIST MANIFESTO TENETS

11. "Man will learn to face the crises of life in terms of his knowledge of their naturalness and probability. Reasonable and manly attitudes will be fostered by education and supported by custom. . . ."

The eleventh tenet speaks of the "crises of life." This refers to the mental, physical, and emotional consequences of sin, which even humanists recognize will occur. The "death technology" now being taught in many schools and the practice of medicine on the basis of "probability" are reinforcing this devastating tenet.

12. "Believing that religion must work increasingly for joy in living, religious humanists aim to foster the creative in man and to encourage achievements that add to the satisfactions of life."

13. "Religious humanism maintains that all associations and institutions exist for the fulfillment of human life. The intelligent evaluation, transformation, control, and direction of such associations and institutions with a view to the enhancement of human life is the purpose and program of humanism. Certainly religious institutions . . . and communal activities must be reconstituted as rapidly as experience allows, in order to function effectively in the modern world."

In order to carry out their plan, humanists must forcibly gain control of all churches and Christian organizations. This is precisely the program which they are pursuing.

Christians are to be the salt of the earth. However, only those who have the inward qualities which Jesus explained in Matthew 5:1–12 will be effective salt.

A major purpose of salt is to stop the spread of decay. When Christians lose their effectiveness, they are "*. . . good for nothing, but to be cast out, and to be trodden under foot of men*" (Matthew 5:13).

The trampling under foot signifies official persecution and judgment against Christians.

What happens when man rejects God's ownership?

● _____

_____

_____

- *Humanistic permissiveness has made suicide the number one cause of teenage death. (Chicago Tribune, May 30, 1982)*

- *Immorality has produced an epidemic of venereal disease. (Herpes II, AIDS)*

- *The humanist's ultimate defiant act against God is to commit suicide.*

5 SCRIPTURAL PRINCIPLE:

FREEDOM

An important aspect of this principle is financial freedom. God wants His people to be free, Satan wants them to be in bondage.

The purpose of freedom, however, is not to be storing up riches for ourselves but to be "distributing to the necessity of saints" (see Romans 12:13), and to be giving to the poor. (See Proverbs 19:17.)

". . . Seek ye first the kingdom of God, and his righteousness; and all these things shall be added unto you" (Matthew 6:33).

Every Christian must realize that he is a steward of what really belongs to God, and that one day he must give an account to God for all that has been entrusted to him. In that awesome day God will set up His eternal Kingdom.

". . . The kingdoms of this world are become the kingdoms of our Lord, and of his Christ; and he shall reign for ever and ever" (Revelation 11:15).

HUMANIST MANIFESTO TENETS

14. "The humanists are firmly convinced that existing acquisitive and profit-motivated society has shown itself to be inadequate and that a radical change in methods, controls, and motives must be instituted. A social and cooperative economic order must be established to the end that the equitable distribution of the means of life be possible. The goal of humanism is a free and universal society in which people voluntarily and intelligently cooperate for the common good. Humanists demand a shared life in a shared world."

Notice the shocking inconsistency in this tenet. It speaks of "voluntarily" sharing assets but then nine words later speaks of demanding a shared life. This tenet is a clear attack on the Biblical principles of finance upon which our nation was built and a blatant proposal of socialistic communism.

15. "We assert that humanism will: (a) affirm life rather than deny it; (b) seek to elicit the possibilities of life, not flee from it; and (c) endeavor to establish the conditions of a satisfactory life for all, not merely for a few. . . ."

This final tenet of the 1933 Humanist Manifesto reveals the true deception behind the innocent-sounding platitudes contained in the document. It speaks of "affirming life rather than denying it." Yet through humanistic laws, 4,000 babies are denied life every day.

It speaks of "elicit[ing] the possibilities of life, not fleeing from it." Yet humanism leads to drugs, liquor, immorality, and many other forms of escape from personal responsibility.

It emphasizes a "satisfactory life for all, not merely for a few." God has made it clear that He wants all to be saved, but this will not be the case, *"because strait is the gate, and narrow is the way, which leadeth unto life, and few there be that find it" (Matthew 7:14).*

What is the political goal of humanism?

* _____

_____

_____

* *World government requires control of all money; thus humanists attack free enterprise, private ownership, and family or business assets.*

GOD HAS ALLOWED HUMANISM TO RISE IN POWER IN ORDER TO MOTIVATE CHRISTIANS TO:

1. Acknowledge transgressions, ours and our forefathers', and turn from them - Jeremiah 14:20; I John 1:9.

2. Establish the home as the basic learning center.

3. Learn Scriptural principles and live by them.

4. Learn to stand alone as individuals, couples, families, churches, and businesses.

". . . The time is come that judgment must begin at the house of God . . ." (I Peter 4:17).

PERSONAL RESPONSE:

On this _____ day of _____, I say with Joshua, *". . . Choose you this day whom ye will serve . . . but as for me and my house, we will serve the Lord"* (Joshua 24:15).

A fortified castle in Europe

"A MAN'S HOME IS HIS CASTLE"

The well known phrase, "A man's home is his castle," is no empty cliché. God designed the home to be a bastion to protect each member from the influences of an often hostile world. It is to be a place of training, preparation, and provision.

It is to give care to its members and hospitality to its visitors. Its potential is to generate resources and skilled warriors who are able to go out to spiritual warfare and to advance the Kingdom of God.

Since the home was designed by God for all these purposes, there should be little wonder that it has been the object of a calculated, systematic, and very effective assault in our generation.

First, the home was robbed of its basic functions; then, ill-trained sons and daughters were lured into enemy territory, where they were easily defeated. Wives and mothers were coerced out of the home with the promise of vocational fulfillment and financial security.

Perhaps the greatest tragedy of all is that the "modern father" has been convinced that he should open up the doors of his castle to any godless influence which desires to come in, plunder his home, and take captive his wife and children.

But God is calling together men who are claiming His power and learning the principles of His Word in order to raise up the foundations of many Godly generations.

5 *BASIC ASPECTS*
OF A DYNAMIC HOME

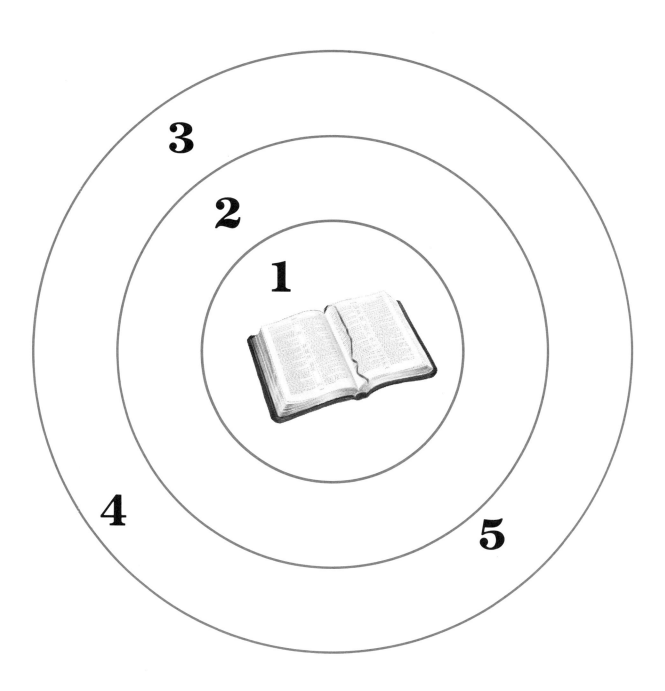

BASIC ASPECTS OF A DYNAMIC HOME

1 A WISDOM CENTER

Why is it important for a father to be the spiritual leader in the family?

● _____
_____
_____

What are the first attitudes that a father must teach his children?

● _____
_____

How can a family identify its present priorities?

● _____
_____
_____
_____

> **An activity is a "number one" priority when nothing but a major emergency can displace it.**

The foundation of a dynamic home must be the Scriptures, and the wise father and mother will begin their day by spending time in them.

An exciting way to make Scripture a living part of daily life is to conduct a *Wisdom Search* each morning and evening. Practical instruction on how to do these will be explained later.

Why doesn't regular Bible reading take place in most Christian families?

● _____
_____
_____
_____

How can parents resolve tensions that result from trying to initiate *Wisdom Searches?*

Precise instruction is given to the father and mother on how to identify and define family responsibilities without unnecessary tensions. It is important to realize that God has designed the father and the mother to excel in the area of decision making that Scripture assigns to each one.

HOW A FATHER HELD THE ATTENTION OF HIS YOUNGER CHILDREN WHILE READING THE BIBLE TO THEM

"When I heard another father tell how he had read the Scriptures for half an hour to his children, I was sure that it would not work in my family. My children would not sit still that long. However, this father gave me a valuable idea. He told me to give the younger children a coloring book or a piece of paper to draw on while I read.

"I practiced reading Genesis chapters one through four so that I could do it in twenty minutes.

"The next evening we gathered around the living room fireplace. My wife kept her fingers productive with handwork while she attentively listened to the Scriptures being read, and my children colored and drew.

"I wondered if they were listening, when all of a sudden my son stopped me and asked me a profound question on what I had just read. As I continued reading, the children asked more questions; and when I finished the four chapters, they begged me to read four more. The twenty minutes extended to over an hour, and the children only let me stop when I promised to read more the next evening."

HOW DO THE COMMANDMENTS OF THE FATHER AND THE LAWS OF THE MOTHER GIVE LIGHT?

LAMP
(Father's Commandment)

LIGHT
(Mother's Law)

Just as Christians have a responsibility to be light to the world, parents have an obligation to give light to their children. The light of the parents is the Biblical teaching and the daily instructions which will direct sons and daughters in their early years and guide them during their later years.

Scripture is very precise in explaining how each parent is to function in the training process. Specific responsibilities and limitations are given to each parent. When these are understood and carefully followed, conflicting commands are avoided and proper instructions are reinforced.

DEFINING RESPONSIBILITIES

> *"My son, keep thy father's commandment, and forsake not the law of thy mother.... For the commandment is a lamp; and the law is light; and reproofs of instruction are the way of life"* (Proverbs 6:20, 23).

Within the analogy of a lighted lamp, there is a wealth of practical direction for the father and the mother as they give discipline to their sons and daughters.

1 HOW DOES A LAMP PICTURE THE COMMANDMENTS OF A FATHER?

The lamp in Proverbs 6:23 was a small clay container filled with oil. A wick was added to the lamp, which drew from the oil the resources to produce light when lit. Just as the lamp required continuous filling with oil, so the father must be filled with the Holy Spirit. (See Ephesians 5:18.) This command is in the present tense, requiring continuous action.

The vessel was kept clean to maintain the efficiency of the light. When fragrance was added to the oil, the light projected a sweet savor throughout the house. Just as the wick will not function without the lamp, nor the lamp without the wick, so the father and mother are to demonstrate oneness in their teaching and discipline of their children.

As the lamp was placed on a higher plane, the outreach of its light was extended, and more people were benefited by it. Similarly, as the father grows to spiritual maturity in his life, he is able to provide clearer commands for his wife to teach the children.

The lamp was the foundation and support of the light, just as the father must assume the greater responsibility in the marriage and for the family.

A lamp was often made of clay and was subject to breakage. Every father must remember that his health and strength continue by the grace of God. A wise father will avoid careless actions or foolish habits which will weaken or damage his body.

The darker the night, the more essential was the lamp. The more difficult the situations faced by a family, the more vital is the need for the father's commands.

Every command that a father gives must be in harmony with the principles of Scripture and the greatest commandment of all:

"... Thou shalt love the Lord thy God with all thy heart, and with all thy soul, and with all thy mind. This is the first and great commandment. And the second is like unto it, Thou shalt love thy neighbour as thyself. On these two commandments hang all the law and the prophets" (Matthew 22:37–40).

2 HOW DOES LIGHT PICTURE THE LAW OF A MOTHER?

The light of a candle provides illumination so that everyone within its range can see clearly how to carry out his responsibilities. The brighter the light, the greater the illumination.

The light of a lamp is fragile. It can be blown out by a sudden gust of wind; it can be extinguished by those around it; or it can be snuffed out by being covered.

When the father gives a Biblically-based command such as "I want our family to be up each morning for *Wisdom Searches*," it is the responsibility of the mother to work out the guidelines in order for this to occur. Her "law" would include bedtime and rising schedules for the children, preparations for breakfast, and coordination of morning routines.

Just as God's Law is an expression of His love, so the law of the mother confirms her love for her husband and her children. She is like the virtuous woman in Proverbs 31, of whom it was said, *"She openeth her mouth with wisdom; and in her tongue is the law of kindness. She looketh well to the ways of her household, and eateth not the bread of idleness. Her children arise up, and call her blessed; her husband also, and he praiseth her" (Proverbs 31:26–28).*

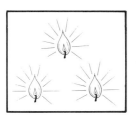

3 WHAT ARE REPROOFS OF INSTRUCTION?

The reproofs of instruction are the consequences that come from the Lord when His Law or His commandments have been violated. If the father gives a command which is not in harmony with the principles of Scripture, he will experience "the reproofs of instruction."

For example, a father may say to his wife, "We need a new car, so I want you to sign this loan agreement with me. With what I am making, we can easily pay it off." This command, of course, violates the many Scriptures which teach us to keep out of debt and warn us that *"...the borrower is servant to the lender."* (See Proverbs 22:7 and Romans 13:8.)

The reproofs of instruction, in this case, may come in the form of financial pressures from unexpected bills.

If a mother prescribes laws which contradict God's Law, she will face the reproofs of God's instruction. These may be expressed by a loss of fellowship with the Lord, pressures within herself, tensions with her husband, and conflicts with her children.

If, for example, the telephone rings and the mother instructs the child to answer it and say that she is not home, this deception would not only violate Scripture, but also teach her child to distrust her and to lie whenever it is not convenient to tell the truth.

If a child disobeys the commandment of the father or the law of the mother, he or she will be in line for both the corrective discipline of the parents as well as the reproofs of God.

EXAMPLES OF THE COMMAND OF THE FATHER AND THE LAW OF THE MOTHER

Father's Command	Mother's Law
Be alert during family *Wisdom Searches*.	Put children to bed early. Share excitement for rising.
Have meals on time.	Organize kitchen, plan menus, assign tasks.
Keep the home neat.	Assign where clothing, toys, books are kept.
Have a grateful spirit.	Teach children to write thank you notes.
Have a growing personal relationship with God.	Schedule personal devotional time.
Learn to be good musicians.	Schedule music lessons and practice time.
Minister to the needs of others.	Invite dinner guests or arrange a meal for a shut-in.

4 WHAT HAPPENS WHEN FATHER FAILS TO GIVE COMMANDS?

When a father fails to fulfill his God-given responsibility as the spiritual leader of the family, the mother and the children become keenly aware of the void and will usually try to fill it in ways which God did not ordain.

If the mother begins giving the commands, the children will tend to become resentful and react to her as a "domineering" mother. The father will either react to his wife for stepping into his position of authority or will further abandon his leadership responsibilities.

The resulting tension between the parents will cause the children to become insecure and motivate them to challenge the authority of both parents. If the children fail to receive proper leadership within the home, they will often react to authority outside the home in an attempt to find leadership that will set limits for them.

5 WHAT IF THE COMMAND OF FATHER VIOLATES SCRIPTURE?

A command which violates God's Word is never to be carried out by the wife or children. God is over the father, and each one in the family is subject to the authority of Scripture.

When a command violates Scripture, the one receiving it should first evaluate his or her own life to see if the command was given as a reaction to rebellion, laziness, ungratefulness, or some other destructive attitude.

Every wrong attitude must be confessed and corrected before dealing with the father's unscriptural command. After evaluating attitudes, the basic intention of the command should be determined. If the objective of the command is right, but the way of achieving it is wrong, then a creative alternative should be suggested.

In the case of the husband asking his wife to cosign the new car loan, the basic intention might have been more reliable transportation. The wife could then have suggested, "Let's use our need for a new car to strengthen our prayer life. We can pray that God will keep this car running, direct us to a good mechanic, provide a better car, or give us grace to respond to irritations when the car doesn't work. Meanwhile, we can re-evaluate our budget and begin setting money aside for a new car."

Notice that in making this appeal, the wife is actually fulfilling her responsibility to work out procedures by which the father's command can be properly achieved. At this point the husband must realize that his wife's suggestions are not a rejection of him, but simply an expression of the ability and responsibility which God has given her.

The human response of the father would be to feel that his authority had been challenged. However, a spiritual response would be to recognize that God gave him a wife as a helpmeet and that He will give her cautions to help him avoid costly mistakes. As the father welcomes and respects his wife's counsel, he affirms both her and God's work through her. The marriage is thus strengthened, and true spiritual light is given to the children.

Scripture gives several illustrations of wives who followed wrong commands and failed to offer creative alternatives. When Abraham told his wife, Sarah, to lie and say that she was his sister, God rebuked her through Abimelech. (See Genesis 20:16.)

Then both Abraham and Sarah experienced the reproofs of life when the same deception they used was repeated by their son Isaac and their grandson Jacob. (See *Character Sketches*, Volume III, pages 263–265.)

6 WHAT IF MOTHER FAILS TO GIVE THE LIGHT OF HER LAWS?

When God designed His "structure of authority," He actually gave the potential of greater power to those who are under authority than to those who are in authority. Those under authority have the power of influence, which if properly exercised can be tremendously helpful in guiding those in authority.

This is especially true in the relationship between a husband and his wife. Many husbands have acknowledged that their motivation for spiritual pursuits can be quickly destroyed by negative attitudes or lack of enthusiasm from their wives.

When a husband gives a command to his family and the wife fails to work out the proper procedures to carry it out, many consequences may occur.

First, the father may attempt to give the laws himself. Very often, however, he is not sensitive to the needs and responses of the children; and thus, he may be too harsh or demanding. The wife will then try to compensate by being more lenient than she should be, and the children will sense a divided authority.

Meanwhile, when the wife does not fulfill her function in the family, she will feel inadequate and inferior. She may try to compensate for these destructive feelings by withdrawing, reacting, or looking outside the family for her approval and fulfillment.

7 HOW SHOULD FATHER AND MOTHER WORK TOGETHER IN GIVING LIGHT?

Even though the father and mother have different responsibilities in family training, there is a constant need for them to communicate with each other in order to gain proper perspective and wise counsel.

The mother will be more alert to details and to immediate consequences if principles are violated. On the other hand, the father will be more alert to attitudes and long-range objectives. The purpose of discussion, prayer, and counsel between parents is for each one to sharpen his or her own perspective and then to help the partner see the situation through that perspective.

It is wise for a husband to ask his wife how she feels about a command before he gives it and also to work out with her the parameters within which she should design her laws. He should then come to the mental resolution that he will not intrude into his wife's area of responsibility. If he has any suggestions about her laws, these should be discussed with her privately.

In a family without a father, the mother should explain to the children that God is their Father and that she will clarify the commands that He has given in His Word by the laws which she makes. (See Psalm 68:5.)

When the mother is missing from the home, the father needs to get a woman's perspective by gaining counsel from his mother, his sister, or a Godly older woman in the church. He also needs to listen much more carefully to his children and learn how to ask questions which will allow them to express their real needs and feelings.

He may overlook the importance of laws, causing his children to become insecure and frustrated by the lack of clear procedural instruction. The father's command tells what he wants done; the law explains how it is to be done.

8 HOW SHOULD PARENTS DISCIPLINE WHEN COMMANDS OR LAWS ARE VIOLATED?

The analogy of the lamp and light is especially useful in determining responsibilities of correction when children disobey. The parents should first determine if the child disobeyed a procedural law established by the mother or if he is rejecting the command issued by the father.

If the disobedience violates a procedural law, the mother should discern whether the child misunderstood her law or is willfully rebelling against it. When laws are misunderstood, further instruction should be given. When laws are purposely disobeyed, Scriptural correction should be administered.

When the mother's discipline does not achieve the desired correction in the child's attitude and behavior, it can be assumed that the child is reacting to the command behind the law and therefore needs further discipline from the father.

In either case, the father must confirm the position of the mother as lawgiver and be ready to support her in whatever way is necessary.

PROJECT

- Write down as many of your mother's instructions as you can remember. Then list the spoken or unspoken commands of your father that stand behind each instruction.
- Discuss how the concept of commands and laws operates in an employment relationship.
- Evaluate how a government's laws must be in harmony with God's commands.
- Discuss how the Church is to work out the laws which will fulfill God's commands of the Great Commission.

2 A LEARNING CENTER

What is God's design for the education of sons and daughters?

● _____

_____

_____

_____

Most parents feel unqualified and inadequate to teach their own sons and daughters, especially when they reach high school or college age. However, what most parents do not realize is that the key to academic achievement at any age level is for the parents to become **enthusiastic learners** along with their sons and daughters.

God always gives the ability to fulfill the tasks which He assigns. With that in mind, study the following verses:

"And thou shalt love the Lord thy God with all thine heart, and with all thy soul, and with all thy might.

"And these words, which I command thee this day, shall be in thine heart:

"And thou shalt teach them diligently unto thy children, and shalt talk of them when thou sittest in thine house, and when thou walkest by the way, and when thou liest down, and when thou risest up.

"And thou shalt bind them for a sign upon thine hand, and they shall be as frontlets between thine eyes.

"And thou shalt write them upon the posts of thy house, and on thy gates" (Deuteronomy 6:5–9).

"We will not hide them from their children, shewing to the generation to come the praises of the Lord, and his strength, and his wonderful works that he hath done. . . .

"That the generation to come might know them, even the children which should be born; who should arise and declare them to their children:

"That they might set their hope in God, and not forget the works of God, but keep his commandments" (Psalms 78:4, 6–7).

"Now I say, That the heir, as long as he is a child, differeth nothing from a servant, though he be lord of all;

"But is under tutors and governors until the time appointed of the father" (Galatians 4:1–2).

Why does teaching knowledge before character lead to arrogance?

● _____

_____

_____

When should education begin with children?

● _____

_____

THE EXCITING POTENTIAL OF PRE-BIRTH TRAINING

In recent years, an increasing amount of research has been carried out to test the potential of prenatal learning.

The Biblical basis of pre-birth perception is found in John the Baptist's leaping in the womb with joy when he heard the voice of Mary as she carried Christ. *"For, lo, as soon as the voice of thy salutation sounded in mine ears, the babe leaped in my womb for joy"* (Luke 1:44).

A further reference for prenatal training is Paul's statement about Timothy having perceived the wisdom of Scripture as a "child" in II Timothy 3:15. The Greek word which Paul used for child was *brephos*. Its precise definition in *Strong's Greek Dictionary of the New Testament* is "an infant (properly, an unborn infant)."

The following testimonies illustrate the potential and importance of reading the Scriptures and providing wholesome music for a child while he or she is still in the womb.

"When my wife was carrying our first son, I decided that it was never too soon to have him hear God's Word, so I began reading a chapter of Proverbs to him each day.

"On the day our son was born, several complications developed. After six agonizing hours in the delivery room, he was finally born. His screams of protest filled the room. . . . This screaming continued until I spoke to him. As soon as he heard my voice, he immediately stopped crying and turned his head toward me.

"While he was in intensive care, I would often come in to see my new son struggling for life. He would be fighting hard just to breathe. When he heard my voice, he would turn his head toward me, and as I continued to speak, the effort it took for him to breathe would lessen. Often he would fall into a much needed sleep.

"The nurses noticed his unusual responses to my voice and frequently commented about it. Today this son, now four years old, has an unusual perception about spiritual matters and a love for the Word of God."

A father from Illinois

"During the labor and birth of our first child, we played beautiful Christian music to him. It was a hectic night for everyone at the hospital, as over twenty babies were born. Every nurse and doctor that came in our room commented on the peaceful and soothing effect of the music. . . .

"Later at home when he would become fussy, I would play those same tapes, and he would quiet down immediately. Even today at five, he is very sensitive and discerning regarding music.

"While driving in the car one day, he opened his window all the way. I asked him why he had done that, and he responded that he wanted the other cars to hear good music about God."

A mother from Illinois

Why is it vital to teach the fear of the Lord?

● _____

_____

"By humility and the fear of the Lord are riches, and honour, and life" (Proverbs 22:4).

Fearing the Lord will result in cleansing the home.

☐ _____ ☐ _____

☐ _____ ☐ _____

☐ _____ ☐ _____

☐ _____

CONSEQUENCES FROM TELEVISION

1. It establishes the practice of tolerating evil to enjoy some good.

"The fear of the Lord is to hate evil . . ." (Proverbs 8:13).

". . . A little leaven leaveneth the whole lump" (I Corinthians 5:6).

2. Its amusement format lowers their resistance to evil.

"Keep thy heart with all diligence; for out of it are the issues of life" (Proverbs 4:23).

3. It provides constant access to the world's system and its false concepts.

"Beware lest any man spoil you through philosophy and vain deceit, after the tradition of men, after the rudiments of the world, and not after Christ" (Colossians 2:8).

4. It deadens their conscience by providing comparison with new lows of immorality.

"And because iniquity shall abound, the love of many shall wax cold" (Matthew 24:12).

5. It allows them to relate to evil individuals whom you would otherwise never allow into your home.

". . . A companion of fools shall be destroyed" (Proverbs 13:20).

6. It devours one of their most precious resources—time.

"So teach us to number our days, that we may apply our hearts unto wisdom" (Psalm 90:12).

7. It stifles creativity by deadening their responses to conscience and Scripture.

"Quench not the Spirit" (I Thessalonians 5:19).

8. It ultimately makes them an enemy of God.

". . . Know ye not that the friendship of the world is enmity with God? whosoever therefore will be a friend of the world is the enemy of God" (James 4:4).

WHAT HAPPENED WHEN GOD'S PEOPLE . . .

". . . were mingled among the heathen, and learned their works. And they served their idols: which were a snare unto them.

"Yea, they sacrificed their sons and their daughters unto devils, And shed innocent blood, even the blood of their sons and of their daughters, whom they sacrificed unto the idols of Canaan: and the land was polluted with blood.

"Thus were they defiled with their own works, and went awhoring with their own inventions.

"Therefore was the wrath of the Lord kindled against his people, insomuch that he abhorred his own inheritance. And he gave them into the hand of the heathen; and they that hated them ruled over them" (Psalm 106:35–41).

CONSEQUENCES FROM SENSUAL MATERIAL

1. It produces guilt by violating God's inborn moral laws.

"Which shew the work of the law written in their hearts, their conscience also bearing witness, and their thoughts the mean while accusing or else excusing one another" (Romans 2:15).

2. It damages the marriage by causing mental adultery.

"But I say unto you, That whosoever looketh on a woman to lust after her hath committed adultery with her already in his heart" (Matthew 5:28).

3. It promotes prostitution by engaging in lewdness for hire.

"Having eyes full of adultery, and that cannot cease from sin; beguiling unstable souls: an heart they have exercised with coveteous practices; cursed children" (II Peter 2:14).

4. It lays the foundation for insanity by encouraging gratification without responsibility.

"A double-minded man is unstable in all his ways" (James 1:8).
(See also Romans 1:28.)

5. It brings destructive temptation and damaging standards.

"Be not deceived; God is not mocked: for whatsoever a man soweth, that shall he also reap" (Galatians 6:7).

6. It results in harsh discipline and child abuse.

"He that soweth iniquity shall reap vanity: and the rod of his anger shall fail" (Proverbs 22:8).

7. It increases violent crime in the nation.

"Do not prostitute thy daughter, to cause her to be a whore; lest the land fall to whoredom, and the land become full of wickedness" (Leviticus 19:29).

8. It violates God's warnings against nakedness and causes sexual obsessions.

". . . I was afraid, because I was naked; and I hid myself" (Genesis 3:10).

9. It dulls spiritual senses and grieves the Holy Spirit.

"For the flesh lusteth against the Spirit, and the Spirit against the flesh: and these are contrary the one to the other . . ." (Galatians 5:17).

10. It promotes the humanistic religion that man's pleasure is the ultimate goal in life.

"Let no man deceive you with vain words: for because of these things cometh the wrath of God upon the children of disobedience" (Ephesians 5:6).

CONSEQUENCES FROM ALCOHOL

1. It brings God's condemnation for violating Scripture which condemns intoxicating drink.

"Look not thou upon the wine when it is red, when it giveth his colour in the cup, when it moveth itself aright. At the last it biteth like a serpent, and stingeth like an adder" (Proverbs 23:31–32).

2. It lowers vital inhibitions for moral standards.

"Thine eyes shall behold strange women, and thine heart shall utter perverse things" (Proverbs 23:33).

3. It leads other people to lower their standards and to experience God's judgment.

"Woe unto him that giveth his neighbour drink, that puttest thy bottle to him, and makest him drunken also, that thou mayest look on their nakedness!" (Habakkuk 2:15).

4. It removes a standard which could spare your son or daughter from wicked and destructive associations.

"Woe unto them that are mighty to drink wine, and men of strength to mingle strong drink: Which justify the wicked for reward, and take away the righteousness of the righteous from him!" (Isaiah 5:22–23).

5. It places your approval on a product which is bringing death and destruction to millions of people.

"Wine is a mocker, strong drink is raging: and whosoever is deceived thereby is not wise" (Proverbs 20:1).

6. It displaces the genuine exhilaration which God gives.

"And be not drunk with wine . . . but be filled with the Spirit" (Ephesians 5:18).

7. It brings physical damage to the one who drinks and to their unborn children.

"They have stricken me, shalt thou say, and I was not sick; they have beaten me, and I felt it not: when shall I awake? I will seek it yet again" (Proverbs 23:35).

8. It leads to addiction and bondage which violates Scriptural freedom.

"All things are lawful unto me . . . but I will not be brought under the power of any" (I Corinthians 6:12).

9. It causes a weaker brother to stumble.

"It is good neither to eat flesh, nor to drink wine, nor any thing whereby thy brother stumbleth, or is offended, or is made weak" (Romans 14:21).

• There are two types of wines identified in the Bible. New wine was unfermented. It was made from freshly squeezed grapes (grape juice). Strong drink was made from fermented grapes. It was an intoxicating beverage.

• Grape juice that ferments on its own is not wine; it is simply spoiled grape juice. To become wine, grape juice must be carefully controlled.

• In Jesus' day, the methods used to prevent grape juice from spoiling included boiling down the grape juice into syrup, bottling it, and storing it in a pond of cool water for thirty days, or soaking raisins in water until juice was reconstituted.

Thus, it is not true that in Jesus' day the people drank only fermented wine due to a difficulty of keeping grape juice from spoiling.

What parents allow in moderation, their children excuse in excess.

". . . Happy is he that condemneth not himself in that thing which he alloweth. . . . For whatsoever is not of faith is sin" (Romans 14:22–23).

NOTES

DIAGRAMS

Replace OBJECTS OF DESTRUCTION with items that reinforce wisdom and Godly character

☐_____ ☐_____

☐_____ ☐_____

☐_____ ☐_____

FURTHER IDEAS:

_____

_____

How can church leaders assist in making your home a Godly center for learning?

● _____

_____

What are the most effective times of learning readiness?

● _____

_____

● Studies and experience indicate that the greatest number of family arguments occur one hour before each meal. This means that to ensure family harmony we must carefully evaluate each aspect of the mealtime. Actually, the mealtime can be one of the most effective times of building each one in the family, but this takes careful planning.

Do you have Scriptural convictions that are worth living for and dying for?

● _____

_____

Have you instilled these convictions in your sons and daughters?

Making Mealtimes More Meaningful

PRIOR TO MEALTIME

NEGATIVE ATTITUDES AND BEHAVIOR	DESIRED POSITIVES	PURPOSE OR GOAL
Unprepared for mealtime: • No regular schedule • Children need to be called three or four times • Younger children in the way of mother while she is cooking	• As regular a schedule as possible so that children know when to be home and ready to eat • Children trained to come on first call • Father assisting by: Keeping younger children out of kitchen Being in charge of "clean up" Encouraging a quiet, relaxed atmosphere by his example Using time for sharing interests and activities of the children	• Obedience on the part of children to their parents • Involvement of father in the children's pre-meal activities

Atmosphere of strife or depression: • Presenting bad news just prior to meal • Sibling arguments • Dislike of food • Father bringing home problems from work • Mealtime conflicting with an evening activity	• Saving bad news or major decisions until after the meal • Not permitting open displeasure of food—expressing positive compliments • Scheduling the meal to allow time for preparation of an evening activity • Father taking the lead in resolving arguments and setting the mood	• Family-centered atmosphere to meal • Harmony among children and parents
Lack of family involvement in meal preparation: • Children and father waiting to be called and served • No help being offered	• Older children assisting with food preparation and table setting • Children selecting appropriate music for the mealtime • Mother preparing a meal that is pleasant to sight and taste	• Mealtime a family project rather than a total serving of the family by the mother

ADDITIONAL IDEAS:

_____   _____
_____   _____
_____   _____
_____   _____

DURING MEALTIME

AREA	POSITIVE SUGGESTIONS	GOAL
PRAYER	Make Prayer Time Meaningful By: • Discouraging memorized prayers • Suggesting the topic for the children's prayers • Using conversational prayer • Holding hands around the table during prayer • Quoting a verse together • Avoiding long prayers and devotions while food is on table • Praying after the meal and thanking God for the food eaten	• A meaningful time of prayer before eating rather than a shallow ritual
FOOD	• Prepare food which is pleasant to sight and taste. Have a variety of foods. • Father encourages the children to thank their mother for food by setting the example. • Parents encourage the children to compliment by commenting on promptness, table setting, etc. • Do not permit criticism of food either orally or visually. • Share turns at different meals for getting up to get forgotten items and allow mother to eat a warm meal, too.	• Demonstrating gratefulness to mother • Demonstrating gratefulness to God for every provision • Appreciation for mother's responsibilities

AREA	POSITIVE SUGGESTIONS	GOAL
CONVERSATION	**Father** • Develop key questions to encourage children to talk about their day's activities. • Daily rotate specific topics or goals to be discussed. • Discuss with the family your interesting observations of the day. • Share your good work experiences with your family. • Avoid criticism and unnecessary discipline at the table. • Steer the conversation away from controversial subjects which might lead to arguments. • Allow for spontaneous humor and free conversation—positive sharing of ideas. **Mother** • Avoid making mealtime a time for relating children's misbehavior and mistakes to father. **Children** • Yield your rights so that each family member is given opportunities to speak without interruptions or negative remarks.	• Father assuming his role as head of the family and as the teacher • Turning negative tendencies and traits into positive qualities
INTERRUPTIONS	• Turn the television off! • Play quiet background music (hymns or classical)—records, tapes, etc. • Definite policies regarding phone calls during meals should be predetermined and followed to avoid unnecessary interruptions. • Misbehavior at the table should be taken care of promptly—temporary "removal" from the table if necessary. • Have one person responsible for quietly getting up to get needed items, to answer the phone, or to change records, etc. • Have each child ask the father to be excused from the table at the end of the meal or during the meal if necessary.	• Family unity • Meaningful exchanges without interruptions • Priorities developed
CLEAN-UP	• Have each person participate in the clean-up activities according to age, ability, and responsibilities. • A partial clean-up to prepare table for a sharing time is a possibility. • Sing together during the clean-up. • Have someone other than mother do the dishes. • Have homework done before mealtime to avoid neglect of responsibility.	• Unity • Responsibility

ADDITIONAL IDEAS:

"LOVE HAS GOOD MANNERS"

HOW WELL DO YOU KNOW YOUR MANNERS?

1. Do you open your napkin when you sit down for a meal or when you are served food?

2. If you are eating a piece of cherry pie and discover a cherry stone, how do you remove it from your mouth? Remove it with your finger, spit it out in your spoon, or deposit it in your glass while taking a drink?

3. When you feel a sneeze coming while sitting at the table, what is the best way to handle it? Quickly leave the table, cover your face with your hands, face your hostess, other?

4. If your partner at a restaurant cannot finish his meat and you are hungry, what is the proper method to transfer part of it to your plate?

5. If you are eating a jelly sandwich and some of the jelly dribbles onto your tie, what should you do? Lift your tie and lick it off, turn the tie around, or begin a scraping operation?

6. If two women are introduced to each other and one is seated, should she rise?

7. When ladies seated at a luncheon table are introduced, do they shake hands?

8. When a husband kisses his wife in public when it is raining, does he have to remove his hat?

9. If a fellow and a girl are going into a room, which one should go in first?

10. If a fellow is walking down the sidewalk with a girl, on which side should he be?

11. If you start to introduce a friend and you forget his name, what do you do?

12. If a boyfriend forgets to open the car door for his girlfriend, should she wait until he remembers, roll the window down and call to him, or open it herself?

13. If you wanted to invite a couple to your home that you met at a neighbor's dinner party, are you obligated to invite your neighbors, too?

14. If you stop dating a fellow who has given you expensive gifts, is it proper to return them or should you figure that is his cost for social life?

15. If you are invited to a formal dinner party which begins at eight, what is the proper time to arrive? Shortly before eight, promptly at eight, or shortly after eight?

16. If you are invited by a hostess as an eligible young man to a dinner where there are eligible young ladies, are you required to send a "thank you" note to her or should she thank you for assisting her to make the dinner a success?

17. If a boy were going to give his girlfriend a Christmas present, should he also give her parents a gift?

18. How much should you tip a taxi driver?

19. Who gets out of a cab first, the fellow or the girl?

20. If you arrange for a taxi to transport your lady friend to her destination, how do you handle the fare and the tip? Give the lady the money, pay the driver first, or have him send you the bill?

21. When a fellow goes out to a restaurant with a girl and the girl insists on picking up the tab, what should the fellow do?

22. How much should you tip a porter for carrying your bags?

23. What should be cleared from the table before serving your guests their dessert?

24. Which way do you pass food, to the left or to the right?

25. Can you take food from a serving dish which someone asks you to pass to him?

26. What do you do if asked a question when your mouth is full of food? Hold up a finger, spit the food into your spoon, talk with your mouth full, or smile at the one asking you the question while you continue chewing your food?

27. If you don't have enough money to pay your restaurant bill, what should you do?

28. If you drop some peas on your hostess's carpet during a formal dinner, what should you do? Smash them into the rug, use your foot to shove them under the table, reach down and pick them up, leave them alone, or none of these?

29. Which way do you tip your soup bowl for the last spoonful?

30. How much should you tip in a restaurant?

31. Should the fellow or the girl lead the way in the restaurant when there is no hostess?

32. Do you refill the water glass from the left or the right of the person?

33. Do you pass your plate for a refill with your knife and fork on or off your plate?

34. Do you butter the whole piece of bread before eating it with your meal?

35. Should you use your knife to cut the big pieces of lettuce?

36. Is it proper to cut up all your meat before starting to eat it?

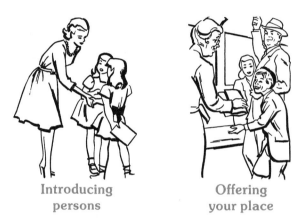

Introducing persons   Offering your place

37. Do you introduce your friend to your mother or vice versa?

38. How do you introduce a minister to your friends: Reverend, pastor, or mister?

39. Is it ever permissible to put your elbows on the table? If so, when?

40. What is the signal that you can start to eat your dessert?

41. How should you remove an olive stone from your mouth?

42. What is the proper way to eat chicken at a formal dinner?

43. Is it ever proper to dunk your food?

44. How should a girl on a date order her meal in a restaurant? Give her order to her date, or give it directly to the waitress?

CHECK YOUR ANSWERS

CORRECT

1. Wait until your hostess has taken up her napkin first.

2. Take it out of your mouth with your thumb and forefinger.

3. Turn your head slightly, use your handkerchief as quietly as possible, and do not excuse yourself.

4. You may transfer part of it only if a fresh fork or spoon is used. The one giving the food should hand the implement, handle first, to you if you want to taste it. If you wish the whole serving, ask the waiter to serve it to you.

5. Take a knife or fork, scoop up the substance, and place it at the side of your plate. Then dip your napkin into your water glass and rub the spot lightly. Do it as inconspicuously as possible.

6. No, they bow. The hostess, however, always shakes hands with her guests, male and female. Anyone acting in the role of hostess should rise and shake hands with the visitors, women as well as men.

7. See #6 answer.

8. Yes. A man kissing his wife on the street (in greeting or farewell only) should always remove his hat, no matter what the weather.

9. The girl should enter first unless it is dark and you wish to make it ready for her.

10. He should walk on the curb side unless a greater danger exists from the building side.

11. Hope that the one being introduced will sense your momentary frustration and help you out. If he should leave you helpless, you may temporarily switch the conversation with, "This is my friend from college days. We were in the same dormitory during our junior year," etc. Finally, you should ask him to refresh your memory.

12. Encourage him to maintain this good manner for his own sake. Thus, wait as long as you can before opening it.

13. You should always invite your host and hostess the first time you entertain a friend first met at their house or in their company.

14. You should not have accepted these expensive gifts in the first place. Now the only thing to do is to tell him that you feel you really should not have accepted them and that you would like to return them, although you want to remain friends.

15. Promptness is always appropriate.

16. You may phone your hostess a day or two after a party or write a brief line of appreciation.

17. It would be nice to give the girl's mother an impersonal gift or give some small gift to the household which the father and mother will both enjoy.

18. If service warrants it, five to fifteen percent.

19. A man always gets out first, then turns and assists the lady by offering her his hand.

20. Ask the driver what the approximate fare will be and pay him in advance, including the tip.

21. Accept it as graciously as possible. It would have been better for the girl to have arranged in advance with the restaurant the payment of the bill.

22. Usually twenty-five cents a bag, but more if he gives extra service.

23. Everything should be cleared except the water glasses and cups and saucers.

24. You should pass food to the left.

25. No, unless they tell you to do so.

26. Nod in acknowledgment. Then take your time, chew your food and swallow before answering. The extra time will allow you

to more carefully consider his question and remind you to always take small bites of food.

27. Excuse yourself from your company and privately explain your dilemma with the manager. He may take your word that you will promptly return that evening with the money or conveniently require either a phone call to your parents or deposit of some security (watch, etc.) until you return.

28. Leave them alone until you have an opportunity to unobtrusively pick them up.

29. You may tip your bowl away from you but not toward you.

30. The standard for tipping in a restaurant is fifteen percent of the bill.

31. The man should go first to a table, pull out a chair for the woman and push it in slowly as she sits down.

32. Refill it on the right of a person.

33. Pass the plate with the utensils on the plate.

34. No. Break it up and butter a bite-size piece at a time.

35. You should use your fork but may sometimes use a knife.

36. No, cut only one or two pieces at a time.

37. You should mention the name of the person to whom greater respect should be given first. "Mother, this is John Smith."

38. It is proper to introduce him as, "Pastor Smith, of the Forest Avenue Church."

39. Before food is served or between courses.

40. When the hostess begins, or at a large dinner, when everyone at your table has been served.

41. You may remove pits from your mouth in the same way the food is eaten. An olive is eaten by holding it in the fingers and biting around the stone which is then laid on a plate.

42. Chicken must be eaten with knife and fork except at picnics.

43. Food should never be dunked unless you are eating alone.

44. A woman should tell her escort, who then gives the order with his own to the waitress.

Answers based on various etiquette books.

3 A HOSPITALITY CENTER

"Be not forgetful to entertain strangers: for thereby some have entertained angels unawares" (Hebrews 13:2).

God commands us to be hospitable

☐ Matthew 25:35-36 _____

_____

☐ Luke 14:13 _____

_____

☐ Romans 12:13 _____

_____

☐ I Peter 4:9 _____

_____

☐ Isaiah 58:7-8 _____

_____

☐ Hebrews 13:1-3 _____

_____

☐ James 1:27 _____

_____

What is hospitality?

_____

_____

_____

Know who should not be invited into your home

☐ I Corinthians 5:11 _____
☐ II Corinthians 6:14 _____

_____

□ II Timothy 3:6_____

_____

□ Titus 1:10-11_____

_____

What is required for good hospitality?

• _____

_____

□ _____

□ _____

_____

Remove or control things which hinder hospitality

□_____

□_____

□_____

□_____

□_____

□_____

□_____

□_____

**WHOM DID GOD CALL
"A GREAT WOMAN"
BECAUSE OF HER
HOSPITALITY?**

• She offers direction for anyone who feels confined to a routine of life that provides no outlet for meaningful ministry.

• She offers counsel to any wife who feels that her husband is incompatible in areas that are important to her happiness.

• She possesses certain character qualities which caused God to refer to her in Scripture as "a great woman."

She is known to us simply as the Shunammite woman. We meet her in II Kings 4:8-17. As we read her story as God wrote it, see if you can detect at least five character qualities that would prompt God to call her a great woman.

(See II Kings 4:8-17.)

1. *ALERTNESS*

The first quality the Shunammite woman displays is alertness. She is alert to the basic needs of others. In this instance she sees a man of God in need of food.

There are two factors we discover which may have contributed to her awareness of the needs of others. First, she has no children of her own. Second, her husband is much older than she is and seems to be busy in his own world. These two factors do not guarantee alertness, but they do free her to reach out from her home to meet the needs of others.

What has God withheld from you or me, or what has He taken away from us that we might be more alert to the needs of others? Instead of using this freedom, have we filled it with pets or possessions that require constant care and absorb our affections? Paul warns, ". . . Seek those things which are above. . . . Set your affection on things above, not on things on the earth" (Colossians 3:1-2).

When God withholds things from us, He is designing our happiness, not destroying it. He knows that the cares of riches choke out the Word. (See I Timothy 6:9.)

2. *INITIATIVE*

The second quality which this woman possesses is initiative. Notice that she takes initiative in the field of her own responsibility when she invites Elisha and his servant to join her and her husband for a meal.

Many of us are prompted by God's Spirit to meet a particular need, but we never take that first step to carry it out. The Shunammite woman could have hardly imagined the rich reward which would come from sharing a meal with one of God's servants. In Hebrews we are advised, *"Be not forgetful to entertain strangers: for thereby some have entertained angels unawares"* (Hebrews 13:2).

A Christian without initiative will be a Christian in a lonely, shrinking world. In fact, a Christian without initiative in good works won't even be recognized by the world as a Christian. Peter tells us that we are to be a unique people. And our uniqueness is in our zealousness to do good works. (See Titus 2:14.)

Not only is initiative vital for accomplishing good works, it is also vital in conquering evil. Romans 12:21 advises that we be not overcome by evil, but that we take the initiative and overcome evil with good.

3. PERSUASIVENESS

The third quality that this great woman from Shunem has is persuasiveness. She persuades others to do what is right. She "constrained him to eat bread." As we study her life we see a possible source of persuasiveness.

Her husband is old and no doubt his friends are also old. To reason with older men requires that you first learn and understand the wisdom which they have gained over the years. As she spoke with the prophet, he was no doubt impressed with the maturity of her insight and the wisdom of her words.

The need for every one of us to communicate with older people is emphasized by God in the way He designed the family. If you take away the grandparents from your family, you remove the richness from your children's heritage.

Many would say to the Shunammite woman, "Your marriage is a mismatch. You have so little in common." But what others would look at as a prison, God looks at as a classroom. The responsibilities we have in our own family will always uniquely prepare us for any ministry we have outside the family.

God has given women an extra ability to exercise persuasiveness. Joab called on a woman to persuade David to forgive Absalom. God used Esther to persuade the king to save her people. Adonijah asked Bathsheba to persuade Solomon to give him a certain girl to be his wife.

On the other hand, the strange woman persuaded the simple young man to follow her to immorality. Eve persuaded Adam to eat the forbidden fruit. God wants us to use all the persuasiveness we have in motivating others to love and good works. *"And let us consider one another to provoke unto love and to good works"* (Hebrews 10:24).

4. HOSPITALITY

The fourth quality that this woman from the town of Shunem has is hospitality. Hospitality is an art that many have never learned. Yet we are commanded in Scripture to be *". . . given to hospitality"* (Romans 12:13).

Hospitality is the ability to make others feel at home in our world. *". . . As oft as he passed by, he turned in thither to eat bread."* The fact that he repeatedly returned reveals that she possessed the true skills of hospitality.

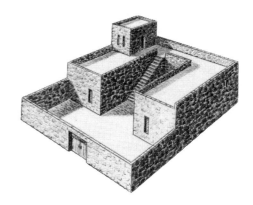

The prophet's chamber made for Elijah

Hospitality involves meeting the needs of others without the appearance of tension or pressure. That effect requires personal organization. Hospitality is meeting the needs of others without desire for personal gain. That requires sincere motives.

Some people invite a guest for dinner to tell him all their problems. Others invite an important guest so they can impress their friends. But this woman from Shunem seems to be free from ulterior motives.

Later, when the prophet wanted to reward her hospitality, she assured him that she was content and had need of nothing. This kind of contentment is a key to hospitality.

5. PERCEPTION

The fifth quality that this Shunammite woman has is perception. She is able to perceive the true character of people. She said to her husband, *"...I perceive that this is an holy man of God...."* Perception into the character of others is an essential element of greatness.

This woman did not bring every passerby into her home. She discerned who God would have grace her table and enrich her family. Scripture warns that there are some people you are not to invite to your home for a meal. I Corinthians 5:11 says, *"...I have written unto you not to keep company, if any man that is called a brother be a fornicator, or covetous, or an idolater, or a railer, or a drunkard, or an extortioner; with such an one no not to eat."*

We are also instructed in II John 10-11, *"If there come any unto you, and bring not this doctrine, receive him not into your house, neither bid him God speed: For he that biddeth him God speed is partaker of his evil deeds."*

We put our approval on the ones we invite into our home. It is important for parents to enlarge their world and the world of their children by bringing guests to their home. But it is equally important that they perceive the character of those who are their guests.

David said that he would make godly men and women the heroes in his home. *"Mine eyes shall be upon the faithful of the land, that they may dwell with me ..."* (Psalm 101:6).

How do we develop perception into the true character of people? This Shunammite woman reveals one secret. We do it by serving people. It didn't take very many meals before she picked up Elisha's attitudes and actions that reflected inner character. One who serves people knows what they are really like because a man's true character is revealed by the way he treats those who serve him.

This Shunammite woman and her husband lived in two different worlds, but it is clear that her initiative in reaching out to the needs of others brought her and her husband closer together. She did not plead, "Will you make a room for our guest?" She said, "Let us make a room for our guest." And from that project new life came to that couple.

The matter of hospitality is clearly demonstrated in the early church. They went from house to house sharing their meals with joy. They used mealtimes to share Scripture with others and to teach young Christians. This was a key to the growth of the church. This practice might have resulted in neighbors wondering why a certain family had become so popular all of a sudden only to learn that they had just become Christians.

Apparently God wanted to give us further encouragement to follow her example by telling us the end of her story in II Kings 8:1-6.

"Then spake Elisha unto the woman, whose son he had restored to life, saying, Arise, and go thou and thine household, and sojourn wheresoever thou canst sojourn: for the Lord hath called for a famine; and it shall also come upon the land seven years.

"And the woman arose, and did after the saying of the man of God: and she went with her household, and sojourned in the land of the Philistines seven years.

"And it came to pass at the seven years' end, that the woman returned out of the land of the Philistines: and she went forth to cry unto the king for her house and for her land.

"And the king talked with Gehazi the servant of the man of God, saying, Tell me, I pray thee, all the great things that Elisha hath done.

"And it came to pass, as he was telling the king how he had restored a dead body to life, that, behold, the woman, whose son he had restored to life, cried to the king for her house and for her land. And Gehazi said, My lord, O king, this is the woman, and this is her son, whom Elisha restored to life.

"And when the king asked the woman, she told him. So the king appointed unto her a certain officer, saying, Restore all that was hers, and all the fruits of the field since the day that she left the land, even until now."

In order to benefit from the example of the great woman of Shunem, there are three questions which we must ask ourselves.

What changes must come in our priorities in order to invite guests into our home for a meal?

- _____
_____
_____

What changes must be made in our home to make it a Godly atmosphere for those guests?

- _____
_____
_____

What preparations must we make in our own life in order to encourage and strengthen the guests we have?

- _____
_____

4 *A HEALTH CENTER*

What is God's directive for increased health?

_____
_____
_____
☐_____
☐_____
☐_____
☐_____

Know why Satan hates our body

☐_____
☐_____
☐_____
☐_____

Discern the causes of sickness — James 5:14-16

☐_____
☐_____
☐_____
_____

Understand God's frame of reference for health

☐_____
☐_____
_____
☐_____
_____
☐_____
☐_____

Recognize false philosophies in medicine

☐_____
☐_____
_____
_____
_____
☐_____
_____
☐_____
_____

5 A CRAFT CENTER

Aquila and Priscilla used their home to make tents and also to start a church.

How does hospitality relate to home industry?

● _____

How does giving to the poor bring unexpected rewards?

● _____

_____

What character is reflected in products and service?

● _____

_____

● _____

THE IMPORTANCE OF ESTABLISHING HOME INDUSTRY WITH THE MOTIVATION OF GENEROSITY

Giving to a ministry

God has richly blessed home industries which were organized with the primary motive of giving to the needs of others.

Forty years ago, a young mother became a Christian through the witness of a Gospel ministry. She desired to send a contribution to this work, so she made up small cartons of salad and sold them to the local stores for resale. Her product was an instant success and the store owners placed more orders.

From that small beginning she now has a large salad-making business managed by her sons-in-law and grandson. She is now a widow and her financial needs are being fully met through this interstate enterprise.

Giving to the poor

Ten years ago the wife of an airline pilot became aware of the needs of poor people. She made arrangements with a wholesale fruit market to buy quantities of fruit at half the resale price. Then she took orders from her neighbors for fruit at forty percent off. The remaining ten percent less expenses was put into a fund to give to the poor.

She spent only one day a week getting the fruit early in the morning and having her neighbors pick it up. Word-of-mouth recommendations caused her business to grow to the point where she had to rent a warehouse, buy trucks, and hire personnel.

When her children came home with boxes of candy to sell for a school fund-raising program, she called the school and offered to organize a "market day" once a month for them.

The children could take home the order blank, and the PTA would supervise the distribution during a three-hour pick-up time in the afternoon. The plan was highly successful, and today she and her company are serving hundreds of schools with a gross annual income of over fifteen million dollars.

What is the key to successful home industry?

● _____

Giving to a need

A fourteen-year-old girl learned the importance of eating whole grain breads in order to maintain good health. The family bought a small grain mill and she began baking bread to give to friends.

The bread was so delicious and nutritious that they and others asked her to continue making it so that they could purchase it from her. She now has all the orders she can handle and still maintain her education training.

What are the cautions for a home industry?

● _____

_____

● _____

_____

6 A MINISTRY CENTER

When the preceding functions are restored to the Christian home, it will become a vibrant hub of life and outreach, and it will attract neighbors and friends who are looking for Spiritual answers and living demonstrations of successful Christians.

A dynamic home will unite grandparents, parents, and children, and it will produce sons and daughters who are mighty in God's Spirit.

Such homes will make a significant impact on our churches, communities, courts, businesses, health care, education, nation, and the world.

All the functions which should take place within the home will prepare sons and daughters to effectively fulfill each of their God-given responsibilities.

BEING MIGHTY IN (GOD'S) SPIRIT

MATURE MAN	SUCCESSFUL BUSINESS-MAN	LOVING HUSBAND	WISE FATHER	DYNAMIC LEADER
MATURE WOMAN	SUCCESSFUL HOME MANAGER	LOVING WIFE	WISE MOTHER	CONFIDENT TEACHER
Life Purpose - Spiritual Gifts	Investments	Relate gifts	Many Godly Generations	Growing Life Message
Moral Freedom	Protection	Six Purposes of Marriage	Transform Drives	Protecting Loved Ones
Yielding Rights	Cautions	Needs of Wife	Priorities of Home	Wisdom Searches
Forgiving	Generosity	Source of Grace	Seven Purposes of Suffering	Responding to Criticism
Under Authority	Management vs. Slothfulness	Preparation for Engagement	Discipline of Children	Education Principles
Clear Conscience	Good Name	Spirit of Marriage	Sins of Forefathers	Counseling Principles
Self-Acceptance	Frugality	Accept Wife	Ten Unchangeables	Rebuilding Marriages
Salvation	Christian Testimony	Covenant	Develop Faith	Soul-Winning and Establishing

* The topics of the Advanced Seminar organized according to life responsibilities.

Natural abilities which accomplish
temporal results, are changed at salvation
to gifts that can accomplish spiritual results

Gifts

Motivational - Given by Holy Spirit
Ministry - given by the Church
Manifestation - what the Holy Spirit does
    thru the use of the gift.

We should "do" all the gifts, but they
will be approached, done thru, the
motivational gift. It becomes
difficult to identify the motivational
gift of a mature Christian, using his
gift thru all the other gifts.

"Suggestions for Identifying your Gift
"Discover the reason you are using what
you think is a gift. The bottom line of
purpose will define the gift

"ask" What irritates you about Christians?
"Your gift will enable you to be very clear
where others are not.
"What stands out to you in the life of Christ?

GIFTS HELP US TO;

1 Understand ourselves 2 Understand others
3 Understand what needs to be developed
in our lives
  a fruitful expression of my gift comes thru
learning to see thru the gifts of others.

HOW TO UNDERSTAND SPIRITUAL GIFTS

GIVER

EXHORTER   TEACHER

SERVER   ORGANIZER

ROPHET   MERCY

GIFTS BALANCE EACH OTHER

The full potential of a life, a marriage, a family, or a church will not be experienced until there is a clear, Biblical understanding of spiritual gifts. For this reason Paul writes in I Corinthians 12:1:

"Now concerning spiritual gifts, brethren, I would not have you ignorant."

NOTES

DIAGRAMS

UNDERSTANDING SPIRITUAL GIFTS

Spiritual gifts are an expression of the "manifold grace of God." (See I Peter 4:10.) Just as there are many gifts, there are many ways to organize them for study and application. The following division has brought joy and freedom to thousands of Christians who have wondered what their spiritual gifts are and how they could effectively use them.

GOD'S GIFTS TO MAKE US MIGHTY IN SPIRIT

1. WHAT ARE SPIRITUAL GIFTS?

Drives opportunities and results given by the Holy Spirit to achieve God's supernatural goals 1 Cor. 12-14

Each person who is born again into God's kingdom takes on a "debt of love." It is designed to motivate us to fulfill the law of God. Thus, we are instructed in Romans 13:8, *"Owe no man any thing, but to love one another: for he that loveth another hath fulfilled the law."* God gives spiritual gifts so that we are able to pay our debt of love.

2. WHO IS GIVEN A SPIRITUAL GIFT?

Every Christian. It is activated at Salvation when the Holy Spirit unites with our Spirit. Roms. 16-17

When we are born physically, we possess certain natural abilities. When we are born again spiritually, God takes these natural abilities and turns them into the means by which He can work through us supernaturally.

Christ *"... gave gifts unto men ... For the perfecting of the saints, for the work of the ministry, for the edifying of the body of Christ: Till we all come in the unity of the faith ..."* (Ephesians 4:8, 12–13).

3. HOW MANY GIFTS DOES EACH CHRISTIAN HAVE?

There are 3 types of gifts: motivation, ministry, and manifestation 1 Cor 12:4-7. We have one motivational gift and the possibility of many ministry and manifestation gifts 1 Pet 4:10; 1 Cor 12:3/

*"Now there are diversities of **gifts**, but the same Spirit. And there are differences of **administrations**, but the same Lord. And there are diversities of operations, but it is the same God which worketh all in all. But the **manifestation** of the Spirit is given to every man to profit withal"* (I Corinthians 12:4-7).

Each Christian's motivational gift is given by the Holy Spirit. The Greek root word for gift is *charisma,* which comes from the word *char* meaning "joy". *Charis* is the Greek word for *grace,* which is God giving us the desire and power to do His will. (See Philippians 2:13.)

The Greek word from which operations comes is *emergeia.* Its English equivalent is *energy.* As God gives power through our motivational gift, the effects produced by it are the operations (*energema*) or manifestions of the Spirit.

Each Christian may also have several ministry gifts given by the local church. After listing the ministry gifts in I Corinthians 12:28-30, Paul concluded by saying *"But covet earnestly the best gifts . . ."* those that would most effectively strengthen believers and advance the kingdom of God.

Peter emphasizes the singularity of the motivational gift when he states, *"As every man hath received the gift, even so minister the same one to another, as good stewards of the manifold grace of God"* (I Peter 4:10).

4. WHY DO WE RECEIVE ONLY ONE MOTIVATIONAL GIFT?

So we can concentrate on it Rom 12:6-8

So we can see our need for each other Rom 12:3-5

The ear is designed to carry out a different function than the eye, and the hand to perform different functions than the foot. Gifts are distributed so that no one Christian will *". . . think of himself more highly than he ought to think; but to think soberly, according as God hath dealt to every man the measure of faith. For as we have many members in one body, and all members have not the same office: So we, being many, are one body in Christ, and every one members one of another. Having then gifts differing according to the grace that is given to us . . ."* (Romans 12:3-6).

If one Christian had all seven motivational gifts, he would certainly be self-sufficient and would not need the other members.

5. HOW DO WE DISCOVER OUR MOTIVATIONAL GIFT?

• Accept Christ for salvation Rom. 10:9-13

• Enter into Christ's victory over sin

It is significant that spiritual gifts are not explained in the first chapter of Romans, but in the twelfth chapter, after sin has been identified and conquered in the believer's life.

• Concentrate on the needs of others Eph 4:12-13

Only as we begin using our gifts will we confirm them and also see the need for others' gifts.

• Discern your real motive in helping others Rom 12:4

• Identify what Christians do to irritate you 1 Jn 3:16

Most Christians fail to understand that their spiritual gifts allow them to see needs which are overlooked by those with other gifts. Rather than frustrating them, this should be their signal to confirm their gifts and use them to help others see what they see.

• Understand the categories of gifts

• Distinguish the characteristic misuses of each gift

Most of the problems which we face come when we try to fulfill our spiritual gift in the energy of the flesh rather than by the energizing power of the Holy Spirit. Most of those who have discovered their spiritual gift have done so by detecting misuses of their natural abilities.

THE PERSONAL REWARDS OF SPIRITUAL GIFTS

Knowing we have a gift that is valuable to the Body of Christ, we are able to achieve a deeper level of self-acceptance and purpose in life.

As we exercise our gifts, we experience personal fulfillment and a deep sense of joy. By concentrating on our gifts, we achieve maximum fruitfulness with minimum weariness.

6. WHAT ARE THE THREE CATEGORIES OF SPIRITUAL GIFTS

Diversities of:
Gifts

Verse: *1 Cor 12:4*

Greek word: *Charismaton-gift*

- *Charis -grace*
- *Char -joy*
-

Category:

1 Motivation

Gifts listed in:

Rom 12: 3-9

". . . Gifts differing according to the grace . . ." (Rom. 12:6)

Basis of classification:

This passage not only emphasizes grace, but it explains the function of faith in recognizing and using our spiritual gifts.

The term *motivation* is simply a definition of the work of God's grace: "the desire and power which He puts within us to accomplish His will."

Diversities of:
Administrations

Verse: *vs. 5*

Greek word: *Diakanion*

It is from this Greek work that we get our English word *deacon.* This word relates to the ministries and outreach of the local church.

Category:

2 Ministry

Gifts listed in:

1 Cor. 12:27-31

". . . God hath set some in the church. . . ." (I Cor. 12:28)

Basis of classification:

Since the ministry gifts are to function within the local church, it is obvious that this list should be classified as ministry gifts.

Ministry gifts are confirmed by ordination, as when Paul said to Timothy, *"Neglect not the gift that is in thee, which was given thee by prophecy, with the laying on of the hands of the presbytery" (I Timothy 4:14).*

Diversities of:
Operations

Verse: *vs. 6*

Greek word: *Energema-Effect*

- *Phanerosis -To show*
-
-

Category:

3 Manifestation

Gifts listed in:

1 Cor. 12: 7-11

The manifestation given ". . . to profit withal . . ." (I Cor. 12:7)

Basis of classification:

Verse 7 continues the thoughts of verse 6, speaking of the result of the Holy Spirit's work.

It is our responsibility to develop our motivational gifts. It is the church's responsibility to confirm ministry gifts, and it is the Holy Spirit's function to reward the use of the gifts for the profit of all.

7. HOW ARE GIFTS USED TODAY?

Motivation	Ministry	Manifestation

Motivation

1. PROCLAIM

proclaim truth
expose sin

Old Testament prophets predicted judgment for the sins of God's people. Today the motivation of a prophet is to use Scripture to reveal unrighteous motives and actions.

2. SERVING *desires to free others to they can serve better*

meet needs
free others

The mature motivation of a server is to minister to Christ by meeting the needs of fellow believers.

3. TEACHING

Clarify truth
validate
information

The motivation of a teacher is to make sure that the facts are accurate so that the decisions which are based upon them can also be correct.

4. EXHORTING

Stimulate faith
promote growth

The motivation of an exhorter is to see Christians grow in faith and maturity so that unbelievers will be attracted to the Gospel by their lives.

Ministry

1. APOSTLES

Sent forth
missionary

In New Testament days, "the Apostles" referred to the Twelve. The meaning of the Greek word for apostle is "one sent forth."

Paul was an apostle to the Gentiles and was sent forth from Antioch along with Barnabas and later Silas. The Latin word for *apostle* is translated "missionary."

2. PROPHETS

Proclaimers,
Confront Christians

A pastor who proclaims God's truth in the pulpit is fulfilling the ministry of a prophet.

3. TEACHERS

Instructors
Clarify message

The ministry of a pastor will also involve teaching. In fact, a qualification for an elder is that he be "apt to teach." All parents are to be teachers of their children, and older women are to be teachers of younger women.

4. MIRACLES

Supernatural deeds
active faith

This ministry gift grows out of believing prayer. As we exercise faith in prayer, God is able to accomplish natural or supernatural events with precise timing in order to bring glory to Himself.

Manifestation

1. WORD OF WISDOM

Seeing life from
God's perspective

As a Christian exercises his gift, one of the results is that he develops a fear of the Lord. This is the "beginning of wisdom." (See Proverbs 1:7.)

2. WORD OF KNOWLEDGE

Comprehending
Christ and His Word

Knowledge comes as the Holy Spirit opens one's understanding, because things of God are spiritually discerned. (See I Corinthians 2:14.)

3. FAITH

Visualizing what
God wants accomplish

Faith is the result of hearing the Word of God as it is proclaimed and taught. (See Romans 10:17.)

4. HEALINGS

Removing diseases
from spirit soul
or body.

The diseases of the spirit are bitterness, greed, and guilt. The diseases of the soul are discouragement, worry, jealousy, and other destructive attitudes. (See Psalm 103:1-3.)

5. GIVING

Extends assets
maximize results

The motivation of a giver is to make wise investments in order to advance the work of the Lord. He is very alert to how funds are used. In order to have more funds available, the giver is frugal with personal spending. Givers who do not have their own assets are motivated to find other sources where funds or resources can be obtained.

6. ORGANIZING

The motivation of an organizer is to coordinate the efforts and resources of many to achieve agreed upon goals. In the same way that the giver views financial resources, the organizer manages assets of human abilities and time. The organizer is able to visualize the final objective and knows how and when to delegate tasks.

7. MERCY

The motivation of one with the gift of mercy is to mentally and emotionally relate to the feelings of those around him. Just as the server focuses on physical needs, the one with the gift of mercy concentrates on giving empathy and comfort during times of distress.

5. HEALINGS

Spiritual, mental
physical restorer

Healing was a part of Christ's earthly ministry. So it should continue to be an outreach of the local church. Just as medical missions are used in other countries, medical clinics operated on Biblical principles should serve the community at home. Bringing healing to the spirit and the soul is often a prerequisite to physical healing.

6. HELPS

assist leadership
aid needy

The Scriptural scope of the responsibility of the local church includes taking care of the fatherless, the widow, and also the poor.

7. GOVERNMENTS

oversees, guides
local church

The ministry of governments involves those in official capacities who guide the local church. It is significant that this ministry gift is included near the end of the list. Organization which is most effective is least visible.

8. TONGUES

various
languages

The four purposes of the ministry of tongues in the early Church are discussed in the following pages.

5. MIRACLES

natural or supernatural
events with precise
timing to bring
Glory to God

Just as the ministry gift of miracles is the expression of prayer, so it is the function of the Holy Spirit to direct our prayers. (See Romans 8:26.)

6. PROPHECY

Bring to light
secret motives of
the heart

It is the ministry of the Holy Spirit to convict of sin, of righteousness, and of judgment to come. (See John 16:8–11.)

7. DISCERNING OF SPIRITS

Recognizing
what is of God
vs. the world the
flesh or the devil.

Discerning of spirits must be done by the power of the Holy Spirit. He bears witness with our spirit when something is or is not of God.

8. VARIOUS TONGUES

Glorifying God
thru language
and music

The Holy Spirit energizes the tongue to edify believers through language and music.

THE HISTORICAL PURPOSES OF TONGUES

Gifts were given "... for the edifying of the body of Christ: Till we all come in the unity of the faith..." (Ephesians 4:12-13). It is ironic that a gift given to unify has brought division.

The material on these next pages is designed for Christians who will diligently seek a common Biblical ground on tongues so that the prayer of Christ in the Garden might be fulfilled:

American Museum of Photography (Philadelphia)

"Neither pray I for these alone, but for them also which shall believe on me through their word; That they all may be one; as thou, Father, art in me, and I in thee, that they also may be one in us: that the world may believe that thou hast sent me" (John 17:20-21).

1 To introduce the Gospel in many languages fulfilling the prophecy of Joel

"... We do hear them speak in our tongues the wonderful works of God" (Acts 2:11).

"But this is that which was spoken by the prophet Joel; And it shall come to pass in the last days, saith God, I will pour out of my Spirit upon all flesh: and your sons and your daughters shall prophesy, and your young men shall see visions, and your old men shall dream dreams" (Acts 2:16-17).

2 To confirm that Gentiles became believers

"And as I began to speak, the Holy Ghost fell on them, as on us at the beginning.... Forasmuch then as God gave them the like gift as he did unto us ... what was I, that I could withstand God?" (Acts 11:15, 17).

3 To provide New Testament truth to the young church before the New Testament was written

The New Testament was completed near the end of the first century. The first letter to the Corinthians was one of the earliest books written after the Church was established (circa A.D. 56, approximately twenty years after the death of Christ).

4 To edify the spirit of a believer

"He that speaketh in an unknown tongue edifieth himself; but he that prophesieth edifieth the church" (I Corinthians 14:4).

SEVEN PREREQUISITES FOR TONGUES FROM THE CORINTHIAN EXPERIENCE

Because of the disturbance which the misuse of tongues created in the Corinthian church, the Apostle Paul established the following conditions to be met before any tongues could be used in the Church. (See I Corinthians 14.)

1 IT MUST EDIFY EVERY BELIEVER

"... Let all things be done unto edifying" (verse 26).

2 IT MUST NOT CONFUSE UNBELIEVERS

"If therefore the whole church be come together into one place, and all speak with tongues, and there come in those that are unlearned, or unbelievers, will they not say that ye are mad." (verse 23).

3 IT MUST BE MINIMAL

"Yet in the church I had rather speak five words with my understanding, that by my voice I might teach others also, than ten thousand words in an unknown tongue" (verse 19).

4 IT MUST BE DONE BY ONLY A FEW

". . . Let it be by two, or at the most by three, and that by course . . ." (verse 27).

5 THERE MUST BE AN INTERPRETER

"But if there be no interpreter, let him keep silence in the church . . ." (verse 28).

6 IT MUST NOT BE DISRUPTIVE

"And the spirits of the prophets are subject to the prophets. For God is not the author of confusion, but of peace, as in all churches of the saints" (verses 32–33).

THE CONCLUSIONS OF SCRIPTURE ON TONGUES

1 Christians are to seek after prophecy which is proclaiming God's Word in a known tongue

"But covet earnestly the best gifts . . ." (I Corinthians 12:31). *"Wherefore, brethren, covet to prophesy . . ."* (I Corinthians 14:39).

2 The mark of a true disciple is whether he loves other Christians

"By this shall all men know that ye are my disciples, if ye have love one to another" (John 13:35).

3 The mark of spirituality is the ability of a Christian to restore another Christian

"Brethren, if a man be overtaken in a fault, ye which are spiritual, restore such an one in the spirit of meekness; considering thyself, lest thou also be tempted" (Galatians 6:1).

4 God's goal is that Christians be like-minded and in one accord

"Fulfil ye my joy, that ye be like-minded, having the same love, being of one accord, of one mind. Let nothing be done through strife or vainglory; but in lowliness of mind let each esteem other better than themselves" (Philippians 2:2–3).

THE BASIS OF UNITY AMONG CHRISTIANS FOR EDIFICATION IS MEDITATION ON SCRIPTURE

1 Meditation is equated with the fulness of the Holy Spirit

". . . Be filled with the Spirit; Speaking to yourselves in psalms and hymns and spiritual songs, singing and making melody in your heart to the Lord" (Ephesians 5:18–19).

"Let the word of Christ dwell in you richly in all wisdom; teaching and admonishing one another in psalms and hymns and spiritual songs, singing with grace in your hearts to the Lord" (Colossians 3:16).

2 Meditation fulfills Paul's requirements to pray and sing with his spirit and with the understanding thereof

"What is it then? I will pray with the spirit, and I will pray with the understanding also: I will sing with the spirit, and I will sing with the understanding also" (I Corinthians 14:15).

The way sheep ruminate illustrates the way Christians are to meditate upon God's Word.

3 Meditation constitutes the worship which God seeks

"But the hour cometh, and now is, when the true worshippers shall worship the Father in spirit and in truth: for the Father seeketh such to worship him. God is a Spirit: and they that worship him must worship him in spirit and in truth" (John 4:23–24).

4 Meditation develops the disciplines of the Holy Spirit

"But the fruit of the Spirit is love, joy, peace, longsuffering, gentleness, goodness, faith, Meekness, temperance: against such there is no law" (Galatians 5:22–23).

NOTES

DIAGRAMS

HOW THE SEVEN SENSE PERCEPTORS IN OUR BODIES ILLUSTRATE THE SEVEN MOTIVATIONAL GIFTS

Analogies between the physical body and the spiritual Body of Christ have their Scriptural roots in such passages as Romans 12:4–5.

"For as we have many members in one body, and all members have not the same office: So we, being many, are one body in Christ, and every one members one of another."

Significantly, this passage precedes the instruction concerning spiritual gifts.

Medical researchers have discovered seven sense perceptors in the human body. These are described in the latest edition of *Gray's Anatomy of the Human Body.* Each perceptor bears a striking resemblance to a spiritual gift.

1. HEAT PERCEPTORS   *PROPHET*

These perceptors send warning messages to the brain when heat passes a certain level of tolerance. When God's judgment was imminent upon His people, the **PROPHET** sounded the alarm.

2. TOUCH PERCEPTORS – *SERVER*

LIGHT

The slightest touch is registered by these perceptors and sent to the brain for a response. When a person taps another, he usually seeks to gain attention in order to have a need met. The **SERVER** would respond to such a situation.

3. BALANCE PERCEPTORS   *TEACHER*

If the body leans too far out of balance, these perceptors will call for muscle response to correct the situation. When doctrine is out of balance, the **TEACHER** is instantly alerted and calls for immediate documentation and correction.

4. STRETCH PERCEPTORS   *EXHORTER*

These perceptors register the amount of stretching which takes place when skin is in the process of growth or use. Similarly, the **EXHORTER** is alert to the spiritual growth and steps of progress that Christians are experiencing.

5. COLD PERCEPTORS   *GIVER*

When an object near the skin is colder than the skin, it draws warmth from the body to itself. This action is detected by cold perceptors. A **GIVER** would respond to the need of a person who is cold and hungry.

6. PRESSURE PERCEPTORS   *ORGANIZER RULER*

Deep pressure in the body triggers these perceptors, which in turn signal the brain to shift the weight of the body and thus avoid pain. When an **ORGANIZER** recognizes that too much pressure is building up on a few people, he will delegate the load to others to avoid serious consequences.

7. PAIN PERCEPTORS   *MERCY*

These perceptors signal the brain when damage is occurring within the body. It is significant that other perceptors can be adapted to or ignored, but these cannot. A person with the gift of **MERCY** will feel the pain of another and will not be able to rest until the cause of the pain is removed.

HOW VARIOUS MANIFESTATIONS CAN RESULT FROM ONE MOTIVATIONAL GIFT

Motivation	Ministry	Manifestation
1. PROPHECY	**1. APOSTLES**	As this exhorter exercises his gift through the ministry of teaching, any one or all of the following results may occur in the hearts and lives of his hearers.
2. SERVING	**2. PROPHETS**	**1. WORD OF WISDOM** One listener saw forgiveness from God's point of view.
3. TEACHING	**3. TEACHER**	**2. WORD OF KNOWLEDGE** Another learned how to gain a clear conscience.
4. EXHORTING Let us suppose that an exhorter is invited to speak to a group of Christians, and he senses the need to guide his hearers to remove guilt. He is motivated to help them clear their consciences so that they are free to grow spiritually.	Let us further assume that the exhorter presents his message in the form of an instructional class and that he was assigned to this opportunity by his church. He would then be using the ministry gift of teaching.	**3. FAITH** Another visualized what God wanted to do in his life through a clear conscience.
	4. MIRACLES	**4. HEALINGS** Another person gained physical health by removing guilt.
5. GIVING	**5. HEALINGS**	**5. MIRACLES** Another experienced supernatural events that allowed him to clear his conscience.
6. ORGANIZING	**6. HELPS**	**6. PROPHECY** Another was deeply convicted and brought to repentance by seeing his true condition.
7. MERCY	**7. GOVERNMENTS**	**7. DISCERNING SPIRITS** Another recognized a root of bitterness within himself.
	8. TONGUES	**8. VARIOUS TONGUES** Another understood the prerequisites of glorifying God through language and music.

WHY EVERY CHRISTIAN MUST KNOW HOW TO EXERCISE ALL THE GIFTS

In the initial excitement of discovering your spiritual gift, you may incorrectly conclude that you cannot exercise any of the other gifts. The ultimate expression of every gift is personified in Christ. The more we become like Him, the more we will express each of the gifts in a balanced manner, even though we will use them all from one basic motivation.

> **It is only as we learn the skills of the other six gifts that we will be able to use our own gift effectively.**

Each of us is commanded in Scripture to perform the functions of all seven gifts regardless of what our particular motivation may be.

1. PROCLAIMING TRUTH (Prophet)

"Follow after charity, and desire spiritual gifts, but rather that ye may prophesy. . . . He that prophesieth speaketh unto men to edification, and exhortation, and comfort" (I Corinthians 14:1, 3).

"Preach the word; be instant in season, out of season; reprove, rebuke, exhort with all long-suffering and doctrine" (II Timothy 4:2).

2. SERVING OTHERS (Server)

"For, brethren, ye have been called unto liberty; only use not liberty for an occasion to the flesh, but by love serve one another" (Galatians 5:13).

". . . Verily I say unto you, Inasmuch as ye have done it unto one of the least of these my brethren, ye have done it unto me" (Matthew 25:40).

"And whatsoever ye do, do it heartily, as to the Lord, and not unto men; Knowing that of the Lord ye shall receive the reward of the inheritance: for ye serve the Lord Christ" (Colossians 3:23–24).

3. INSTRUCTING OTHERS (Teacher)

"Let the word of Christ dwell in you richly in all wisdom; teaching and admonishing one another . . ." (Colssians 3:16).

"Go ye therefore, and teach all nations, baptizing them in the name of the Father, and of the Son, and of the Holy Ghost: Teaching them to observe all things whatsoever I have commanded you: and, lo, I am with you alway, even unto the end of the world. Amen" (Matthew 28:19-20).

4. EXHORTING OTHERS (Exhortation)

"But exhort one another daily, while it is called To-day; lest any of you be hardened through the deceitfulness of sin" (Hebrew 3:13).

". . . Exhorting one another: and so much the more, as ye see the day approaching" (Hebrews 10:25).

5. SHARING WITH OTHERS (Giver)

". . . Freely ye have received, freely give" (Matthew 10:8).

"Give, and it shall be given unto you; good measure, pressed down, and shaken together, and running over, shall men give into your bosom. For with the same measure that ye mete withal it shall be measured to you again" (Luke 6:38).

"Distributing to the necessity of saints; given to hospitality" (Romans 12:13).

6. ORGANIZING (Ruler)

"[Every father must be] one that ruleth well his own house, having his children in subjection with all gravity; (For if a man know not how to rule his own house, how shall he take care of the church of God?)" (I Timothy 3:4–5).

"He that is slow to anger is better than the mighty; and he that ruleth his spirit than he that taketh a city" (Proverbs 16:32).

"Let all things be done decently and in order" (I Corinthians 14:40).

7. SHOWING MERCY (Mercy)

"Blessed are the merciful: for they shall obtain mercy" (Matthew 5:7).

"Bear ye one another's burdens, and so fulfil the law of Christ" (Galatians 6:2).

"Put on therefore, as the elect of God, holy and beloved, bowels of mercies, kindness, humbleness of mind, meekness, longsuffering; Forbearing one another, and forgiving one another, if any man have a quarrel against any: even as Christ forgave you, so also do ye. And above all these things put on charity, which is the bond of perfectness" (Colossians 3:12-14).

• **If you are not sure what your motivational gift is, choose any gift and begin practicing it.**

NOTES   **DIAGRAMS**

DISCOVERING YOUR

SPIRITUAL GIFT

THREE STAGES OF DISCOVERING YOUR SPIRITUAL GIFT

1 YOU ARE NOT SURE WHAT YOUR GIFT IS.

There may be several reasons for this including the tendency to confuse a ministry gift with a motivational gift.

2 YOU ARE SURE WHAT YOUR GIFT IS.

At this stage, you enjoy having fellowship with others who have the same gift. Beware of isolating yourself from interaction with all the gifts, since you will then tend to have a limited response to a given need or situation.

3 YOU DEMONSTRATE ALL THE GIFTS.

By learning to see a need or situation from the perspective of all seven gifts, you will greatly enhance the exercise and effectiveness of your own spiritual gift.

1 WHAT ARE THE CHARACTERISTICS OF THE GIFT OF PROPHECY?

GIFT	CHARACTERISTICS	MISUSES
PROPHECY  Bible Art Series, Standard Publishing, Cincinnati **Who in Scripture best illustrates the motivational gift of prophecy?** PETER Rom 12:9 **What guidelines are given for the gift of prophecy in Romans 12:9?** • Love w/out hipocrisy • Abhor evil • cling to good **What basic principle does the prophet most need to exercise?** Clear Conscience **Why is this true?** It allows the prophet to speak the truth boldly with love.	• need to express themselves Prophets need to express their thoughts and ideas verbally, especially when matters of right and wrong are involved. In the written account of the Gospels, Peter spoke more often than any other disciple. He also became the spokesman for the early Church. (See Acts 2:14; 3:12; 4:8; 11:4.) • Quick impressions of people. Prophets tend to make quick judgments on what they see and hear. They also tend to express their views before others speak. In the Gospels, Peter spoke first more than any other disciple. (See Matthew 14:28; 15:15; 16:16; 16:33; 17:4; 19:27; John 6:38; 13:6.) • alertness to dishonesty Prophets have an amazing ability to sense when someone or something is not what it appears to be. They react harshly to any form of deception or dishonesty. Peter must have sensed deception in Ananias and Sapphira since he was prompted to question them about it. His condemnation resulted in their deaths. (See Acts 5:3–10.)	• Exposing without restoring A prophet's primary concern about stopping the spread of evil tends to cause him to expose a sinner rather than restore him. In so doing, the prophet will fail a test of spirituality. (See Galatians 6:1.) The prophet, however, believes that exposure of sin is the first step of restoration. • Jumping to conclusions Prophets tend to draw conclusions from a few known facts. Once a hasty conclusion has been made, prophets tend to look for confirming evidence. This action can result in their taking words and actions of the accused out of context in order to prove their points. • Reacting harshly to sinners When a prophet sees sin, he tends to denounce it so strongly that it appears to others as an "overkill." After exposing the sin, the prophet tends to expect immediate repentance regardless of whether his rebuke was given in love or was even fully accurate. His motive in magnifying sin is to promote repentance.

CHARACTERISTICS	MISUSES
• Desire for justice	• Being unforgiving
Prophets tend to cut off those who sin so that justice will be done and others will be warned. Peter desired to cut off his offenders, and he asked Jesus how often he would have to forgive them. (See Matthew 18:21.) A prophet knows that "a little leaven leaveneth the whole lump."	It is very difficult for a prophet to make a separation between sin and the sinner. Therefore, he tends to reject them both with equal vigor. Those who hear his harshness interpret his denunciations as angry tirades. Peter's epistles provide a balance of truth and love.
• Open about their own faults	• Condemning themselves
Prophets are as open about their own failures as they want others to be about theirs. When Christ appeared to the disciples, Peter fell on his knees and said, "...Depart from me; for I am a sinful man, O Lord" (Luke 5:8).	The harsh judgments which prophets have for others, they also have for themselves. They tend to be extremely self-critical and feel worthless when they fail. After Peter denied Jesus, the heavenly messenger knew his need for extra reassurance and said, "...Go...tell his disciples and Peter..." (Mark 16:7).
• Wholehearted involvement	• Being impetuous
Once prophets are committed to a cause, they are wholeheartedly involved in it. Within the context of their commitment, they are quick to respond to situations and opportunities. When Peter recognized Jesus walking on the water, he asked Jesus to bid him to come. (See Matthew 14:28.)	Because of his tendency to make quick decisions, a prophet can be very impulsive and can vacillate between extremes. At first Peter refused to allow Jesus to wash his feet; then he asked Jesus to wash his whole body. (See John 13:6–10.)
• Loyalty to truth vs people	• Cutting off people who fail
Prophets are loyal to truth even if it means cutting off relationships. When Jesus asked the disciples if they were also going to leave Him, Peter replied that he would stay because Christ had the words of eternal life. (See John 6:67–69.)	Whenever prophets see or hear something that is wrong, they feel responsible to speak out against it. It does not occur to them to ask: "Whose responsibility is this? Do I have all the facts? Do I need to take action at this time?"
• Willingness to suffer for right	• Lacking tactfulness in rebuke
Prophets are eager to suffer when it comes to standing for the truth or doing what is right. Peter rejoiced that he was counted worthy to suffer shame for Jesus when he was beaten for obeying God rather than men. (See Acts 5:29–42.)	Prophets tend to be painfully direct when correcting others, no matter who they are. This bluntness can cause the prophet embarrassment, as when Peter rebuked Jesus for telling the disciples of His death. (See Mark 8:31–32.)
• Persuasive in defining truth	• Dwelling on the negative
Prophets have a special ability to be articulate in defining what is right and what is wrong. Great conviction was brought to thousands on the Day of Pentecost when Peter pointed out, "...Ye have taken [Jesus], and by wicked hands have crucified and slain [Him]" (Acts 2:23).	Prophets tend to divide everything into two classes — right or wrong. Once they label a person or activity, that judgment tends to be fixed in their minds, and they often feel compelled to persuade others to agree with them.

2 WHAT ARE THE CHARACTERISTICS OF THE GIFT OF SERVING?

GIFT	CHARACTERISTICS	MISUSES

GIFT

SERVING

Who in Scripture best illustrates the motivational gift of serving?

TIMOTHY

What guidelines are given for the gift of serving in Romans 12:10?

- _Kind affection_

- _Brotherly love_

- _Honor others_

What basic principle does the server most need to exercise?

Authority (must be under God given authority to best
Why is this true? _carry out gift)_

It gives the server protection for the management of his time.

CHARACTERISTICS

- _See and meet practical needs_

Important needs that would seem insignificant to others catch the eye and attention of the server. These needs are usually physical; however, the server knows that by meeting them he will bring encouragement and strength to those who receive his help.

Timothy's serving ability is noted by Paul: _"For I have no man like-minded, who will naturally care for your state"_ (Philippians 2:20).

- _Free others to achieve_

The joy of the server is not just initiating tasks, but knowing that through them he is bringing a peace of mind to another person which will allow that person to be more productive in the tasks which God has called him to do.

Timothy served Paul so that Paul could carry out his ministry. His serving was _". . . as a son with the father . . ."_ (Philippians 2:22).

- _Disregard for weariness_

Because the server sees the importance of the tasks which he has begun, he will freely use up personal assets of time, money, and strength. His focus is not on himself, but rather on the completion of the tasks which he knows will benefit the individual and bring joy to himself.

MISUSES

- _Giving un-requested help_

Sometimes the tasks which the server sees appear to be more important to the server than the one being served. It may even be that the one who has the needs is not aware of them to the degree that the server is. In either case, a server who uses his initiative in meeting these needs may be judged as "pushy or intrusive."

- _Letting things be too important_

In order to meet the needs of others, servers will often neglect their own home and personal responsibilities. They will meet the serving needs at home, but leave the other needs unmet. This transfer of attention may cause reaction by the server's family and the feeling by the one being served that too much attention is being put on physical things.

- _Working beyond physical limits_

Inner tension resulting in physical ailments and especially stomach problems often occurs in servers. This condition is the consequence of extending themselves on either one job or taking on too many jobs.

We know that Timothy had physical ailments by Paul's instruction to him to take medication _". . . for thy stomach's sake and thine often infirmities"_ (I Timothy 5:23). (Grape juice is very effective in calming stomach tensions.)

CHARACTERISTICS	MISUSES

CHARACTERISTICS

• _Difficulty in saying no._

As the server effectively meets one need, others may ask for similar help, not realizing the inner motivation of the server. These requests, however, are difficult to turn down because they represent needs, and the server feels obligated at having been asked.

• _alert to likes and dislikes_

Those with the gift of serving have an amazing ability to find out and remember the special interests of the people they serve. Thus, birthdays and anniversaries are special occasions for them. They can often recall favorite foods, special colors, types of home furnishings, and favorite activities and use this knowledge in making occasions special.

• _need approval_

Appreciation confirms to the server that his work is necessary, and it is being blessed by the Lord. The server also desires clear direction. Paul gave Timothy more praise and precise instructions than any other assistant. (See I and II Timothy.) Servers prefer working with a person rather than for a person.

• _Like_

The tasks which attract a server are usually immediate needs. The server often becomes frustrated with long-range planning or a continuous task which seems to have no visible progress. Timothy was urged to maintain endurance as a good soldier and to continue in the calling which he was given of God. (See I Timothy 4:16, and II Timothy 2:3.)

•_____

The server knows that by doing more than is expected he will not only delight the one being served, but demonstrate that he is doing it unto Lord. "Going the second mile" for a server may be trimming and sweeping after mowing the lawn or putting a bow and flower around a lunch box.

•_____

In an effort to complete tasks, a server will try to avoid committees and what to him appears to be unnecessary "red tape." In order to avoid delays, the server will use personal funds.

MISUSES

•_____

Servers are often placed in positions of responsibility because they are diligent workers. It is then easy for them to volunteer a helping hand or become involved in tasks which they should be delegating to others. This imbalance causes the server's authority to become frustrated because assigned tasks are not completed on schedule.

•_____

A server may react to people around him who, in his judgment, walk right past obvious needs. He assumes that others see what he sees. If he tells someone about a need and that person does not follow through on his suggestion, the server may become resentful.

•_____

If a server is given a physical job simply because he is a server and is expected to get his joy from doing it, he may feel misused and react in anger. He will then fail to remember that he is working for the Lord. A server's perspective may also be lost if the one whom he is serving is not making wise use of his time.

•_____

Because of the server's lack of desire or ability to properly delegate tasks, he will often develop his own time schedule and force others to adapt to it. Lack of delegation may also hinder the family from feeling involved in his serving and cause them instead to feel that they are taken for granted.

•_____

A server may react to a rigid schedule, not realizing that it is for his own protection. He may feel that it hinders him from the joy of additional serving. Twice Timothy was told by Paul not to get sidetracked. _"Do thy diligence to come shortly unto me. . . . Do thy diligence to come before winter . . ."_ (II Timothy 4:9, 21).

•_____

The purposes of God may be frustrated when a server meets a need that God intended to bring about repentance. If a server would have met the physical needs of the prodigal son while he was in the sty, it would have hindered his return. (See Luke 15:11–31.)

3 WHAT ARE THE CHARACTERISTICS OF THE GIFT OF TEACHING?

GIFT	CHARACTERISTICS	MISUSES
TEACHING  Who in Scripture best illustrates the motivational gift of teaching? _____ What guidelines are given for the gift of teaching in Romans 12:11? • _____ • _____ _____ • _____ What basic principle does the teacher most need to exercise? _____ Why is this true? It allows the teacher to become mighty in spirit.	• _____ When a teacher hears important statements, whether given privately or publicly, he will desire to verify them. His motivation is to confirm that the statements are true and accurate and would, therefore, have the authority to bring spiritual freedom. Luke wrote his Gospel to Theophilus, *"That thou mightest know the certainty of those things, wherein thou hast been instructed"* (Luke 1:4). • _____ A person with the gift of teaching will be very alert to false teachers. He will want to find out their background before listening to them. He will also assume that others want to know his qualifications; thus, he will tend to give these before speaking. Luke began his Gospel by affirming that he was an eyewitness and that he *". . . had perfect understanding of all things from the very first . . ."* (Luke 1:3). • _____ A teacher has a need to go to primary sources to validate truth. He will also use accepted works of recognized authorities to further confirm statements which others make. Luke praised the Bereans for daily checking out Paul's statements against the Old Testament Scriptures. (See Acts 17:11.) Luke also related his writings to the other Gospel accounts and to the Old Testament.	• _____ With the teacher's thoroughness in checking out facts, he will acquire much knowledge. Since *". . . knowledge puffeth up . . ."* (I Corinthians 8:1), it is very easy for him to become proud. He may also appear prideful by giving far more information than is needed to prove a point. Further pride can be communicated by the attitude "It isn't right until I check it out and say that it is right." • _____ Many teachers attempt to control misinformation by requiring approved courses of instruction. By depending only on these courses, credentials can be overemphasized, and the practical wisdom of those whom teachers consider uneducated can be despised or minimized. In such cases, teachers make the mistake of concentrating on intellectual knowledge rather than spiritual perception. • _____ Since he is able to use scholarly resources, a teacher can easily give the impression that he is the only source of truth and that his gift is more important than the other gifts. The teacher may also react to the need to bring his intellect under the control of the Holy Spirit, thus putting his scholarship ahead of the spiritual insight that comes through meditating on Scripture.

CHARACTERISTICS	MISUSES

Teachers tend to feel more comfortable when material is laid out in an orderly sequence. The teacher wants to know the events in the order in which they occurred. Luke emphasized the chronological structure of his Gospel when he explained that his approach was *"...to write unto thee in order..."* (Luke 1:3).

Those with the gift of teaching often have a greater delight in researching facts than they do in teaching them. When they do speak or write, they feel constrained to give as many facts as possible. Luke's Gospel is the longest of the four; he includes information left out by other writers, and he emphasizes the completeness of his account. (See Acts 1:1.)

A teacher enjoys giving details which are not noticed or mentioned by others. Luke gives precise descriptions of events, conversations, circumstances and physical conditions. He detailed more names, titles, cities, dates, events, and sidelights than any other Gospel writer.

A teacher is concerned that truth be presented in balance. He recognizes the danger of using personal experience as a foundation for truth. He wants to go from Scripture to experience, rather than from experience to a proof text in Scripture. A teacher tends to remain silent until information has been heard, observed, and verified. Luke's silence is conspicuous in the New Testament; none of his own statements are recorded.

A teacher tends to remain loyal to a mentor or a school as long as any truth remains and does what he can to promote the truth. Luke demonstrated amazing loyalty to Paul and his message in prison, even after others left him. *"...Only Luke is with me"...* (II Timothy 4:11).

If a teacher learns that his facts are wrong, he will not simply accept the conclusion but will want to retrace his own investigation to determine at what point he got off the track. He will desire to use the same procedure in helping others who have strayed from the truth.

A teacher's motivation to verify all statements by the authority of Scripture may hinder him in making wider Scriptural application. As he focuses on textual studies, he may miss the underlying principles that tie all Scripture together *"... for doctrine, for reproof, for correction, for instruction in righteousness"* (II Timothy 3:16).

When a Christian with the gift of teaching shares a conclusion, he feels obligated to explain how he arrived at it. He often assumes, wrongly, that because he enjoyed the research so much, others will also. Concentration on research may also cause a teacher to live in an unreal world which he has created by his exclusion of other people.

If a teacher fails to subject his intellect to the teaching ministry of the Holy Spirit, he will need to reexamine the "foundational truths of Scripture." These are to be understood by faith. His theology will become the reorganization of Scripture around a philosophical base.

The most effective way for anyone to keep his intellect under the control of the Holy Spirit is to meditate upon God's Word day and night. Neither the inspiration or the true meaning of Scripture will be understood intellectually, but will be discerned spiritually. If a teacher fails to become mighty in Spirit, he will tend to become trusting of his own intellect.

Truth out of balance leads to heresy. Imbalance begins by studying a doctrine out of its moral setting (i.e., the second coming without its purifying hope; communion without self-examination). Argumentation and division result. Imbalance also occurs by separating related truths (i.e., mercy without justice, grace without law).

If a teacher leans on his own understanding, it is easy for him to reject an important spiritual truth because he detects a minor flaw in the presentation of it. He may further reject this truth because he is being asked to intellectually accept a conclusion without knowing how the other person arrived at it.

4 WHAT ARE THE CHARACTERISTICS OF THE GIFT OF EXHORTING?

GIFT	CHARACTERISTICS	MISUSES

EXHORTING

Bible Art Series, Standard Publishing, Cincinnati

Who in Scripture best illustrates the motivational gift of exhorting?

_____

_____

What guidelines are given for the gift of exhorting in Romans 12:12?

• _____

_____

• _____

_____

• _____

_____

What basic principle does the exhorter most need to exercise?

_____

Why is this true?
It allows the exhorter to understand and explain God's sovereignty.

CHARACTERISTICS

• _____

_____

The motivation of an exhorter is to see spiritual growth take place in practical living, and he is willing to become personally involved to see it achieved. Paul said, "... I travail in birth again until Christ be formed in you" (Galatians 4:19). Paul further declared that he worked night and day to "... present every man perfect [mature] in Christ Jesus" (Colossians 1:28).

• _____

_____

An exhorter can discern the spiritual maturity of another person. Based on this, the exhorter is motivated to search out hindrances in the lives of those who are not growing spiritually and to give further encouragement to those who are. Paul saw the Corinthians as spiritual infants and therefore could not speak unto them "... as unto spiritual, but as unto carnal . . ." (I Corinthians 3:1).

• _____

_____

An exhorter has the ability to visualize spiritual achievement for another Christian and then help him work out practical steps of action to achieve it. These steps are designed to remove hindrances and develop personal disciplines through which the Holy Spirit can work. Paul told Timothy to flee youthful lusts, to avoid foolish questions, and to follow righteousness with a pure heart. (See II Timothy 2:22-23).

MISUSES

• _____

_____

An exhorter's willingness to give people whatever time is necessary to help them grow spiritually often cuts into family time and personal responsibilities. He often assumes that his family will understand, until major resentments surface. Paul understood the sacrifices that he was making in his ministry; however, if an exhorter is married, his priority must be his marriage. (See I Corinthians 7:32-34.)

• _____

_____

As an exhorter gains experience and success in counseling, he tends to categorize problems as he hears them and arrive at conclusions before getting all the facts. By failing to listen completely and sense direction from the Holy Spirit, an exhorter can be guilty of the folly of giving the wrong direction. (See Proverbs 18:13.)

• _____

_____

When an exhorter gives steps of action, he assumes that they will be carried out. He bases this expectation on the fact that he has "come alongside" and is working with the person to achieve agreed upon goals. As spiritual growth becomes visible, it is easy for an exhorter to take personal credit for it. He may also be tempted to settle for outward conformity rather than true inward change.

CHARACTERISTICS	MISUSES
• An exhorter tends to use examples from the lives of others to help Christians see the potential of daily victory. Paul used the testimony of one church to motivate another church. (See II Corinthians 9:2.) He used his own life to illustrate God's grace since he was the chief of all sinners. (See I Timothy 1:15.)	• Exhorters tend to jump into new projects without finishing existing ones. They use projects to motivate others, and then when others are involved, the exhorters find a better project. After several projects, those who are working on them may become frustrated. The exhorter, however, sees the projects as simply a means to accomplishing a bigger perspective.
• Mature exhorters have learned by experience that God gives special grace during trials. Based on this, Paul gloried in tribulation. His credentials were the persecutions which he experienced and the counseling God gave him during his afflictions. (See II Corinthians 1:1-7.)	• The exhorter is constantly on the lookout for steps of action which will bring lasting results. As he works with his family or friends, they may get the impression that they are simply another counseling project rather than real people who need personal attention.
• An exhorter knows that true growth will not take place where there is guilt. Paul told Timothy that his chief weapon was a clear conscience. (See I Timothy 1:19.) An exhorter desires an open life to gain a wider hearing for the Gospel. Paul explained, "... I am made all things to all men, that I might by all means save some" (I Corinthians 9:22).	• The problem of treating family and friends as "projects" rather than people is made even worse as the exhorter shares private illustrations which came out of his counseling experiences. Exhorters depend heavily on illustrations to communicate their message. However, when these are used without permission, listeners become uneasy and those who were counseled become resentful.
• The exhorter is motivated to learn "cause-and-effect sequences" and through them to discover underlying principles of life. He studies both Scripture and experience to find these. His motivation is to promote spiritual growth and to bring diverse groups of Christians together.	• Exhorters tend to avoid heavy doctrinal teaching which does not have immediate practical application. The result of this emphasis can be an imbalance of teaching which will eventually show up as doctrinal error. Thus, the exhorter needs the balancing ministry of the teacher.
• An exhorter tends to explain truth with logical reasoning in order to motivate people to act upon it. Paul's writings in I Corinthians 15 have been studied in law schools for their logic. He reasoned with the Jews, the Greeks, King Agrippa, and others. (See Acts 18:4; 26:28.)	• Exhorters often visualize long-range projects and goals for people. These are usually presented without reference to the amount of time that will be required to achieve them. Those whom the exhorter motivates assume that the projects and goals will be achieved much sooner than they can be. This situation raises expectations and breeds disillusionment.
• An exhorter needs to see the facial expressions of his listeners in order to determine their response and to ensure a positive result. Paul's longing to see his fellow believers was constantly reaffirmed. (See I Thessalonians 2:17; 3:10; II Timothy 1:4.) He used personal conferences extensively. (See I Thessalonians 2:11-12.)	• Exhorters tend to lose hope with people who do not quickly and consistently respond to the steps of action which are given for spiritual growth. By surrounding himself with only those who do respond quickly, he loses valuable personal character training and insights which God must then teach in other ways.

5 WHAT ARE THE CHARACTERISTICS OF THE GIFT OF GIVING

GIFT	CHARACTERISTICS	MISUSES

GIVING

Who in Scripture best illustrates the motivational gift of giving?

_____

What guidelines are given for the gift of giving in Romans 12:13?

• _____

_____

• _____

_____

• _____

_____

What basic principle does the giver most need to exercise?

_____

Why is this true?

It allows the giver the freedom to respond to God's direction.

CHARACTERISTICS

• _____

_____

A giver has an ability to discern wise investments. His motivation is to use assets of time, money, and possessions to advance the work of the Lord. If a person with the gift of giving has limited funds, he is still able to use his ability of recognizing available resources and draw upon them when needed.

• _____

_____

A giver needs continuous reassurance that his decisions are in God's will whether he has little or much to give. To achieve this, he will first give himself and then his gift to the Lord. Since all believers must practice giving, Paul explained how the Macedonians "... first gave their own selves to the Lord, and unto us by the will of God" (II Corinthians 8:5).

• _____

_____

The giver's ability to discern value motivates him to provide quality gifts. He wants them to last. Matthew recorded in greater detail than any other Gospel writer the gifts given to Christ. He is the only writer who mentioned "the treasures" brought by the Magi; he described Mary's ointment as "very precious," and Joseph's tomb as "new." (See Matthew 2:11; 26:6–11; and 27:57-60.)

MISUSES

• _____

_____

An effective use of the gift of giving depends upon having the fear of the Lord. One way we learn the fear of the Lord is by regular giving. It was for this purpose that the tithe was established. (See Deuteronomy 14:22-23.) If a giver stops exercising his gift, he will not only begin to lose the fear of the Lord, but his storing up will cause him to become stagnant.

• _____

_____

A giver has a desire to make sure that his gifts are wisely invested and used. Thus, he will often buy a good quality item rather than giving the money for it. However, if items are purchased or projects are sponsored by a giver, he may be viewed as using his gifts to control lives and ministries.

• _____

_____

If a giver's focus is more on the quality of the gift than the need that it is meeting, he can cause the receiver to be dissatisfied with the quality of other things which he owns. A giver could also excuse personal luxuries on the basis that he is generous with his money. However, when he is not faithful in little, God will not trust him with much.

CHARACTERISTICS	MISUSES
• _____	• _____
A giver who is in fellowship with the Lord will be prompted to give even when a need is not obvious. His ultimate confirmation that this gift was according to God's will comes when he learns that it fulfilled an unknown need or answered a special prayer.	A giver who is not in fellowship with the Lord will begin to feel guilt as he stores up funds. Even if he is preparing for a special need, he must have the reassurance from the Lord that his plans are according to God's will.
• _____	• _____
Just as the giver looks to the Lord for direction, so he wants recipients to look to the Lord for provision. The giver knows that future reward is more valuable than present praise, thus he will give quietly and often anonymously. Matthew is the only Gospel writer who emphasized secret giving. (See Matthew 6:1–4.)	If a giver reacts to all appeals for funds and looks only for the hidden and unannounced needs, he may fail to get the mind of the Lord in a particular situation. He may also miss an important opportunity to give wise counsel as well as needed funds to a worthy ministry.
• _____	• _____
A mature giver understands the destructiveness of the love of money. He is very aware that the disciplines that God taught him in acquiring assets may not have been learned by those who need his assistance. Therefore, he looks for ways of giving which avoid dependency, slothfulness, or extravagance.	The frugality of a giver is often extended to his own wife and children. However, if he does not show the same concern, care, and delight in meeting their needs as he does others, they will react to his generosity. By listening to the Lord and the counsel of his wife, he will avoid the damaging consequences of unwise gifts or investments.
• _____	• _____
The personal assets which the giver has are often the result of consistent personal frugality while being content with basics. A giver will always be concerned in getting the best buy, not with how much he has left. He will spend extra effort in saving money and being resourceful with what he has.	If a giver loses his focus on meeting the needs of people, he may be unduly attracted to projects. His desire for measuring value may prompt him to build a "memorial to his generosity." The emphasis of Scriptural giving is distributing to the necessity of saints. Paul's collection was for the needy Christians.
• _____	• _____
The motivation of a giver is to encourage others to give. He wants them to experience the joy and spiritual growth that comes by sacrificial giving. Thus, the giver may provide matching funds or the last payment in order to encourage others to give.	When a giver lets others know what he is giving, he will cause many to turn their attention from the Lord to him. He also runs the danger of attracting carnal Christians with wrong motives. These people are trained to appeal to his human inclinations and extract funds which were not directed by the Lord.
• _____	• _____
A giver reacts to pressure appeals. He looks instead for financial needs which others tend to overlook. A husband who has the gift of giving will often confirm the amount that he should give by seeing if his wife has the same amount in mind.	If a giver is not instantly obedient to the promptings of the Holy Spirit, he may lose the joy of seeing God accomplish a miraculous provision through him. The one who was to receive the gift will also be denied the opportunity of seeing God provide funds precisely when needed.

6 WHAT ARE THE CHARACTERISTICS OF THE GIFT OF ORGANIZING?

GIFT	CHARACTERISTICS	MISUSES

ORGANIZING

Who in Scripture best illustrates the motivational gift of organizing?

_____

What guidelines are given for the gift of organizing in Romans 12:14?

• _____

_____

• _____

_____

• _____

_____

What basic principle does the organizer most need to exercise?

_____

Why is this true?

It causes the organizer to learn to be sensitive to the needs of others.

• _____

_____

When a major project is given to an organizer, he is able to picture the completed task and what it will take to accomplish it. When Nehemiah was given the task of removing the "great affliction and reproach of God's people in Jerusalem," he immediately visualized the need to rebuild the walls. (See Nehemiah 1:2–3.)

• _____

_____

In order for an organizer to visualize the completion of a task, he needs to know who and what his resources are. Since the efficiency of his entire operation depends upon the faithfulness of the workers, he would rather have fewer that he can count on than more that he cannot count on. Nehemiah required an oath of cooperation from the rulers, nobles, and people. (See Nehemiah 5:1–13.)

• _____

_____

An organizer knows which tasks to delegate and which he must do himself. He also is able to sense which workers will need more assistance than others. Organizers are able to naturally maintain a continued accountability with their workers. Nehemiah delegated the building of the walls, but he retained responsibility for dealing with the enemies. (See Nehemiah 4:13.)

• _____

_____

If an organizer is in the position of authority, he can simply direct people based upon his gift of seeing the bigger picture. However, if he is not in this position, he must earn the right to be heard. Then he must patiently explain that all the steps which he sees are required to reach the goal. An organizer will tend to make suggestions and then react or become discouraged when these are not followed.

• _____

_____

An organizer is very sensitive to loyalty. He depends upon it to accomplish his goals or the goals others have for him. An organizer in charge of a work may single out individuals whom he thinks are especially important to his goals and show them favoritism or partiality. If he is not in charge, he may cause disharmony by openly expressing frustration.

• _____

_____

When a person with the gift of organization is not in charge, it is easy for him to delegate his responsibilities to others. His work may be completed; however, he will miss the character training and other objectives which the one who assigned him the task had in mind. His authority and others may then react to him and accuse him of laziness and irresponsibility.

CHARACTERISTICS	MISUSES
•_____	•_____

<table>
<tr><td>

•_____

Once an organizer commits himself to a task, he is willing to endure much opposition to his leadership. This reaction may come from insiders or outsiders. However, he knows that without the continuous pressures that he must exert, the final goal will not be achieved. Nehemiah responded to persistent opposition from outside enemies and fellow workers. (See Nehemiah 4:8-18.)

•_____

An organizer has the ability to take seemingly impossible tasks and break them down into achievable goals. Nehemiah took the huge task of rebuilding the walls of Jerusalem and broke it down into smaller sections which each family or group was able to complete. (See Nehemiah 3:1-32.)

•_____

An organizer notices what others might consider small details, but which he knows are essential in order for the project to be completed in the proper way. He also tends to remove himself from distracting details in order to focus on the ultimate goal. Nehemiah did not get involved in actual building; however, he removed obstacles such as financial pressures which would have hindered the workers. (See Nehemiah 5:1-13.)

•_____

The efficiency of organizers begins before they start a project by checking out and securing needed resources. Nehemiah secured timber from the king's forest before the rebuilding began. Organizers also place workers according to their strengths and weaknesses so that maximum productivity can be achieved.

•_____

Because the final goal is clearly visualized by the organizer, he is able to quickly evaluate requests and situations and make firm decisions. Nehemiah was consistently invited by his enemies to come and have a conference with them. His decision not to come was immediate and decisive.

•_____

In an organizer's mind the job is not finished until everything is back in its place. He will inspire and encourage workers to complete a job by approval, praise, reproof, and challenge. The organizer's final joy is seeing all the parts come together. It doesn't matter to him if others appreciate the job as long as he knows it was accomplished according to the plans laid out.

</td><td>

•_____

When an organizer who is in charge of a project rejects valid suggestions or closes his ears to grievances, pressures result. These cause him to become harsh or even resign. When an organizer is not responsive to directions from his authorities, he must be disciplined. If he reacts, he will build patterns of resentment and pride.

•_____

When an organizer reacts to people who do not have his spiritual gift, he is usually focusing only on their inefficiency and disorganization. By reacting, he overlooks their real needs and potential and damages important relationships and the potential ministry which God intended for him.

•_____

If an organizer is given a position of authority in the local church, he will appoint workers on the basis of their ability to get the job done. If serious character flaws are discovered in a valuable worker, the organizer will be reluctant to dismiss him. Failure to do so, however, will communicate approval and acceptance of the behavior and will cause reaction or imitation by others.

•_____

When an organizer is put in charge of several people to accomplish a job, he may tend to give instructions without explanation. This neglect causes fellow workers to feel like pawns in a chess game. Their feelings of being used are intensified if they are not given proper praise or appreciation when the work is done.

•_____

An organizer can misuse his special abilities of persuasion and decisiveness by coercing others to help him achieve personal ambitions. They can also be misused on legitimate jobs by insensitivity to the schedules, weariness, or personal priorities of his workers.

•_____

The fulfillment of an organizer is to see a job completed. However, before moving on to a new job he must make proper provision for maintenance of the completed job. When this trait is carried over into the personal life of an organizer, he is never content with the things that he has or that he has done.

</td></tr>
</table>

7 WHAT ARE THE CHARACTERISTICS OF THE GIFT OF MERCY

GIFT	CHARACTERISTICS	MISUSES
MERCY Who in Scripture best illustrates the motivational gift of mercy? _____ What guidelines are given for the gift of mercy in Romans 12:15? •_____ _____ •_____ _____ What basic principle does the one with the gift of mercy most need to exercise? _____ Why is this true? It protects the one with the gift of mercy from improper relationships.	•_____ _____ A person with the gift of mercy will demonstrate loyalty to a friend by even reacting harshly toward those who attack him. When the Apostle John watched the Samaritans reject Jesus whom he loved, John wanted to call down fire from heaven to consume them. (See Luke 9:54.) •_____ _____ The very nature of a person with the gift of mercy requires close friendships. These friendships, however, must have mutual commitment which is often reaffirmed. John enjoyed such a friendship with Christ. He was not only closer to Christ than most of the other disciples, but he referred to himself as the "disciple whom Jesus loved." (See John 13:23; 19:26; 20:2; 21:7, 20.) •_____ _____ The gift of mercy enables the one having it to sense which individuals are hurting and to share the pain with them. Along with the pain, a mercy senses the full scope of emotions. John wrote his first epistle to give joy, fellowship, hope, and confidence and to cast out fear and torment. (See I John 1:3-4; 3:2-3; 4:18; 5:13-14.)	•_____ _____ The tendency of one with the gift of mercy is to take up an offense for someone who is being hurt by another person, especially if the one being hurt is a friend. Before comfort is given, a prophet should check out what caused the hurt, and an exhorter should give steps for properly responding to it. •_____ _____ The deep need for commitment in a close friendship can cause those with the gift of mercy to monopolize the time and attention of others. As he experiences disappointments in one friendship, the mercy tends to place greater demands on a new friendship. •_____ _____ If those with the gift of mercy do not have spiritual discernment as to why people suffer, they may give sympathy and encouragement to those who are suffering as a direct result of violating God's moral laws. The one with the gift of mercy can learn discernment by seeing people through the eyes of the other spiritual gifts.

CHARACTERISTICS	MISUSES

CHARACTERISTICS

• _____

Those with the gift of mercy find it hard to be firm because they do not want to offend other people. Therefore, the mercy must see that greater hurt and offenses will occur if he fails to be decisive. When John was faced with denying Jesus, he demonstrated a boldness and decisiveness which caused the Sadducees to marvel. (See Acts 4:13.)

• _____

The gift of mercy carries with it the ability to sense genuine love. It, therefore, carries a greater vulnerability to deeper and more frequent hurts from those who fail to demonstrate sincere love. John used the word "love" more than any other disciple in his Gospel and epistles.

• _____

One with the gift of mercy has a deep understanding of people who are going through mental or emotional distress. This sensitivity causes those with hurts to be drawn to him and to confide in him. When Christ died, he transferred responsibility for his grieving mother to John.

• _____

Whereas an exhorter will try to help a person find benefit from his hurts, the one with the gift of mercy will try to remove the source of them. The message of John's first epistle was for Christians to stop hurting and hating each other. (See I John 3:11, 15.)

• _____

A person with the gift of mercy tends to need physical closeness in order to be reassured of acceptance. The closeness includes rich times of fellowship. John sought out the closest place to Christ at the Last Supper and leaned upon the Lord. His need for physical closeness may also have prompted his request to sit next to Christ in glory. (See Mark 10:35-37.)

• _____

The statement that opposites attract is certainly true with the motivational gifts. Those with the gift of mercy are attracted to those with the gift of prophecy. The firm truth of the prophet is thus balanced with the gentle love of the mercy. John spent more time with Peter than with any other disciple. (See Luke 22:8; Acts 3:1-11; 4:13-19; 8:14.)

MISUSES

• _____

When a person with the gift of mercy is given a position of leadership, he will tend to avoid disciplinary action which is needed. As a result, the person who should have been disciplined is not brought to repentance, prophets react to his leadership, and other "mercies" react to the prophets.

• _____

Because those with the gift of mercy have such sensitive feelings, they tend to base their decisions on emotions rather than on principles. Their subjective reasoning can easily cause them to reject Biblical doctrines which seem harsh to them.

• _____

A person of the opposite sex tends to be drawn to one who has the gift of mercy. This attraction comes about because of the ability of the "mercy" to be a sensitive, understanding, and responsive listener. This factor must be considered in any relationship which a "mercy" has with a person of the opposite sex.

• _____

Unlike exhorters, who look at suffering as a means of receiving more grace and growing spiritually, those with the gift of mercy tend to react to the idea that God would allow a good person to suffer. Unless the person with the gift of mercy maintains a proper perspective, he can easily become bitter toward God.

• _____

When a person with the gift of mercy demands physical closeness in a friendship, he may fail to consider the desires of others who need that person's time and attention. For this reason, John was gently reproved for his request to be next to Jesus in His kingdom.

• _____

A person whose words and actions reflect insensitivity to the feelings of other people will be quickly recognized and reacted to by one with the gift of mercy. Rather than trying to help this insensitive person, the "mercy" will tend to close off his spirit and cut off fellowship with him.

WHICH ONE OF THESE SEVEN PERSONS BEST DESCRIBES YOU?

PERSON NUMBER 1

- ☐ You want to make sure that statements are true and accurate.
- ☐ You desire to gain as much knowledge as you can.
- ☐ You react to people who make unfounded statements.
- ☐ You check the credentials of one who wants to teach you.
- ☐ You use your mind to check out an argument.
- ☐ You enjoy spending hours doing research on a subject.
- ☐ You like to tell others as many facts as you can on a topic.
- ☐ You pay close attention to words and phrases.
- ☐ You tend to be silent on a matter until you check it out.
- ☐ You like to study material in a systematic sequence.

PERSON NUMBER 2

- ☐ You can visualize the final result of a major undertaking.
- ☐ You enjoy coordinating the efforts of many to reach a common goal.
- ☐ You can break down a large task into achievable goals.
- ☐ You are able to delegate assignments to others.
- ☐ You see people as resources that can be used to get a job done.
- ☐ You are willing to endure reaction in order to accomplish a task.
- ☐ You require loyalty in those who are under your supervision.
- ☐ You remove yourself from petty details to focus on the final goal.
- ☐ You can encourage your workers and inspire them to action.
- ☐ You move on to a new challenge once a job is finished.

PERSON NUMBER 3

- ☐ You see actions as either right or wrong.
- ☐ You react strongly to people who are not what they appear to be.
- ☐ You can usually detect when something is not what it appears to be.
- ☐ You can quickly discern a person's character.
- ☐ You feel a responsibility to correct those who do wrong.
- ☐ You separate yourself from those who refuse to repent of evil.
- ☐ You explain what is wrong with an item before you sell it.
- ☐ You let people know how you feel about important issues.
- ☐ You enjoy people who are completely honest with you.
- ☐ You are quick to judge yourself when you fail.
- ☐ You are willing to do right even if it means suffering alone for it.

PERSON NUMBER 4

- ☐ You can sense when people have hurt feelings.
- ☐ You react to those who are insensitive to other's feelings.
- ☐ You are able to discern genuine love.
- ☐ You desire deep friendships in which there is mutual commitment.

☐ You seem to attract people who tell you their problems.
☐ You find it difficult to be firm or decisive with people.
☐ You tend to take up offenses for those whom you love.
☐ You need quality time to explain how you feel.
☐ You want to remove those who cause hurts to others.
☐ You often wonder why God allows people to suffer.

PERSON NUMBER 5

☐ You motivate people to become what you see they could be.
☐ You like to give counsel in logical steps of action.
☐ You can usually discern a person's level of spiritual maturity.
☐ You enjoy working out projects to help people grow spiritually.
☐ You sometimes raise expectations of results prematurely.
☐ You dislike teaching which does not give practical direction.
☐ You like to see the facial responses of those whom you counsel.
☐ You often take "family time" to counsel others.
☐ You enjoy giving examples from the lives of others.
☐ You soon give up on those who do not follow your counsel.
☐ You find it hard to follow through on the project you have started.
☐ You identify with people where they are in order to counsel them.

Bible Art Series, Standard Publishing, Cincinnati

PERSON NUMBER 6

☐ You notice the practical needs of others and enjoy meeting them.
☐ You enjoy serving to free others for more important things.
☐ You are willing to neglect your own work to help others.
☐ You sometimes go beyond your physical strength in serving others.
☐ You can remember the likes and dislikes of others.
☐ You can usually detect ways to serve before anyone else can.
☐ You will even use your own funds to get a job done quickly.
☐ You do not mind doing jobs by yourself.
☐ You do not want public praise, but you do need to feel appreciated.
☐ You find it difficult to say "no" to those who ask for help.
☐ You like to put "extra touches" on the jobs you do.

PERSON NUMBER 7

☐ You are very frugal with money for yourself and your family.
☐ You enjoy investing money in the ministries of other people.
☐ You have an ability to make money by wise investments.
☐ You desire to keep your giving a secret.
☐ You react negatively to pressure appeals for money.
☐ You like to encourage others to give with your gifts.
☐ You want the ministries you support to be as effective as possible.
☐ You enjoy giving to needs which others tend to overlook.
☐ You sometimes fear that your gifts will corrupt those who get them.
☐ You desire to give gifts of high quality.
☐ You enjoy knowing that your gifts were specific answers to prayer.

Which person did you check the most?

1-Teacher; 2-Organizer; 3-Prophet; 4-Mercy; 5-Exhorter; 6-Server; 7-Giver.

NOTES

DIAGRAMS

HOW TO USE THE IRRITATIONS FROM OTHERS TO HELP YOU DISCOVER YOUR MOTIVATIONAL GIFT

1 Ask yourself: "What do Christians do or not do that disappoints me and causes unbelievers to reject the Christian life?

Bible Art Series, Standard Publishing, Cincinnati

David's sin brought reproach upon God's people and gave great occasion to the enemies of the Lord to blaspheme His Name. Nathan exercised his gift of prophecy in bringing David to repentance.

2 Realize that your answer to this question will be greatly influenced by your spiritual gift:

☐ They compromise with the world. **(Prophet)**

☐ They fail to demonstrate true Christian concern. **(Server)**

☐ They are substituting experience for sound doctrine. **(Teacher)**

☐ They are not growing to spiritual maturity. **(Exhorter)**

☐ They are not trusting God for their finances. **(Giver)**

☐ They are not accomplishing any major goals. **(Organizer)**

☐ They do not have genuine love for each other. **(Mercy)**

3 Determine what you can do **now** to begin resolving the problem that concerns you the most.

☐ Explain your understanding of the problem to God.

☐ Dedicate yourself to being part of the solution, whatever the cost.

☐ Ask God for wisdom as you read and memorize His Word daily.

☐ Take advantage of every little opportunity that He gives to you.

☐ Constantly evaluate your results in the light of God's Word and lasting fruit.

MY MOTIVATIONAL GIFT

Based upon what I have learned thus far, I believe that my motivational gift is:

_____

_____

I am not certain what my motivational gift is; however, I have been able to narrow it down to the following two:

_____

_____

UNDERSTAND THE BASIC MOTIVATION OF EACH SPIRITUAL GIFT

If each of the seven motivational gifts were represented in a family and someone dropped the dessert on the floor, here is what each one might say and why they would say it.

PROPHET
"That's what happens when you're not careful!"
(Motivation: To correct the problem.)

MERCY
"Don't feel badly. It could have happened to anyone."
(Motivation: To relieve embarrassment.)

SERVER
"Oh, let me help you clean it up."
(Motivation: To fulfill a need.)

TEACHER
"The reason that it fell is that it was too heavy on one side."
(Motivation: To discover why it happened.)

EXHORTER
"Next time, let's serve the dessert with the meal."
(Motivation: To correct the future.)

GIVER
"I'll be happy to buy a new dessert."
(Motivation: To give to a tangible need.)

ORGANIZER
"Jim, would you get the mop. Sue, please help pick it up; and Mary, help me fix another dessert." (Motivation: To achieve the immediate goal of the group.)

HOW TO USE QUESTIONS TO IDENTIFY YOUR BASIC MOTIVATION

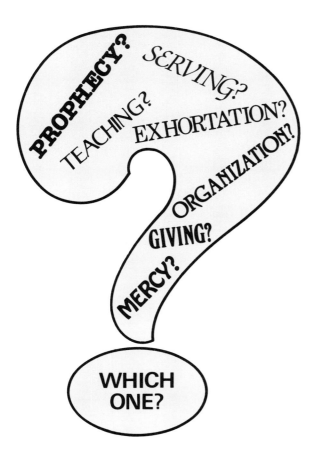

PROPHECY? TEACHING? SERVING? EXHORTATION? ORGANIZATION? GIVING? MERCY?

WHICH ONE?

Many Christians are confused about their motivational gift because they enjoy practicing many gifts. Use the following types of questions to help yourself analyze why you enjoy doing a certain activity. Let us suppose, for example, that you enjoy teaching a Bible class.

1. QUESTION: What would your basic motive be in teaching a Bible class?

   ANSWER: To encourage people to be honest before God and others. **(A prophet's motivation)**

2. QUESTION: But why do you want people to be honest with God and others?

   ANSWER: So that they will not hurt each other's feelings. **(A mercy's motivation)**

3. QUESTION: Why do you not want Christians to hurt each other?

   ANSWER: So that they will be able to grow spiritually. **(An exhorter's motivation)**

4. QUESTION: Why do you want Christians to grow spiritually?

   ANSWER: So that they can appreciate the true message of the Bible. **(A teacher's motivation)**

5. QUESTION: Why do you want Christians to understand the true message of the Bible?

   ANSWER: So that they can get their lives in order and be useful for God. **(An organizer's motivation)**

6. QUESTION: Why do you want Christians to be organized for God?

   ANSWER: So that they will be free to give to the Lord's work. **(A giver's motivation)**

7. QUESTION: Why do you want Christians to give to the Lord's work?

   ANSWER: So that we can meet the practical needs of Christians and unbelievers. **(A server's motivation)**

QUESTION: Why do you want to meet the practical needs of others?
ANSWER: I think that is most important.
CONCLUSION: Your gift must be serving.

SERIOUS MARRIAGE CONFLICTS ARE CAUSED WHEN ONE PARTNER FAILS TO UNDERSTAND THE MOTIVATIONAL GIFT OF THE OTHER OR WHEN ONE OR BOTH PARTNERS DEMONSTRATES THE NEGATIVE CHARACTERISTICS OF HIS OR HER SPIRITUAL GIFT.

UNDERSTAND HOW EACH GIFT RESPONDS IN A SITUATION

If seven Christians representing each of the motivational gifts visited a sick person in the hospital, here is what each one might say, based on the perspective of his gift.

SERVER
"Here's a little gift! Now, I brought your mail in, fed your dog, watered your plants, and washed your dishes."

TEACHER
"I did some research on your illness and I believe I can explain what's happening."

MERCY
"I can't begin to tell you how I felt when I learned you were so sick. How do you feel now?"

GIVER
"Do you have insurance to cover this kind of illness?"

ORGANIZER
"Don't worry about a thing. I've assigned your job to four others in the office."

PROPHET
"What is God trying to say to you through this illness? Is there some sin you haven't confessed yet?"

EXHORTER
"How can we use what you're learning here to help others in the future?"

HOW TO BEGIN PRACTICING OTHER GIFTS

1 DISCOVER WHAT GIFTS ARE AROUND YOU.

God has already placed around your life people whose gifts will complement yours. Your parents, brothers and sisters, marriage partner, Christian friends, and working associates all have spiritual gifts (if they are Christians) that will enrich your life as you find out what they are and how they operate.

Help those around you to discover their spiritual gifts by reviewing the characteristics of each motivational gift. Ask each person to identify the list which most accurately describes him or her.

THE MOTIVATIONAL GIFTS OF THOSE IN MY FAMILY

_____

_____

_____

_____

_____

THE MOTIVATIONAL GIFTS OF OTHERS

_____

_____

_____

_____

_____

2 TAKE A NEW LOOK AT CONFLICTS.

Most of the conflicts which we have with other Christians are simply the result of our misunderstanding their motivational gift or of their misusing that gift.

The most important point to remember in understanding other people is that each person sees a given situation from the perspective of his or her motivational gift.

Furthermore, each person will expect you to see those things which stand out to him or her. At the same time, you will probably expect others to see what is obvious to you in a given situation.

Not only will others expect you to see things from their perspective, but they will expect you to be as concerned about them as they are. Any lack of concern may be translated as a lack of spiritual maturity on your part or even as a sign that you are rejecting them.

3 LEARN TO SEE THROUGH THE EYES OF OTHERS.

Begin asking those with other gifts to tell you what things are important to them. Ask them to describe what they see in a particular situation. Encourage them to point out "blind spots" in your life or service for Christ.

Find Christians who are successfully using their gifts and study how they go about doing various things:

☐ How does a **prophet** identify and expose sin?

☐ How does a **server** see and meet practical needs?

☐ How does a **teacher** validate truth?

☐ How does an **exhorter** visualize steps of action?

☐ How does a **giver** make wise investments?

☐ How does an **organizer** get jobs done?

☐ How does a **mercy** know what hurts others?

NOTES   **DIAGRAMS**

UNDERSTAND HOW GIFTS ARE TO BE USED IN THE CHURCH

If seven Christians met together to organize the ideal church and each Christian represented a different motivational gift, here is what they would probably emphasize based on their spiritual outlook.

WHAT WE NEED IN OUR CHURCH:

PROPHET
Well-prepared sermons exposing sin, proclaiming righteousness, and warning of judgment to come.

GIVER
Generous programs of financial assistance to missionaries and other ministries.

SERVER
Practical assistance to every member of the church to encourage them and to help them fulfill their responsibilities.

ORGANIZER
Smooth-running organization throughout the church so that every phase will be carried out decently and in order.

TEACHER
In-depth Bible studies with special emphasis on the precise meaning of words.

MERCY
Special outreach and concern for the precise and varying feelings of individuals with a readiness to meet their needs.

EXHORTER
Personal counseling and encouragement for every member to assist them in applying Scriptural principles to their daily living.

TO WHAT DEGREE ARE YOU FINANCIALLY FREE?

PERSONAL EVALUATION:

YES NO

1. This morning, did you consciously ask God for the things you would need to get through this day? (See Matthew 6:9–15.) ☐ ☐

2. Can you list three of God's basic purposes for money? (See I Timothy 6:8; Malachi 3:10; II Corinthians 8:14–15.) ☐ ☐

3. Does a man need more than careful planning and hard work to be wealthy? (See Deuteronomy 8:18.) ☐ ☐

4. Has your study of God's Word increased since your last financial crisis? (See Haggai 1:9.) ☐ ☐

5. Have you ever lost money, a promotion, a job, or a friend because you refused to compromise your convictions? (See Proverbs 29:25.) ☐ ☐

6. Are you consistently giving at least ten percent of your income to your church? (See Malachi 3:10.) ☐ ☐

7. Have you paid all of your debts? (See Romans 13:8.) ☐ ☐

8. Does God intend for victorious Christians to suffer financial need? (See Philippians 4:12.) ☐ ☐

9. When you read a sales catalog, do you always check the price before studying the product? (See Luke 14:28.) ☐ ☐

10. If someone were to offer you a quick way to legally make a large amount of money, would you tend to turn it down? (See Proverbs 28:22.) ☐ ☐

11. Have you ever researched items in a consumer guide or consumer report? (See Proverbs 14:15.) ☐ ☐

12. Do you have accurate records for all of your expenditures? (See I Corinthians 4:2.) ☐ ☐

13. Is it your policy to refuse to co-sign for anyone? (See Proverbs 6:1–2.) ☐ ☐

14. Do you believe that mothers are able to accomplish more for the family's finances from within the home than outside of the home? (See Proverbs 31:10–31.) ☐ ☐

15. Have you ever kept a verbal promise even though it was costly to do so? (See Psalm 15:4.) ☐ ☐

16. Can you recall three instances in which you received money, goods, or services in answer to specific prayer? (See John 16:24.) ☐ ☐

17. Have you avoided business partnerships, especially equal partnerships? (See Matthew 6:24.) ☐ ☐

18. Is it wise for a man to work beyond retirement age as long as he is physically able? (See Luke 12:19–20.) ☐ ☐

19. Have you ever avoided an unwise business decision because you listened to the cautions of your wife? (See Proverbs 31:11, 26.) ☐ ☐

20. Have you ever sacrificially given a large sum of money to God? (See Matthew 6:19–20.) ☐ ☐

TOTAL CORRECT ☐

EVALUATION SCORE:

20 correct	=	Financial freedom
19–15 correct	=	Financial warning
14–10 correct	=	Financial danger
9–0 correct	=	Financial bondage

Answers:

The answer to each question is yes.

HOW TO GAIN FINANCIAL FREEDOM

Nebuchadnezzar

PRIDE AND BONDAGE

". . . Is not this great Babylon, that I have built for the house of the kingdom by the might of my power, and for the honour of my majesty? . . . And he was driven from men, and did eat grass as oxen . . ." (Daniel 4:30, 33).

FREEDOM BY HUMILITY

"Now I . . . praise and extol and honour the King of heaven, all whose works are truth, and his ways judgment: and those that walk in pride he is able to abase" (Daniel 4:37).

HOW TO GAIN FINANCIAL FREEDOM

1 LEARN THE IMPORTANCE OF FINANCIAL FREEDOM

* _____
_____

The importance of this point is illustrated in the program and methods of the coming antichrist. He will gain world domination by controlling all buying and selling. *"And that no man might buy or sell, save he that had the mark, or the name of the beast, or the number of his name"* (Revelation 13:17).

* _____
_____
_____

A man who has financial freedom can build his job around his family. A man without financial freedom is often forced to build his family around his job.

A man who lacks financial control with his money usually lacks self control in his morals. *"For by means of a whorish woman a man is brought to a piece if bread. . . . He that keepeth company with harlots spendeth his substance"* (Proverbs 6:26; 29:3).

One symptom of being "a lover of pleasure more than a lover of God" is exchanging the eternal riches of heaven for the passing enjoyments of this world. *"Lo, children are an heritage of the Lord: and the fruit of the womb is his reward. As arrows are in the hand of a mighty man; so are children of the youth: Happy is the man that hath his quiver full of them . . ."* (Psalm 127:3-5).

Financial debt damages God's reputation, since Scripture assures us *". . . My God shall supply all your need according to His riches in glory by Christ Jesus"* (Philippians 4:19).

* _____
_____
_____

Being forced to borrow is always a sign of God's judgment.

". . . The borrower is servant to the lender" (Proverbs 22:7).

"For the Lord thy God blesseth thee, as he promised thee: and thou shalt lend unto many nations, but thou shalt not borrow . . ." (Deuteronomy 15:6).

"But it shall come to pass, if thou wilt not hearken unto the voice of the Lord thy God, to observe to do all his commandments and his statutes which I command thee this day; that all these curses shall come upon thee, and overtake thee. . . . He shall lend to thee, and thou shalt not lend to him: he shall be the head, and thou shalt be the tail" (Deuteronomy 28:15, 44).

What is true for a nation is just as true for an individual. Some require the discipline of God's judgment for a time, but it is not something that we should seek or voluntarily enter into.

* _____
_____
_____

When Solomon asked for wisdom rather than money, God assured him that because he asked for wisdom he would get both, since they are related. (See I Kings 3:12-13.)

2 KNOW GOD'S FOUR PURPOSES FOR MONEY

* _____
_____
_____

Security is only possible as we build our lives around that which can never be destroyed or taken from us. Only the Lord and His Word qualify for this quality of security. *"And having food and raiment let us be therewith content"* (I Timothy 6:8).

A person who is not content with food and clothing will always have financial problems and spiritual problems. *"But godliness with contentment is great gain"* (I Timothy 6:6).

● _____

_____

_____

During the time of Christ, the Jews and Gentiles had no dealings with each other. God overcame this disunity among Christians by using the Jewish Christians to bring the Gospel to the Gentiles and then using the Gentile believers to bring financial relief to the Jews in Jerusalem who were experiencing famine.

The concept of this purpose for money was explained by Paul: *"But by an equality, that now at this time your abundance may be a supply for their want, that their abundance also may be a supply for your want: that there may be equality"* (II Corinthians 8:14).

> When was the last time that God prompted you to give to the need of another Christian?
>
> ● _____
>
> Did you obey God's prompting?

● _____

_____

"Bring ye all the tithes into the storehouse, that there may be meat in mine house, and prove me now herewith, saith the Lord of hosts, if I will not open you the windows of heaven, and pour you out a blessing, that there shall not be room enough to receive it.

"And I will rebuke the devourer for your sakes, and he shall not destroy the fruits of your ground; neither shall your vine cast her fruit before the time in the field, saith the Lord of hosts." (Malachi 3:10–11).

> **"For the eyes of the Lord run to and fro throughout the whole earth, to shew himself strong in the behalf of them whose heart is perfect toward him . . ." (II Chronicles 16:9).**

● _____

_____

One of the greatest protections that Christians can have from making wrong financial decisions is purposing to not move forward on any program unless and until the funds are available. This commitment will give both direction and timing for God's will.

God is just as able to give direction through the lack of funds as He is through the provision of funds.

When funds are not available for a purchase or a project, it could be for one or more of the following reasons:

1 WE DON'T NEED IT.

Life does not consist of the things that we possess but rather in our relationship to God and His power. God knows which items and activities will be damaging to us, and He will often use the lack of funds to protect us if we are committed to only act when funds are available.

If you have resources that could be used for some purchase or project which you are not completely sure is in the Lord's will, ask God to provide additional funds in a significant way in order to confirm the decision that God wants you to make. Many can give exciting testimonies of God's faithfulness to confirm direction in this way.

2 WE MISSPENT THE MONEY.

Many people who do not have sufficient money for food or clothing have a brand new television set in their home or other items which God never intended for them to possess. Some justify these items on the basis that they were purchased on time. This only compounds the financial aspects of the problem because of the interest payments.

If people give you funds designated for one purpose and they are used for another purpose, givers will not only be disappointed but will tend to eliminate further assistance.

3 GOD IS TESTING YOUR FAITH.

Very often God will provide funds or other items just when they are needed. He delights in the precise timing of a gift. The timing comfirms the gift's miraculous nature and causes us to rejoice in Him.

By having easy access to credit we do not need to trust God. (Until the bill comes and then we get our spiritual spanking.) But by waiting upon the Lord right up until the time that a decision must be made, we are forced to trust in the Lord, follow principles, and thereby grow in faith.

If you are waiting for funds and the bills are past due, you can be sure that God is not testing your faith. God always pays for what He orders and His payments are always on time.

4 YOU NEED TO MAKE A MAJOR CHANGE.

If you are in Christian work and the Lord is not providing funds for necessities, you can be confident that God is directing you to make a change in methods, location, or vocation. Sometimes a Christian worker will limit his ministry to just one age group. Lack of provisions may be God's way of saying, "Work with the whole family."

If the people to whom you are ministering are not open to your message, follow the example of Christ, Paul, and others by going to a new area. If these steps are taken and needed funds are still lacking, do what Paul did and get a "tent making job" so that you can have the privilege of ministering without charge.

5 YOU NEED TO CHECK YOUR ATTITUDES.

This point may actually be the most important of all. It might be the cause of more lost resources than any other, especially within employment. One man who had worked in a company for seventeen years without a promotion decided in anger to quit.

However, he remembered the instruction at the Basic Seminar on working at making your boss successful. From that day forward this became the secret motivation of his work on the job: to make his boss successful and to do his work as unto the Lord.

Within a short time his boss called him in and gave him a promotion after saying, "I do not know what has happened to you, but you have a whole new attitude on the job." Within a year, this employee became the vice president of that company.

A further testimony of the importance of this point is given in the following report:

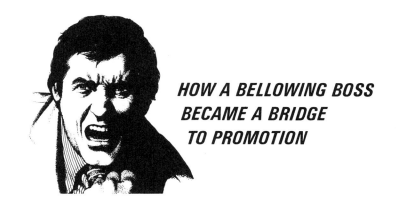

HOW A BELLOWING BOSS BECAME A BRIDGE TO PROMOTION

"A few years ago I really didn't like my job or much else. I had gotten pretty far away from God (really far). I knew God was the only way to really "get with it" and be happy, so I started seeking the Lord and putting my life right with Him.

"Shortly thereafter, I attended a Seminar and learned about making things right with our authorities. As a result, I asked my boss to forgive me for my bad attitudes. I stopped arguing and did all I could to please him. I worked in a packing house, which I considered to be a step above slave labor (or maybe a step below). My boss always hollered at me. Then my boss quit and went to another company. I thought, 'Real cool. Here I work, work, work, and then he leaves.'

"I could tell that God was wanting me to look at my job as though I were working for Him and not just for my earthly employer. I had been on the night shift, but within two weeks after deciding to really apply Scripture and let the Lord control my life, I got a day shift job and $100 a week raise. Shortly after this, my former boss asked me to go to his new company with him. Now I see why God wanted me to work as hard as I could.

"Actually, I thought that when I first started applying Scripture at work I'd get fired pretty fast. Now less than three years later, I have seven foremen and about 270 people working under me.

"I still can't believe how true the Scriptures are! When I first started reading Proverbs, it was as though someone were writing a book about my life. Now when I have a problem, I just look in the Bible and see what it says to do. It's really neat!

Used by permission.

3 SEE FOUR TYPES OF POVERTY

1. _____

_____

Samson was conquered by Delilah.

"For a whore is a deep ditch; and a strange woman is a narrow pit. She also lieth in wait as for a prey, and increaseth the trangressors among men" (Proverbs 23:27–28).

Blind Samson grinding in prison

"For by means of a whorish woman a man is brought to a piece of bread: and the adulteress will hunt for the precious life" (Proverbs 6:26).

2. _____

_____

_____

Doré Bible Illustrations

Job being informed about the loss of all his possessions and the death of all of his children.

"And said, Naked came I out of my mother's womb, and naked shall I return thither: the Lord gave, and the Lord hath taken away; blessed be the name of the Lord" (Job 1:21).

3. _____

_____

Bible Art Series, Standard Publishing, Cincinnati

Christ went from heaven's riches to a stable.

"For ye know the grace of our Lord Jesus Christ, that, though he was rich, yet for your sakes he became poor, that ye through his poverty might be rich" (II Corinthians 8:9).

NOTES

DIAGRAMS

4. _____

Bible Art Series, Standard Publishing, Cincinnati

Moses standing before the Pharaoh of Egypt, whose wealth he gave up to serve God's people

"By faith Moses, when he was come to years, refused to be called the son of Pharaoh's daughter; Choosing rather to suffer affliction with the people of God, than to enjoy the pleasures of sin for a season; Esteeming the reproach of Christ greater riches than the treasures in Egypt: for he had respect unto the recompence of the reward. By faith he forsook Egypt, not fearing the wrath of the king: for he endured, as seeing him who is invisible" (Hebrews 11:24-27).

4 RECOGNIZE GOD'S FINANCIAL REPROOFS (BONDAGE)

• _____

"He shall lend to thee, and thou shalt not lend to him: he shall be the head, and thou shalt be the tail" (Deuteronomy 28:44).

• _____

"No man can serve two masters: for either he will hate the one, and love the other; or else he will hold to the one, and despise the other. Ye cannot serve God and mammon" (Matthew 6:24).

• _____

"But they that will be rich fall into temptation and a snare, and into many foolish and hurtful lusts, which drown men in destruction and perdition" (I Timothy 6:9).

• _____

"The sleep of a labouring man is sweet, whether he eat little or much: but the abundance of the rich will not suffer him to sleep" (Ecclesiastes 5:12).

• _____

"He also that received seed among the thorns is he that heareth the word; and the care of this world, and the deceitfulness of riches, choke the word, and he becometh unfruitful" (Matthew 13:22).

• _____

"No man that warreth entangleth himself with the affairs of this life; that he may please him who hath chosen him to be a soldier" (II Timothy 2:4).

• _____

"He that hasteth to be rich hath an evil eye, and considereth not that poverty shall come upon him" (Proverbs 28:22).

• _____

"Now therefore there is utterly a fault among you, because ye go to law one with another. Why do ye not rather take wrong? why do ye not rather suffer yourselves to be defrauded?" (I Corinthians 6:7).

• _____

"Go to now, ye rich men, weep and howl for your miseries that shall come upon you" (James 5:1).

"Turn you at my reproof: behold, I will pour out my spirit unto you, I will make known my words unto you. Because I have called, and ye refused; I have stretched out my hand, and no man regarded; But ye have set at nought all my counsel, and would none of my reproof: I also will laugh at your calamity . . ." (Proverbs 1:23-26).

5 CHOOSE TO SERVE GOD, NOT MONEY

Each of us has at least one "Isaac" in our life. Our "Isaac" is the center of our affection. It could be a possession, or an ambition, or a person. It draws our attention throughout the day and brings delight whenever we think about it. It is what we build our plans around. Others know that it is a priority in our life.

We sacrifice other things for it and push away the thought that it could be taken from us someday. It is important that we identify our "Isaac" before the Lord and place it on His altar.

My "Isaac" is:

• _____

It is a serious step to give something to God. From the moment that it is turned over to Him, we have no more rights over it or authority to use it as we would choose. It now belongs to Him. The real test of whether or not we have fully yielded something to God comes when we are prepared to thank Him for whatever happens to it.

The purpose of giving our most cherished affection to God is so that He can work supernaturally through it, and that we can gain more of Christ. Paul testified, *"But what things were gain to me, those I counted loss for Christ. Yea doubtless, and I count all things but loss for the excellency of the knowledge of Christ Jesus my Lord: for whom I have suffered the loss of all things, and do count them but dung, that I may win Christ"* (Philippians 3:7–8).

"Though he slay me, yet will I trust in him: but I will maintain mine own ways before him" (Job 13:15).

"But without faith it is impossible to please him; for he that cometh to God must believe that he is, and that he is a rewarder of them that diligently seek him" (Hebrews 11:6).

HOW A WIFE TRADED WORLDLY PRESTIGE FOR SPIRITUAL POWER

The "Isaac" was an exciting career in a hospital operating room.

"Both my husband and I were deeply influenced at the Basic Seminar, but the big change occurred after my husband attended the Advanced Seminar in 1974. He grasped the concept of being an active member of the Lord's army. The disciplines that followed tested my submissiveness and willingness to trust him to be our spiritual leader.

"My husband had a good teaching position, and I was an operating room registered nurse—a job I loved even more than being the creative homemaker God intended me to be [her "Isaac"]. In spite of this, we were $10,000.00 in debt. My husband asked me to quit my job. It was a difficult decision; however, I did it!

"Next, we sold our brand new four-bedroom house and moved into a two-bedroom apartment! An even bigger adjustment was moving from Los Angeles to a farm in Texas. What a change—from the prestige and excitement of working in a hospital operating room to the privilege of hoeing in a cotton field during the summer. At times I felt that the Lord had completely forgotten about me, but I soon learned that the wisdom of the Lord is so much bigger than my tiny frame of reference.

"It was during the following three years that my husband and I really began to establish our goals and sincerely apply the teachings of God's principles to our lives. We had a time to memorize and meditate on God's Word. We also had the privilege of really experiencing God's grace because we were humbled, and humbled, and humbled some more.

"My husband worked for his father as a hired hand. When things looked bleak, he continued to be faithful in claiming God's promises for us. His desire was for us to get our home in order and then reach out to others. It would have been so much easier to reach out to others than to go through the painful process of getting our home in order.

"On the farm our salary is much smaller than we were used to, but now we are almost entirely out of debt. From the world's eyes it seemed impossible, and many times I thought, "If only my husband would let me work, we could get out of debt much faster. Now I praise the Lord that I did not work, because during this time God illustrated His power through miraculous answers to prayer for the things we needed. Among them was a car and a sewing machine.

"My learning will continue, but meanwhile I never could have imagined the results of these last three years. My husband and I enjoy a growing oneness of spirit. Our son is reflecting the character which we are learning; we are achieving financial freedom; and through the changes in our lives, our relatives have wanted to attend a Seminar.

"My father was led to salvation when he did attend, plus my brother-in-law. The spiritual revival in my immediate family is unbelievable. It makes any price we paid seem like a very small investment."

6 GIVE TITHES AS WEEKLY REMINDERS

"And blessed be the most high God, which hath delivered thine enemies into thy hand. And he gave him tithes of all" (Genesis 14:20).

"Thou shalt truly tithe all the increase of thy seed, that the field bringeth forth year by year. And thou shalt eat before the Lord thy God, in the place which he shall choose to place his name there, the tithe of thy corn, of thy wine, and of thine oil, and the firstlings of thy herds and of thy flocks; that thou mayest learn to fear the Lord thy God always" (Deuteronomy 14:22–23).

The significance of learning to fear the Lord is emphasized in the following passage:

"By humility and the fear of the Lord are riches, and honour, and life" (Proverbs 22:4).

"And I will rebuke the devourer for your sakes, and he shall not destroy the fruits of your ground; neither shall your vine cast her fruit before the time in the field, saith the Lord of hosts" (Malachi 3:11).

"Bring ye all the tithes into the storehouse, that there may be meat in mine house, and prove me now herewith, saith the Lord of hosts, if I will not open you the windows of heaven, and pour you out a blessing, that there shall not be room enough to receive it" (Malachi 3:10).

NOTES

DIAGRAMS

FURTHER QUESTIONS ABOUT TITHING
ANSWERED IN MEN'S MANUAL, VOLUME II:

☐ WHAT IS THE TITHE?

☐ IS TITHING A PART OF THE LAW THAT DOES NOT APPLY TODAY?

☐ WHAT IS THE REAL PURPOSE OF THE TITHE?

☐ WHERE IS THE TITHE TO BE GIVEN?

☐ WHEN SHOULD WE PAY THE TITHE?

☐ DOES THE TITHE INCLUDE MORE THAN MONEY?

☐ SHOULD A MAN TITHE IF HE IS IN DEBT?

☐ SHOULD A WIFE TITHE IF HER HUSBAND DOES NOT WANT HER TO?

☐ WHAT IF I HAVE NOT TITHED FOR SEVERAL YEARS?

☐ SHOULD A PERSON TITHE ON A DESIGNATED GIFT?

☐ SHOULD WE TITHE ON OUR GROSS INCOME OR OUR NET INCOME?

☐ SHOULD WE TITHE ON AN INHERITANCE THAT WAS GAINED BY SELLING HARMFUL ITEMS?

☐ SHOULD A PERSON TITHE FROM HIS SOCIAL SECURITY CHECK?

☐ CAN THE TITHE BE USED TO PAY THE TUITION AT A CHURCH SCHOOL?

☐ ARE THERE ONLY ETERNAL CONSE-QUENCES FOR NOT TITHING?

☐ SHOULD AN OLDER CHILD BE GIVEN MONEY TO PUT IN THE OFFERING PLATE IN ORDER TO TEACH HIM TO TITHE?

☐ IF WE INCREASE OUR TITHE, WILL GOD INCREASE OUR FINANCIAL REWARD?

ARE MY RESOURCES BEING DEVOURED BECAUSE I HAVE NOT FAITHFULLY TITHED?

Satan is the devourer of our money, possessions, family, and health. His means to bring about these losses are accidents, fires, natural disasters, excessive taxation, disease, or loss of employment.

God promises to rebuke the devourer when we tithe.

Yes No

☐ ☐ Have I been faithful in giving back to God as He has prospered me?

☐ ☐ Have I given God the first part of all my increase?

☐ ☐ Have I given it on the first day of every week?

"Upon the first day of the week let every one of you lay by him in store, as God hath prospered him..." (I Corinthians 16:2).

• Can I recall major financial losses that could be related to the devourer?

• Can I report instances of God's outpouring of blessing after I have given tithes and offerings to Him?

"... He which soweth sparingly shall reap also sparingly; and he which soweth bountifully shall reap also bountifully" (II Corinthians 9:6).

7 KEEP OUT OF DEBT

One of the most important initial steps in reaching financial freedom is to come to the conviction that you will not go into debt. This decision requires the following commitments:

☐ I will look to the Lord rather than rely on credit for the provision of my daily needs.

☐ I will reduce my standard of living to the level of God's provision.

☐ I will sell things of lesser importance, if necessary, to purchase things of greater importance.

☐ I will live without things rather than purchasing them on time payments or credit.

HERE ARE SOME OF THE REASONS WHY THIS COMMITMENT IS SO IMPORTANT:

• _____

_____

The message of Scripture on borrowing is quite clear: *Do not do it.* God commands Christians to keep out of debt altogether. *"Owe no man any thing, but to love one another..."* (Romans 13:8).

Strong's Exhaustive Concordance amplifies the message behind these words: "Owe to no one, no not anything, nothing at all."

• _____

_____

"The rich ruleth over the poor, and the borrower is servant to the lender" (Proverbs 22:7).

• _____

"Go to now, ye that say, To-day or to-morrow we will go into such a city, and continue there a year, and buy and sell, and get gain" (James 4:13).

• _____

"Ye ask, and receive not, because ye ask amiss, that ye may consume it upon your lusts" (James 4:3).

• _____

_____

_____

_____

_____

"Thou shalt not lend upon usury to thy brother; usury of money, usury of victuals, usury of any thing that is lent upon usury" (Deuteronomy 23:19).

• _____

_____

"But my God shall supply all your need according to his riches in glory by Christ Jesus" (Philippians 4:19).

ADDITIONAL CONSEQUENCES OF BORROWING EXPLAINED IN MEN'S MANUAL, VOLUME II:

☐ **IT GIVES THE ILLUSION OF INDEPENDENCE.**

☐ **IT ALLOWS THE BORROWER TO EVADE SELF-EXAMINATION.**

☐ **IT INTERFERES WITH GOD'S PROVISION.**

☐ **IT DEMONSTRATES DISCONTENT WITH BASIC PROVISIONS.**

☐ **IT STIFLES RESOURCEFULNESS.**

☐ **IT PROMOTES IMPULSIVE BUYING.**

☐ **IT WEAKENS PERSONAL FAITH.**

☐ **IT EXCLUDES HELP FROM OTHERS.**

☐ **IT CAUSES OVERSPENDING.**

HOW CAN A HOME BE PURCHASED TODAY WITHOUT GOING INTO DEBT?

In order to apply Scriptural principles of finances to the purchase of a home, it is first essential to comprehend God's purposes for the family.

God designed the family to be a dynamic functioning unit with each member supplying what other members need in terms of encouragement, training, counsel, health care, and financial assistance.

When a special need arises, the family's first purpose is to draw its members together. Only as resources are not available in the extended physical family is a member to appeal to the "family of the church." (See I Timothy 5:4–8.) This special need in the church is then to have the similar result of bringing all the members of the body together.

On the basis of this instruction, the family, especially the father, is to assist the son in preparing a home for the son's family.

"House and riches are the inheritance of fathers . . ." (Proverbs 19:14).

This same principle is beautifully illustrated in the relationship of Christ and His Father in the preparing of a home for the Bride of Christ.

It is significant that in the early part of this century, when the family was a strong unit, over ninety percent of the homes were built or purchased without mortgages.

Today, as the size of the family has been decreased and as the members have been encouraged to "be on their own," over ninety percent of the homes are purchased with mortgages.

Depleted families are in bondage to the bank and other creditors, and elderly parents give away what assets they have left to enter nursing homes.

In the light of God's priorities, every wise parent needs to re-examine the matter of expenditures for higher education and expensive cars. The Scriptural direction for receiving the best professional education is to study under a master in the trade.

In the times of unsurpassed quality in craftsmanship, it was not a question of what school you attended, but under whom you studied. Paul studied under Gamaliel; Timothy studied under Paul. The disciples studied under Christ. The potential of apprenticeship has been largely neglected in our day. Yet, its costs are much lower and results are far more superior than most people imagine.

With regard to the matter of an automobile, many people who say they are unable to purchase a home would be shocked to add up how much they have unnecessarily spent on depreciation and interest on new cars. If these resources had been better invested, the potential of a home would be within the reach of many young couples.

HOW ONE FAMILY DISCOVERED GOD'S SECRET OF OBTAINING A DEBT-FREE HOME

"Several years ago, my husband left the teaching profession and entered the building business. Months later, the economy and building prospects were at an all-time low. We were in debt for a car, a house, and four building lots.

"Our boys had always been in Christian schools and we were falling behind paying for their tuition, as well as loans, taxes, and living expenses. So we joined a direct sales company that kept us too busy and spending more money than we earned. We had the great promise and dream that within months our money problems would be over.

"Then my husband signed a contract to be a representative for a Christian organization. We were thrilled, as this was the culmination of a dream—to be in full-time Christian work. However, there was one "catch" to this opportunity—we had to borrow $2,500 to buy video equipment. We also bought another car on credit so my husband could travel more economically.

"About this time, I felt an urgency that we attend the Advanced Seminar in Atlanta. It was a joke to think we could afford a trip to Georgia since we lived on the West Coast. However, as we committed our priorities to the Lord, money came in from a variety of sources until we had all that we needed.

"After that week at the Seminar, we had new direction. The day spent on financial freedom changed our lives! We came home from Atlanta purposing to do three things."

THE PAINFUL FIRST STEPS

"First, we asked to be released from the contract with the Christian organization. By then the parent company was in financial distress, so we met some opposition. We wrote letters trying to settle the matter, but with no satisfaction. After several months, we dropped the issue and accepted the fact that none of this would have happened if we had waited for God to supply the resources for His work. We lost $2,500, plus the equipment.

"The second thing we purposed to do was to write a letter of resignation to the direct sales company outlining our new set of financial principles. Here again, we met with opposition, and our "friends" in this business no longer had any time for us.

"Our third purpose was to get out of debt, no matter how long it would take. It seemed as though we were going at life backwards, as far as our own understanding and that of those around us were concerned. But our own ways had caused problems, and we were now ready to do it God's way.

"At this point we either had to make more money or spend less—the choice was obvious. We examined our budget and canceled everything but necessities. We sold our economy car and bought one for $500. It ran well, but was hard on my pride.

"As if that wasn't enough, the ultimate sacrifice came when my husband informed me that we had to take our children out of the Christian school. We decided that I would teach them at home. Without carpooling and tuition, we saved $250 a month.

"There we were—not much work or money, home-bound, and no entertainment or extras. When we would get low and think God had surely gone to another country, He would send a check or a money order, often anonymously. Each month we would be in total amazement that we had enough to pay our bills.

"We could see that the major expense we had now was our house payment. Years before, we had refinanced our house to buy other property. We decided to try to sell our home, and with the equity we would build another house and pay our debts.

"In the meantime, my husband's former vice principal called to see if my husband would be interested in taking a half-time teaching position. Now we were sure that the Lord was working, because my husband would be able to teach half-time to provide for our family and work half-time on building a new house.

"It was as though once we committed our way to the Lord in our finances and He saw that we were willing to suffer the consequences of our previous wrong decisions, He began to "move our mountains." The next spring, the four lots we bought were all sold. Then, our house sold when houses were not selling.

"We began to build. Lumber prices were the lowest they had been in eight to ten years. The Lord provided many building materials through the classified ads and garage sales. We bought windows for $10 that should have cost $100. For $10 we found thirteen old turned table legs that we used for the balcony railing. Tile that would have cost over $400 in the store was $50. Sinks, faucets, molding—somehow it was available just when we needed it. We stood in amazement!

"For five years we have experienced God's provisions, and it has been etched in our minds that when we truly seek His kingdom first, all these things will be added to us. For $52,000 spent, He has given us a home which is appraised at $120,000, and we have reached our goal of "owing no man anything.""

THE DOUBLE BITE OF THE DEBT TRAP

If you increase your indebtedness by only $1,000 a year at 12% interest, compounded annually, the interest after 15 years will be $26,754, and your total indebtedness will be $41,754!

If you should then attempt to get out of debt by repaying the loan at $6,000 per year, it will take you almost 16 more years and cost an additional $53,696 in interest.

Your debt accumulation of $1,000 per year for 15 years has cost you a total of $80,450 in interest. This averages out to be $2,595 per year for the 31-year period.

Financial freedom is achieved far more quickly by decreasing expenses than by increasing income. Every dollar saved is equivalent to over $1.50 earned when taxes and expenses to earn it are taken into consideration.

> "God's work done in God's way will not lack God's support. He is just as able to supply funds ahead of time as afterward and He much prefers doing so."
>
> *J. Hudson Taylor*

Borrowing Years	Debt Addition	Interest	Total Debt
1	$1,000	$ 120	$ 1,120
2	1,000	254	2,374
3	1,000	405	3,779
4	1,000	574	5,353
5	1,000	762	7,115
6	1,000	974	9,089
7	1,000	1,211	11,300
8	1,000	1,476	13,776
9	1,000	1,773	16,549
10	1,000	2,106	19,655
11	1,000	2,479	23,134
12	1,000	2,896	27,030
13	1,000	3,363	31,393
14	1,000	3,887	36,280
15	1,000	4,474	41,754
		$26,754	

Repaying Years	Repayment	Interest	Balance Due
16	$6,000	$5,010	$40,764
17	6,000	4,892	39,656
18	6,000	4,759	38,415
19	6,000	4,610	37,025
20	6,000	4,443	35,468
21	6,000	4,256	33,724
22	6,000	4,047	31,771
23	6,000	3,813	29,584
24	6,000	3,550	27,134
25	6,000	3,256	24,390
26	6,000	2,927	21,317
27	6,000	2,558	17,875
28	6,000	2,145	14,020
29	6,000	1,682	9,702
30	6,000	1,164	4,866
31	5,450	584	—
		$53,696	

TOTAL INTEREST	**$80,450**

From *Men's Manual*, Volume II, page 82.

NOTES

DIAGRAMS

MEN OF GOD WHO REFUSED TO BORROW

NOAH

He could have borrowed money to build the ark. In fact, it would have been a shrewd move for him to have "floated" a loan; but it would have damaged his faith and his message. (See Genesis 6-7.)

JOASH

He could have borrowed money to pay the workmen who refurbished the temple. Instead, he collected the money ahead of time and gave it to the workmen as they had need of it. This caused joy among the people. (See II Chronicles 24:4-14.)

MOSES

He could have borrowed material to construct the tabernacle; but that would have made God the servant of the people, rather than teaching the people how to serve the true and living God. (See Exodus 25-27.)

EZRA

He could have borrowed money to rebuild the temple, but it would have been a poor testimony to the king and the heathen. God provided the funds through the king whom Ezra served. (See Ezra 7:11-28.)

DAVID

He could have borrowed money to build the temple. Instead, he spent his lifetime gathering the materials, and his son was then able to build a far more glorious structure —debt free.(See I Chronicles 17, 22.)

NEHEMIAH

He could have borrowed money to rebuild the walls of Jerusalem; but because of his obedience to the king, the king provided all that he needed for the building. (See Nehemiah 2:3-8.)

ABRAHAM

He could have borrowed money to buy the tomb for his wife, but it would have been a point of contention for many generations. Instead, he secured the land and the trees with a public contract. (See Genesis 23.)

PAUL

He could have borrowed money for his missionary journeys. He could have even asked people to support him. Instead, he earned his support by laboring night and day. He became an example to every Christian after him. (See Acts 18:3; 20:33-35.)

From *Men's Manual*, Volume II, page 83.

8 LIVE WITHIN YOUR INCOME

_____

_____

> "For ye know the grace of our Lord Jesus Christ, that, though he was rich, yet for your sakes he became poor, that ye through his poverty might be rich" (II Corinthians 8:9).

_____

_____

> "Hearken, my beloved brethren, Hath not God chosen the poor of this world rich in faith, and heirs of the kingdom which he hath promised to them that love him?" (James 2:5).

When the poor are given faith, they are enabled by it to receive all the provisions they need. Thus, they experience God's blessing which "makes rich and adds no sorrow with it." (See Proverbs 10:22.)

_____

> "I know both how to be abased, and I know how to abound: every where and in all things I am instructed both to be full and to be hungry, both to abound and to suffer need" (Philippians 4:12).

_____

FURTHER INSIGHTS ON POVERTY AND WEALTH FROM MEN'S MANUAL, VOLUME 2.

☐ 1. Is a man poor when he does not have enough money to pay his bills?

☐ 2. If a man really sets his mind to making money, can he become wealthy?

☐ 3. Is one of God's ways of punishing those who violate His Word to cause them to lose money?

☐ 4. Does God choose to make some people rich and other people poor?

☐ 5. Are some people destined to remain poor, while others are destined to remain rich?

☐ 6. Can government programs eliminate poverty?

☐ 7. Does God have a cycle which takes people from riches to poverty to riches?

☐ 8. Is God's only remedy for slothful people not to give them food?

Continued on page 90.

VIOLATIONS OF GOD'S WORD THAT BRING FINANCIAL LOSS

VIOLATION	FINANCIAL CONSEQUENCES
• Being immoral with a woman	". . . Strangers [shall] be filled with thy wealth . . ." (Proverbs 5:10).
• Spending too much time sleeping	"So shall thy poverty come . . ." (Proverbs 6:11).
• Getting money by doing evil	"The Lord . . . casteth away the substance of the wicked" (Proverbs 10:3).
• Failing to be diligent	"He becometh poor that dealeth with a slack hand . . ." (Proverbs 10:4).
• Cosigning a note	"He that is surety for a stranger shall smart for it . . ." (Proverbs 11:15).
• Having a stingy attitude	". . . It tendeth to poverty" (Proverbs 11:24).
• Provoking your family to anger	You ". . . shall inherit the wind . . ." (Proverbs 11:29).
• Getting money without labor	It ". . . shall be diminished . . ." (Proverbs 13:11).
• Refusing to listen to reproofs	"Poverty and shame shall be to [you] . . ." (Proverbs 13:18).
• Talking too much	It ". . . tendeth only to penury" (Proverbs 14:23).
• Being slothful	You ". . . shall suffer hunger" (Proverbs 19:15).
• Rejecting the cry of the poor	You ". . . shall cry . . . but shall not be heard" (Proverbs 21:13).
• Loving pleasure	You ". . . shall be a poor man . . ." (Proverbs 21:17).
• Loving wine	You ". . . shall not be rich" (Proverbs 21:17).
• Giving to rich people	You ". . . shall surely come to want" (Proverbs 22:16).
• Overeating	You ". . . shall come to poverty . . ." (Proverbs 23:21).
• Charging usury on loans	You ". . . shall gather . . . [your money] for him that will pity the poor" (Proverbs 28:8).
• Following vain persons	You ". . . shall have poverty enough" (Proverbs 28:19).
• Trying to get rich quickly	". . . Poverty shall come upon [you] . . ." (Proverbs 28:22).

9. Does God have special punishments for those who take advantage of the poor?

10. Has God ordained the government to provide jobs for the poor?

11. Would a guaranteed income violate the principles of God's Word?

12. Does God compensate the poor by giving them things that the rich do not have?

13. Does God allow wicked people to prosper financially?

14. Is it possible for a truly dedicated Christian to be financially poor?

15. Is it Scripturally right for our government to take from the rich and give to the poor?

16. Is wealth measured by how much money or how many possessions a person has?

17. Is poverty more a state of mind than a condition of the pocketbook?

18. Are the riches of the wicked valuable because they provide personal security?

19. Should we adjust our standard of living to the income that God allows us to receive?

20. Is it unscriptural for a dedicated Christian to have an abundance of riches?

See Men's Manual, Volume II, pages 91-95.

9 DEVELOP SALES RESISTANCE

"The simple believeth every word: but the prudent man looketh well to his going" (Proverbs 14:15).

"The slothful man roasteth not that which he took in hunting: but the substance of a diligent man is precious" (Proverbs 12:27).

"A gracious woman retaineth honour: and strong men retain riches" (Proverbs 11:16).

LEARN THE SUBTLE TACTICS OF DECEPTIVE ADVERTISING.

1. It uses beautiful and successful-appearing models.

2. It appeals directly to those who are under authority.

3. It creates doubts about established rules.

4. It rejects warnings.

5. It creates discontent.

6. It promotes an independent spirit.

7. It depends on human reasoning.

8. It overrides cautions to meet basic needs.

9. It appeals to the lust of the *eye.*

10. It offers fulfillment apart from God.

11. It uses misleading phrases.

12. It denies the product's weakest point.

For more information, see Men's Manual, Volume II, 106-109.

10 FLEE THE TRAPS OF SWINDLERS

Swindlers are experts in their trade. Once given a hearing, few swindlers miss their mark. Thus, every year millions of people fall victim to clever schemes which exchange their money for worthless ideas, products, or services.

Swindlers prey upon the greed, guilt, pride, and other human weaknesses in their intended victims. There are various types of frauds; however, the following aspects of the trap are common to many of them.

- _____

- _____

- _____

- _____

For more information, See Men's Manual, Volume II, pages 116-129.

11 GET THE BEST BUY

A good buy simply means not paying more than is necessary for a product or a service. The more skillful a buyer is in paying only for value, the freer he can be in rewarding the individuals who provided it when they do a good job.

A Christian should have the testimony of being both frugal in purchases and generous with the individuals who serve him.

A purchase should never be evaluated on the basis of how much money we have left, but rather "Are we getting the best buy for our money?"

How can I establish value?

* _____

_____

What if there is only a small difference in price between two identical items?

* _____

_____

How can I build discipline in spending?

* _____

_____

How can I avoid getting my heart set on an item that is too expensive for me to buy?

* _____

_____

How do I avoid hidden cost?

* _____

_____

How can I be sure that I am getting the best buy?

* _____

_____

How can I be doubly sure?

* _____

_____

For further information, see *Men's Manual*, Volume II, pages 130-141.

12 KEEP RECORDS AS A FAITHFUL STEWARD

_____

_____

13 REFUSE TO LEND TO FRIENDS OR TO COSIGN

Why do we lose a friend the instant that we lend him money?

* _____

_____

The rich ruleth over the poor, and the borrower is servant to the lender" (Proverbs 22:7).

Why were the loans mentioned by Christ actually gifts?

* _____

"Give to every man that asketh of thee; and of him that taketh away thy goods ask them not again" (Luke 6:30).

How can we be sure that cosigning for anyone is wrong?

* _____

"Deliver thyself as a roe from the hand of the hunter . . ." (Proverbs 6:5).

"My son, if thou be surety for thy friend, if thou hast stricken thy hand with a stranger, Thou art snared with the words of thy mouth" (Proverbs 6:1).

"He that is surety for a stranger shall smart for it: and he that hateth suretyship is sure" (Proverbs 11:15).

"A man void of understanding striketh hands, and becometh surety in the presence of his friend" (Proverbs 17:18).

"Take his garment that is surety for a stranger: and take a pledge of him for a strange woman" (Proverbs 20:16).

"Be not thou one of them that strike hands, or of them that are sureties for debts" (Proverbs 22:26).

"Take his garment that is surety for a stranger, and take a pledge of him for a strange women" (Proverbs 27:13).

Although it is permissible to get interest on our money in a bank or to lend it for business purposes, why is it not Scriptural to charge interest to a friend in need?

● _____

_____

"If thou lend money to any of my people that is poor by thee, thou shalt not be to him as an usurer, neither shalt thou lay upon him usury" (Exodus 22:25).

The Scriptural basis of not lending to a needy Christian friend is that we are in a covenant relationship with him through Christ. In such a covenant relationship, our possessions are to be shared as God directs.

For further information, see *Men's Manual,*
Volume II, page 154-165.

14 *DEVELOP THE FULL POTENTIAL OF YOUR HOME*

● _____

_____

Christ gave specific guidelines regarding the motives of such hospitality. We are not to look to guests to reward us financially, because God promises that He will. *". . . When thou makest a dinner or a supper, . . . call the poor, the maimed, the lame, the blind: And thou shalt be blessed; for they cannot recompense thee: for thou shalt be recompensed at the resurrection of the just"* (Luke 14:12-14).

● _____

_____

God explains the qualities of a praiseworthy mother in Proverbs 31. A significant amount of space is devoted to her ability to use available resources in providing quality items for her family, as well as for others.

- *"She seeketh wool, and flax, and worketh willingly with her hands"* (vs. 13).

- *"She considereth a field, and buyeth it: with the fruit of her hands she planteth a vineyard"* (vs. 16).

- *"She perceiveth that her merchandise is good: her candle goeth not out by night"* (vs. 18).

- *"She layeth her hands to the spindle, and her hands hold the distaff"* (vs. 19).

- *"She maketh herself coverings of tapestry . . ."* (vs. 22).

- *"She maketh fine linen, and selleth it . . ."* (vs. 24).

"She riseth also while it is yet night, and giveth meat to her household, and a portion to her maidens. . . . Her children arise up, and call her blessed . . ." (vss. 15, 28).

● _____

For more information, see *Men's Manual,*
Volume II, pages 164-179.

15 *REJECT THE CONCEPT OF A "WORKING MOTHER"*

When the Scriptural functions of the home are restored, there will not be the time or the desire for the mother to work for someone else outside the home. God designed a wife to find her fulfillment by being a helpmeet to her husband. (See Genesis 2:18.)

Some of the consequences of a mother working ouside the home are as follows. Further consequences are described in *Men's Manual,* Volume II, pages 174–175.

● _____

"To be discreet, chaste, keepers at home, good, obedient to their own husbands, that the word of God be not blasphemed" (Titus 2:5).

● _____

"I will therefore that the younger women marry, bear children, guide the house, give none occasion to the adversary to speak reproachfully" (I Timothy 5:14).

● _____

"She is loud and stubborn; her feet abide not in her house" (Proverbs 7:11).

● _____

"No man can serve two masters: for either he will hate the one, and love the other; or else he will hold to the one, and despise the other. Ye cannot serve God and mammon" (Matthew 6:24).

NOTES

DIAGRAMS

THE MYTH OF A MOTHER'S PAYCHECK

The following costs have come from independent sources and accurately reflect the expenses which a wife and mother would incur by working outside the home.

Annual wage	**$14,000.00**
Monthly salary	**1,166.66**

EXPENSES (Monthly)

1. Federal income tax (15%)	$175.00
2. State income tax (3%)	35.00
3. Social Security tax (7%)	81.66
4. Tithe	117.00
5. Transportation* (400 miles @ 30¢ per mile)	120.00
6. Meals ($3 a day)	60.00
7. Restaurant and carry-out meals (From lack of time for preparation)	80.00
8. Extra clothes and cleaning	100.00
9. Forfeited savings on thrift shopping (10%)	116.60
10. Hairdresser	20.00
11. Employee insurance	15.00
12. Day care ($50 a week, one child)	200.00
13. "I owe it to myself" expenses	95.00
	$1215.26
Net Loss	(48.60)

*This does not include the additional costs of a second car, which might be needed because of the mother's job.

16 *LEARN TO PRAY FOR MONEY*

God delights in showing His love and supernatural power by providing for specific needs in answer to believing prayer. For this reason, we are to tell God every detail of our need in earnest and thankful prayer, and the peace of God which transcends human understanding will keep constant guard over our hearts and minds as they rest in Christ Jesus.

There are three perspectives about life that a Christian should have before he asks God for funds. Based on these, the following prerequisites must be followed in order to properly base our requests for funds on the principles of Scripture. These are further explained in *Men's Manual*, Volume II, pages 197–202.

- _____
- _____
  _____
- _____
  _____

BASIC PRINCIPLES OF PRAYING FOR MONEY

1. We must be in "right standing" with God.
We become members of His family by faith and trust in the Lord Jesus Christ for our personal salvation. Only then are we in "right standing."

2. Our request must be based on the name of Christ.
When Christ taught us to pray in His name, He was referring to the character and the functions for which His name stands. A request for bread is consistent with His name because He is the bread of life. (See John 6:35.)

3. We must base our appeal on guarding God's reputation.
Moses effectively appealed to God not to destroy the nation of Israel because doing so would damage His reputation.

4. The authority of our appeal must be God's Word.
When we pray for God to provide, we must base our petition on His will as it is clearly revealed in His Word.

5. Our appeal must fulfill the clear will of God.
Daniel discerned that it was God's will for His people to return to the promised land. This was the basis of his successful prayer.

6. We must separate basic needs from project funds.
Paul made a very clear separation between funds for personal living and funds for public ministry. We must do the same.

George Mueller founded many orphanages in England during the 1800s. His underlying purpose was to demonstrate to Christians how God could provide funds in direct answer to prayer. He received millions of dollars in this way.

GEORGE MUELLER'S METHODS FOR DETERMINING THE WILL OF GOD

1. I seek to get my heart into such a state that it has no will of its own in a given matter. When you're ready to do the Lord's will, whatever it may be, nine-tenths of the difficulties are overcome.

2. Having done this, I don't leave the result to feeling or simply impression. If I do so, I leave myself liable to great delusion.

3. I seek the will of the Spirit of God through, or in connection with, God's Word. The Spirit and the Word must be combined. If I look to the Spirit alone without the Word, I lay myself open to great delusions also. If the Spirit guides us, He'll do it according to the Scriptures, not contrary to them.

4. Next, I take into account providential circumstances. These often plainly indicate God's will in connection with His Word and Spirit.

5. I ask God in prayer to reveal His will to me.

6. Thus, through prayer, the study of the Word, and reflection, I come to a deliberate judgment, according to the best of my ability and knowledge.

   If my mind is thus at peace, and continues after two or three more petitions, I proceed accordingly.

   I have found this method always effective in trivial or important issues.

For further information on this very important topic, see *Men's Manual*, Volume II, pages 218-233.

17 *AVOID BUSINESS PARTNERSHIPS*

How can a business partnership endanger a valuable asset?

● _____

How can partnerships run ahead of God?

● _____

What is the consequence of getting into partnership with one who is violating God's principles?

● _____

What can be the Spiritual consequences of partnerships?

● _____

● _____

When one partner takes a week off in the business, it cannot help but cause the other partner to realize, "Half the money I make this week will be shared with my partner, and he didn't earn it."

This builds up a feeling of indebtedness by the partner who took time off, whereas if the Lord would bless the business so that the owner could take several months off, the managers and employees would not have the same basis for such an attitude.

Larger partnerships, such as medical or legal groups, can be restructured from a partnership basis to a cooperative association with individual responsibilities and rewards.

For further information, see *Men's Manual*, Volume II, pages 206-217.

18 *LISTEN TO THE CAUTIONS OF YOUR WIFE*

Most husbands will smile or agonize with painful remembrance when asked, "Did you ever make a bad investment that your wife tried to warn you about?" Happily, there are a growing number of wise husbands who are learning the following principles of being attentive to the spoken and unspoken cautions of their wives.

☐ 1. A wife often has unexplainable cautions regarding financial decisions.

☐ 2. A wife has special alertness to the moral aspects of a business relationship.

☐ 3. A wife can express her cautions from four conflicting viewpoints.

☐ 4. A wife has a basic human need for security.

☐ 5. A wife is not as concerned about the amount of her husband's earnings as she is about his management of it.

☐ 6. A wife loses her feeling of self-worth when her husband rejects her financial cautions.

☐ 7. A wife's agreement with a business decision does not in itself make it right.

For further information, see *Men's Manual*, Volume II, pages 232-245.

19 CHOOSE A GOOD NAME RATHER THAN RICHES

A good name is not only essential to financial freedom but also to the important relationships for which we are responsible. The quality of our name as a Christian affects the reputation of the Lord. Thus when David sinned, the prophet said, "*... Thou hast given great occasion to the enemies of the Lord to blaspheme [His name]..."* (II Samuel 12:14).

If we damage our name by bad business practices, we bring shame to our parents and their name. "*Whoso keepeth the law is a wise son: but he that is a companion of riotous men shameth his father*" (Proverbs 28:7).

A further importance of a good name is the value and benefit which it represents to children and grandchildren. "*The memory of the just is blessed: but the name of the wicked shall rot*" (Proverbs 10:7).

BASIC REQUIREMENTS TO EARN A GOOD NAME

☐ **1. Be true to your word.**

☐ **2. Return borrowed items.**

☐ **3. Use "just weights and measures."**

☐ **4. Reject gain that comes from another's loss.**

☐ **5. Be punctual in paying bills.**

☐ **6. Associate with wise and Godly people.**

For further information on this very important topic, see *Men's Manual*, Volume II, pages 181-193.

20 RECOGNIZE THE SYMPTOMS OF SLOTHFULNESS

God's reproofs of slothfulness are very painful. A sluggard has trouble all through his life. For this reason, we must conquer slothfulness in ourselves and avoid hiring a sluggard. "*The way of the slothful man is as an hedge of thorns..."* (Proverbs 15:19).

● *Seven symptoms of a slothful man:*

1. *He does not believe that he is slothful.*
2. *He makes little, soft choices in life.*
3. *He does not value the importance of time.*
4. *He will not finish tasks.*
5. *He lives in a world of wishful thinking.*
6. *He brings damage to his employers.*
7. *He has self-induced fears.*

● *Steps to conquer slothfulness*

☐ *1. Counteract slothfulness with hunger.*

☐ *2. Learn the principles of diligence.*

☐ *3. Realize that slothfulness develops in stages.*

☐ *4. Learn the discipline of rising early.*

☐ *5. Learn to respect time.*

A discouraged wife wondered if her family would ever be free from financial pressures. Her husband could never seem to get the right employment. She was working to help support the family. On two occasions he had used the family savings for businesses which had failed.

The following sequence defines the causes which produced their financial pressures.

For further information on this very important topic, see *Men's Manual*, Volume II, pages 218-233.

NOTES

DIAGRAMS

DEVELOPMENT OF A SLOTHFUL MAN

INWARD CAUSES	RESULTING CONFLICTS	RELATED SCRIPTURE
1 Childhood wants were provided without personal effort	☐ Laziness - "I can get what I want without work." ☐ Stealing	The hands of the slothful refuse to labor - Prov. 21:25
2 The easy job; highest pay for least work	☐ Complaining ☐ Lack of initiative ☐ Increased pressure from employer	The field of the slothful is full of weeds - Prov. 24:30–31
3 Self-employment to escape the boss' pressure	☐ Indebtedness ☐ Entanglement with get-rich-quick schemes	Haste to be rich will bring poverty - Prov. 28:22
4 Gifts to the rich or influential to get ahead	☐ Arguments with parents or wife on spending	Giving to the rich results in poverty - Prov. 22:16
5 The "Temporary Job"; putting up with the job to repay debts	☐ Lack of advancement ☐ Lack of fulfillment ☐ Contempt for manual labor	Bread is the reward of sweat - Gen. 3:19
6 Hoping for the "Big Opportunity"	☐ Damaged self-image ☐ Lack of achievement ☐ Constant search for a prestige position (Full-time Christian work)	All work is for God - Col. 3:23–24 Labor with hands - Eph. 4:28 Prides himself as wiser than 7 men - Prov. 26:16

REINFORCE PRINCIPLES OF FINANCE AS YOU LEARN CHARACTER

The following character qualities are related to financial freedom and are developed in *Character Sketches*, Volume III.

CAUTIOUSNESS

☐ 1. Living within the protection of my God-given resources.

☐ 2. Realizing that my greatest ability is also the point of my greatest vulnerability.

☐ 3. Remembering that greed crouches at the door of every heart.

☐ 4. Recognizing that the majority is often wrong.

CONTENTMENT

☐ 5. Valuing God-given relationships more than earthly possessions.

☐ 6. Realizing that I am indestructible until my work is done.

☐ 7. Avoiding the bondage of personal expectations.

☐ 8. Rejoicing in the way that God designed me.

GRATEFULNESS

☐ 9. Giving expressions of appreciation that will honor the design of God.

☐ 10. Paying my debt of love out of the firstfruits of all my increase.

☐ 11. Multiplying the ministry of those who have given to me.

☐ 12. Accepting difficulties as part of God's loving provision.

PUNCTUALITY

☐ 13. Responding immediately when God directs me to give a gift.

☐ 14. Honoring God's way by the timing of a gift.

☐ 15. Meeting basic needs when others are unable to do so.

☐ 16. Remembering anniversaries that are important to others.

RESOURCEFULNESS

☐ 17. Seeing resources that are overlooked by those around me.

☐ 18. Using time, money, and possessions to extend the work of God.

☐ 19. Recognizing that valuable resources come out of right relationships.

☐ 20. Extending my ability to give by avoiding entrapments.

THRIFTINESS

☐ 21. Making the most of limited resources.

☐ 22. Preparing for known needs during times of plenty.

☐ 23. Learning how to live with basic provisions.

☐ 24. Taking care of what I have to extend its usefulness.

KINDNESS

☐ 25. Using a gift to show the worth of a person.

☐ 26. Bringing joy out of sorrow.

☐ 27. Giving honor to whom honor is due.

☐ 28. Returning good for evil.

HOW TO USE THIS BOOK

The *Character Sketches* series is designed to strengthen families and individuals in an exciting new approach to education. The goal is to encourage each family member to learn the facets of God's character, understand basic Biblical concepts, and by knowledge and application become mighty in God's Spirit.

One of the best times to go through this book as a family is after the evening meal. Whenever possible, the father should lead the discussion. Spending twenty to thirty minutes of preparation *beforehand* will greatly multiply the enjoyment and effectiveness of each session. Sessions should last between half an hour and one hour.

FIRST EVENING

1 Read the character definitions.

"Cautiousness is knowing the importance of right motives, timing, methods, and amounts in carrying out wise giving."

The first step in doing this is "Living within the protection of my God-given resources."

2 Give the quiz question on pages 24–27.

"Who can tell me what animal buries its enemies alive?" (Answer on page 32.)

3 Read the nature story caption.

"How is living within the protection of God-given resources illustrated in the world of nature?"

4 Read the nature story.

Practice beforehand adding feeling, emphasis, and curiosity. Adapt difficult words to the children's understanding.

5 Read the animal Scripture references.

Encourage further discussion.

6 Read the nature material.

Begin with the introductory paragraph. As you read, make as many analogies as you can to the Christian life and encourage your family to do the same.

7 Look for ways to apply the quality.

Consider family situations or decisions such as requests to borrow money or possessions, and ask "Will this help you to learn to live within the protection of your God-given resources?"

SECOND EVENING

1 Read the concept question for the chapter from pages 18–23.

"How would you respond to the following situation?" ... After reading the situation, ask each person to give a response. Do not allow any answer to be criticized. Express appreciation for each answer without indicating if it is correct.

2 Read the Scripture story introduction.

"Can you tell from the following description who the person is who illustrates this aspect of the character quality?" Allow for responses; however, do not reveal whether their answer is correct or incorrect. The purpose is to build background and curiosity for the story.

3 Read the Scripture story title.

"How is the protection of living within God-given resources illustrated in Scripture?"

4 Read the story quiz question.

Allow for responses without indicating whether or not the answer is correct.

5 Read the Scripture story.

Before reading to your family, read the Scripture upon which the story is based and practice reading the story.

6 Allow for discussion.

"Do you see a further application of this story to our lives?" Be ready to give an illustration from your own experience.

7 Read the historical background and character sketch.

In your preparation write down points for discussion and application. Suggest a project that the family could work on which would reinforce the character quality: "Let us watch for God-given limitations such as time or money and discuss them."

THE IMPORTANCE OF
CHOOSING A GOOD NAME WHATEVER THE COST

From a "Life Message."

- *"A good name is rather to be chosen than great riches. . . ." Proverbs 22:1*

What does it mean to have a good name?

- _____
  _____
  _____
  _____

Why is a good name vital?

- _____
  _____
  _____
  _____

How is a good name damaged?

- _____
  _____
  _____
  _____

FIVE "LITTLE" WAYS SATAN WANTS US TO COMPROMISE

1 _____
  _____

"But now I have written unto you not to keep company, if any man that is called a brother be a fornicator, or covetous, or an idolater, or a railer, or a drunkard, or an extortioner; with such an one no not to eat" (I Corinthians 5:11).

Other people will evaluate our name on the basis of the company we keep. There is the continual danger of damaging a good name by wrong friendships. Scripture makes this quite clear. *"Be not deceived: evil communications corrupt good manners" (I Corinthians 15:33).*

Not only do our friends cause others to make judgments about our character, but they also influence us to make judgments about basic decisions in life. *"He that walketh with wise men shall be wise: but a companion of fools shall be destroyed" (Proverbs 13:20).*

Do all of your close friends have good reputations as wise and Godly people?

2 _____
  _____

"And he saith unto them, Whose is this image and superscription? They say unto him, Caesar's. Then saith he unto them, Render therefore unto Caesar the things which are Caesar's; and unto God the things that are God's" (Matthew 22:20–21).

A false weight or measure is not a large theft; in fact, it is a small theft repeated many times to many people. Yet, notice how severely God condemns and punishes the corruption of the marketplace for even a small unjust gain. *"Shall I count them pure with the wicked balances, and with the bag of deceitful weights? . . . Therefore also will I make thee sick. . . . Thou shalt eat, but not be satisfied. . . . Thou shalt sow, but thou shalt not reap; thou shalt tread the olives, but thou shalt not anoint thee with oil . . ." (Micah 6:11, 13–15)*

LITTLE WAYS OF DISHONESTY	Guilty?
• Getting to work a few minutes late	☐
• Leaving work a few minutes early	☐
• Taking extra time for breaks	☐
• Not fulfilling expected services	☐
• Charging more than an item is worth	☐
• Failing to reveal defects	☐
• Reducing the quality of items	☐
• Making exaggerated claims	☐
• Not giving full amount of a purchase	☐
• Misusing "sick-day" policy	☐

3 _____

_____

"In the house of the righteous is much treasure: but in the revenues of the wicked is trouble" (Proverbs 15:6).

God condemns "unjust gain." He warns that those who receive it will gather it to their own hurt. *"And they lay wait for their own blood; they lurk privily for their own lives. So are the ways of every one that is greedy of gain; which taketh away the life of the owners thereof"* (Proverbs 1:18–19).

There will be severe and lasting damage to the name of any person who profits by another's loss.

GAIN AT ANOTHER'S LOSS	Guilty?
• Winning in a lottery or bingo game	☐
• Gaining through any form of gambling (races, cards, etc.)	☐
• Making, selling, or delivering liquor, cigarettes, harmful drugs, or pornography	☐
• Rewards for getting friends to buy high-priced items that they do not need	☐
• Taking advantage of the poor	☐

Although a way of getting money may be legal, it violates God's Word if it takes advantage of the poor. *"Blessed is he that considereth the poor: the Lord will deliver him in time of trouble. The Lord will preserve him, and keep him alive; and he shall be blessed upon the earth: and thou wilt not deliver him unto the will of his enemies"* (Psalm 41:1–2).

4 _____

_____

"Be ye not unequally yoked together with unbelievers: for what fellowship hath righteousness with unrighteousness? and what communion hath light with darkness? And what concord hath Christ with Belial? or what part hath he that believeth with an infidel?" (II Corinthians 6:14–15).

If God calls a person to accomplish a certain task, He will either give him the ability to do it himself, or He will give him the financial resources to hire the skill and assistance that are needed.

The lack of ability or resources is usually a motivation for a person to form a partnership. God, however, may have intended this lack as a signal to pray and receive from Him what is needed.

God may also have intended this lack of funds or abilities to be a message to wait, which is a vital part of God's way of working. He gives us a "vision" and then takes us through the "death of a vision" in order to prepare us for His ultimate supernatural fulfillment of that "vision."

During our "death of a vision," Satan usually appears as an angel of light. He prompts us to fulfill God's goals with human effort. If we follow his leading, we may achieve our goal but miss God's will. Instead of blessing, there will be continual conflict.

5 _____

_____

"Holding faith, and a good conscience; which some having put away concerning faith have made shipwreck" (I Timothy 1:19).

MY VOWS AND PROMISES		Kept?
TO GOD	• Marriage vows	☐
	• Vows to serve God	☐
	• Daily Bible reading	☐
	• Tithes and offerings	☐
	• Other	☐
TO FAMILY	• Promises made to wife (Ask her to list them.)	☐
	• Promises made to children (Ask them for a list.)	☐
	• Promises to relatives (List them.)	☐
TO OTHERS	• Promises to friends	☐
	• Promises in business	☐
• **Ask a trusted person to keep you accountable to fulfill each vow and promise. (See Hebrews 3:13.)**		

Steps I must take to restore a good name.

_____

_____

_____

NOTES

DIAGRAMS

HOW TO RECOGNIZE "THE LIE" IN CONTEMPORARY MUSIC

Bible Art Series, Standard Publishing, Cincinnati

"Woe unto them! for they have gone in the way of Cain, and ran greedily after the error of Balaam for reward, and perished in the gainsaying of Core" (Jude 11).

Balaam was a prophet during the early days of the nation of Israel. He had a special power. Those whom he cursed were cursed, and those whom he blessed were blessed. The king of Moab hired Balaam to curse Israel; but God warned Balaam not to curse His people, so he blessed them instead.

However, Balaam's greed and his continued fellowship with God's enemies brought spiritual blindness. His donkey and an angel of God tried to bring him to his senses. He persisted in his own way, got his money, and caused Israel to become morally corrupt. (See Numbers 22–24; Revelation 2:14.)

NOTES

DIAGRAMS

HOW FAR DOES THE KINGDOM OF SATAN EXTEND?

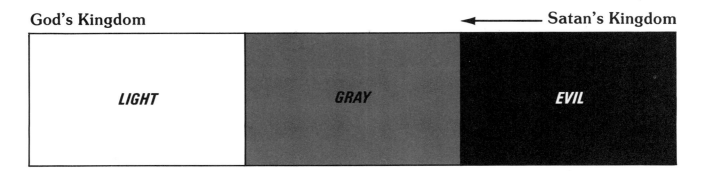

God's Kingdom   ← Satan's Kingdom

| LIGHT | GRAY | EVIL |

SCOPE OF DEMONOLOGY

	LIGHT	II Cor. 11:14	GRAY	EVIL
GUIDANCE				
HEALING				
AWARENESS				

NOTES

DIAGRAMS

BASIC PRINCIPLES OF MUSIC EVALUATION

WHAT IS THE PRIMARY AXIOM OF MUSIC EVALUATION?

1 _____

_____

Accurate evaluation of music is only possible as we integrate it with the related disciplines of mathematics, science, history, and medicine. The laws of these disciplines act as an authoritative reference to confirm that the musical expression is either following or violating established principles.

Chemistry	Language	Math
Cl Na Ph	a b c	2 7 5
Elements	Letters	Numbers

Art	Music
Lines	Notes

The individual parts in each of these disciplines are amoral. However, this status changes once any two elements are combined.

● _____

_____

● _____

"But I say unto you, That every idle word that men shall speak, they shall give account thereof in the day of judgment" (Matthew 12:36).

● _____

"For we must all appear before the judgment seat of Christ; that every one may receive the things done in his body, according to that he hath done, whether it be good or bad" (II Corinthians 5:10).

● _____

● _____

_____

_____

_____

HOW IS MUSIC INTERRELATED TO THE STUDY OF OTHER DISCIPLINES?

Just as there is a balance of power in the three branches of United States government, so the laws of related disciplines provide checks and balances for music.

Notice how this interrelationship between disciplines works out in the following questions and answers:

● ACOUSTICAL ANALYSIS OF TIMBRE

Why does the middle section of a Gospel song or hymn usually modulate to the dominant or relative minor key of the beginning and ending sections?

Answered by the historical development of symphonic form, classical symmetry in art and architecture, and acoustical analysis of variety in tonal levels.

● ACOUSTICAL ANALYSIS OF VIBRATIONS AND TUNING

Why does the leading tone (seventh degree) of the scale demand resolution to the tonic?

Answered by acoustical analysis of the number of vibrations each tone has—the leading tone is closer in pitch to the tonic than other scale tones are to each other.

● BEHAVIORAL EFFECTS OF SOUND

Why do sliding and sagging pitches in a singer's performance give a sensuous impression to the hearers?

Answered by the study of science and behavior in the ability of the sound to suggest erotic movement.

• CULTURAL SIGNIFICANCE OF ATONALITY

How did atonality come to be an accepted mode of expression in twentieth century music?

Answered by a historical understanding of the trends in art forms as they reflect the thoughts and desires of the people of various time periods.

• EFFECTS OF RHYTHM ON THE FUNCTION OF THE HEART

How can an imbalanced beat in music actually cause the loss of physical strength?

Answered by studying medicine and the acoustical effect of external rhythms countering heart rhythms in the body.

• EXPRESSIONS OF SUBJECTIVITY IN MUSIC

Why is there an increasing focus on man's personal experience in the lyrics of twentieth century songs?

Answered by understanding the historical development of philosophy—an increasing emphasis on existentialism and humanism, motivating glorification of subjective experience as the most desired legitimate expression.

• ACOUSTICAL EVALUATION OF DECIBEL LEVEL

Why is rock music consistently performed at high volume levels?

Answered by a study of acoustics and behavior—recognizing that the high volume levels are required to consume the listener totally and to block out the internal communication of personal conscience.

• HUMAN PERCEPTION OF LIGHT, COLOR, AND TIMBRE

Why does the minor key tend to communicate sadness and the major key sound tend to communicate joyfulness?

Answered by an understanding of light and human perception of color—dark colors and the minor mode are perceived as having a somber message; lighter, warmer colors and the major mode are perceived as a joyful spirit.

• EFFECTS OF RHYTHM PATTERNS ON THE BODY

Why is triple meter used more often in songs of personal testimony than for hymns of praise to God?

Answered by an understanding of science—the effects of rhythm patterns on the body. Duple meter tends to communicate objectivity and control, especially in a military sense of march or triumph. Triple meter tends to communicate a circular movement with much greater subjectivity.

• MICROPHONE TECHNIQUES RELATED TO TERRITORIES

Why does a singer's breathing into a microphone communicate a sensual message?

Answered by an understanding of science—the territorial domains of creatures. All animals and human beings have an innate sense of "private space" around them. Heavy breathing into a microphone creates an impression of implied intimacy because the breathing sounds as if it were right next to your ear.

WHY MUST ALL MUSIC BE BROUGHT UNDER THE CONTROL OF THE HOLY SPIRIT?

2 _____

The worship of God must be carried out in purity. The very name of the Holy Spirit through Whom we worship the Lord emphasizes this vital point. The following disciplines illustrate how the purity of an item can be corrupted by adding even a small amount of another element.

Chemistry	Language	Math
H_2O + CN	Truth + Lie	Solution + 1
Poison	Untruth	Incorrect

Art	Music
Figure + Nudity	**Rhythm + Imbalance**
Pornography	**Acid Rock**

The holiness of God is no trifling matter. When the nation of Israel lost sight of Who God was and mixed heathen elements into their worship, they brought the judgment of God upon themselves. The following elements of worship are essential:

● _____

_____

"I am the Lord: that is my name: and my glory will I not give to another, neither my praise to graven images" (Isaiah 42:8).

● _____

"Whether therefore ye eat, or drink, or whatsoever ye do, do all to the glory of God" (I Corinthians 10:31).

> **Worship ascribes glory to someone or something. To whom does this music give glory?**
> ☐ Composer
> ☐ Musician(s)
> ☐ Man's philosophies
> ☐ Musical instrument(s)
> ☐ God and His Word

● All music must glorify God, just as everything we do must glorify Him.

● A musician is not capable of glorifying God unless the Word of God is a living reality in his daily life.

"Let the word of Christ dwell in you richly in all wisdom; teaching and admonishing one another in psalms and hymns and spiritual songs, singing with grace in your hearts to the Lord" (Colossians 3:16).

● _____

"This then is the message which we have heard of him, and declare unto you, that God is light, and in him is no darkness at all" (I John 1:5).

● _____

"Your glorying is not good. Know ye not that a little leaven leaveneth the whole lump?" (I Corinthians 5:6).

HOW DOES THE LOGIC OF "NEEDING TO USE THE WORLD'S MUSIC TO REACH THE WORLD" BREAK DOWN?

3 _____

_____

The confusion of trying to teach the world about God using worldly music is graphically illustrated in Scripture. When Babylonians were resettled in Israel and began to be devoured by lions, they asked the king to send them a prophet of God so they could learn how to worship Him.

The priest came and taught them how they should fear the Lord. However, he did not require them to destroy their gods. The result is described in II Kings 17:33: *"They feared the Lord, and served their own gods. . . ."*

Chemistry	Language
Do we take drugs to win addicts?	**Do we use curse words to witness?**

Math	Art	Music
Do we steal to identify with robbers?	**Do we draw lewd pictures to present Christ?**	**Do we use carnal music to gain a hearing?**

125

NOTES

DIAGRAMS

Why is carnal music ineffective for achieving lasting spiritual results?

● _____

_____

"(For the weapons of our warfare are not carnal, but mighty through God to the pulling down of strong holds;) Casting down imaginations, and every high thing that exalteth itself against the knowledge of God, and bringing into captivity every thought to the obedience of Christ" (II Corinthians 10:4–5).

Do Biblical words make a worldly song Christian?

● _____

_____

_____

_____

"If one bear holy flesh in the skirt of his garment, and with his skirt do touch bread, or pottage, or wine, or oil, or any meat, shall it be holy? And the priests answered and said, No. Then said Haggai, If one that is unclean by a dead body touch any of these, shall it be unclean? And the priests answered and said, It shall be unclean" (Haggai 2:12–13.)

● _____

"Wherefore come out from among them, and be ye separate, saith the Lord, and touch not the unclean thing; and I will receive you" (II Corinthians 6:17).

Did God design music to present the Gospel?

● _____

_____

"For after that in the wisdom of God the world by wisdom knew not God, it pleased God by the foolishness of preaching to save them that believe" (I Corinthians 1:21).

What are the two purposes of Christian music?

● _____

_____

"Speaking to yourselves in psalms and hymns and spiritual songs, singing and making melody in your heart to the Lord" (Ephesians 5:19).

"Let the word of Christ dwell in you richly in all wisdom; teaching and admonishing one another in psalms and hymns and spiritual songs, singing with grace in your hearts to the Lord" (Colossians 3:16).

Why can't carnal music be mixed with Godly words?

● _____

_____

"For the flesh lusteth against the Spirit, and the Spirit against the flesh: and these are contrary the one to the other: so that ye cannot do the things that ye would" (Galatians 5:17).

Who was severely punished for trying to use worldly methods to carry out God's work?

● _____

_____

King David attempted to transport the ark of the covenant to Jerusalem.

However, he used the wrong method. He put the ark on an ox-drawn cart. David copied this method from the heathen. The Philistines had used a cart to transport the ark several years earlier.

Some methods may work for non-Christians that will not work for Christians! The results of this method were disastrous for David. One man was killed; David became angry at God; and the huge procession ended without success.

There was a clear reason why the method of transporting the ark on a cart did not work. God had given precise instructions on how the ark was to be moved.

It was to be carried on the shoulders of the four priests. (See II Samuel 6:1–19 and *Character Sketches*, Volume I, pages 99–101.)

NOTES

DIAGRAMS

The Ark of God

WHAT IS REQUIRED IN MUSIC IF IT IS TO REPRESENT THE CHARACTER OF GOD?

4 _____

_____

_____

The orderly nature of God is reflected in all of His creation. It is Satan who introduced disorder and confusion into God's world. Scripture affirms, however, that God is not the author of confusion. (See I Corinthians 14:33.)

Chemistry	Astronomy	Medicine
Precise order of elements	Cycles of Days, Months, Years	Rhythm of heartbeat and organs

Art	Music
Principles of light and color	Patterns of vibration and chords

Where in Scripture are we commanded to make all of our music appropriate, fitting, and orderly?

• _____

_____

"Let all things be done decently and in order" (I Corinthians 14:40).

How does Satan corrupt music?

• _____

What is the ultimate purpose of music elements?

• _____

_____

Why must melody be dominant?

• _____

"Speaking to yourselves in psalms and hymns and spiritual songs, singing and making melody in your heart to the Lord" (Ephesians 5:19).

The elements of music are melody, harmony, rhythm, form, performance, and, in vocal music, text.

A MELODY IS A SERIES OF TONES HEARD AS A MUSICAL THOUGHT.

Melodies do not just happen. Rather they are specifically designed to move in certain ways. A composer arranges a few pitches to make a short melodic formula called a **motive**.

These motives are combined to produce **phrases**, and the phrases are combined to create **themes**.

Each individual melody has its own **contour** or outline of ascending and descending **pitches**. A good melody will have a definite high place near its conclusion so that a sense of **climax** and **resolution** can be achieved.

Melodies must be balanced in their design of rising and falling pitches. A melody line which descends for too long a time before an upward turn creates a sense of despair in the listener. A rising line that is too long builds tension in the listener, and **static** movement, or constant repetition of pitches, gives a chantlike quality which produces a hypnotic effect or trance in the listener.

If a melody is designed to be sung, its rising and falling pattern must match the inflection of the words in the text. It is possible for inappropriate melody lines to neutralize the effectiveness of the textual message if this is not done.

A melody is usually heard against a background of harmony. **Harmony** relates to **chords** and their movements, or **progression**. The Greek word *harmos* means "joining place." The perception of depth, perspective, mood, color, and atmosphere is joined to the melody through harmony.

In a well-written piece of music, the harmony will be supportive of the melody and play a subservient, though crucial role. A definite procedure exists by which chordal patterns must be applied to melody.

Each scale has its own "home base" or **tonal center** known as the **keynote** or **tonic**. Chords may be built on each of the scale tones, and they move through prescribed formulas toward the tonic for resolution or away from the tonic to build tension.

> ### A SCALE IS OFTEN SUNG WITH THE SYLLABLES
>
> DO RE MI FA SOL LA TI DO
>
> ### THE CHORDS BUILT ON THESE SCALE TONES ARE IDENTIFIED WITH ROMAN NUMERALS.
>
> I II III IV V VI VII I

A HIERARCHY OF MOVEMENT SIMILAR TO A CHAIN OF COMMAND EXISTS IN THE TRADITIONAL HARMONIC STRUCTURE OF THE MAJOR-MINOR TONAL SYSTEM:

Home (Key Center):	I
Resolution to Home:	V or VII
Movement to V:	IV or II
Movement to IV or II:	VI
Movement to VI:	III

The longer it takes to reach the resolution point in the tonic, the greater is the tension built in the listener. The tonic is home or the place of rest.

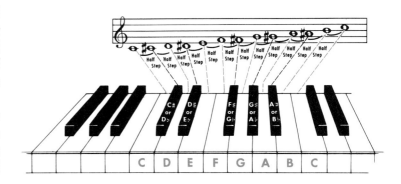

The chromatic, or twelve-tone scale consists of all the black and white keys within an octave, such as from C to C on the piano. Tones in the chromatic scale are always a half step apart.

This means, for example, that the V chord of one scale could be the same as the I chord of another scale or **key**. Because this fact is true, a whole system of **modulation** from key to key is possible for the musician.

The relationship of these keys to one another can be charted on a circle usually called the **Circle of Fifths**. Keys immediately adjacent to one another on the circle provide simple modulation formulas for greater variety.

CIRCLE OF FIFTHS (MAJOR KEYS)

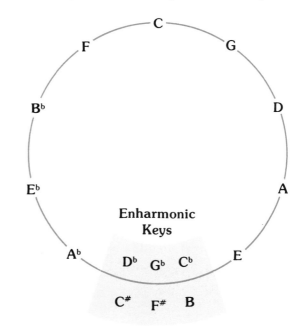

Key signatures tell what key the music is written in. If it has no flats or sharps, the music may be in the key of C major or its relative minor, A minor. Each major key has a relative minor key.

C Major or A Minor

G Major or E Minor

F Major or D Minor

D Major or B Minor

B Flat Major or G Minor

A Major or F Sharp Minor

E Flat Major or C Minor

E Major or C Sharp Minor

A Flat Major or F Minor

B Major or G Sharp Minor

D Flat Major or B Flat Minor

F Sharp Major or D Sharp Minor

G Flat Major or E Flat Minor

C Sharp Major or A Sharp Minor

C Flat Major or A Flat Minor

Great regularity and order exist in the relationships of chords, pitches, scales, and tonalities. As with melody, too much repetition produces a hypnotic effect on the listener.

Too much **consonance** provides no interest in the composition. Too much **dissonance** provokes excessive unrest in the listener. Balance is necessary in the harmonic structure of well-written music.

> **RHYTHM IS THE ORDERLY MOVEMENT OF MUSIC THROUGH TIME.**

Just as the heartbeat is the life of the body, **rhythm** is the life of music. Melody and harmony must unfold together. Rhythm makes this simultaneous unfolding possible. There is rhythm in nature—cycles of night and day, tides, seasons, and cycles in the body. All the arts have rhythm patterns of their own in their design.

Time in our music is organized in units known as **measures**. Each measure contains a fixed number of **beats**. The first beat of any metrical grouping is a strong beat or **accent**. Metrical patterns created by accents are heard as **duple** or **triple patterns**. Duple patterns have accents every other beat, while triple patterns have their accents every third beat.

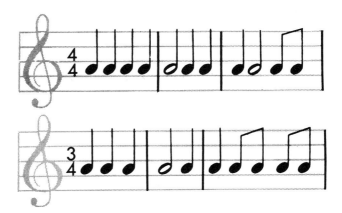

A **measure** contains a set number of beats. Its **time signature** appears as a fraction, showing **how many beats each measure has** (four or three in the examples below) and **what kind of note gets one beat** (quarter notes in both examples illustrated below).

Accents can be shifted for emphasis or to create variety in a composition. This shifting is called **syncopation**. Syncopation occurs whenever an accent appears in a place where it is normally not expected or an accent is left out in a place where the listener expects it. The strongest syncopation occurs when both are done at the same time.

Some forms of contemporary music alternate triple and duple measures. This creates a sensation of constant syncopation and thereby produces a great amount of tension.

A well-written piece of music has a subtle rhythm or sense of pulsation with a balance of regular accent patterns and occasional syncopation for variety and interest.

Balance does not mean equal amounts. For example, in a balanced diet, equal amounts of spices and vegetables would not be eaten. Syncopation is to music as spices are to a well-cooked meal. Used sparingly, it provides great delight.

The artist shapes his material in such a way that the observer should be able to grasp its outlines easily and clearly. **Form** is important in each of the arts, but it is even more crucial in musical design. In the visual arts, the entire work lies before the observer as a whole.

However, music is always in motion. The composition is never before the listener as a whole. Therefore, the music must be written with a clear design so that the beginning may be related to the middle, and the middle to the ending by an astute listener.

The basic law of musical form is **repetition and contrast**. The composer repeats his material to help the listener grasp the meaning. But if he constantly repeated, soon the composition would become boring. Thus, he introduces new material.

But if he constantly introduces new material, he soon bewilders the listener. Again a balance is necessary between the two. **Repetition** creates a sensation of **unity. Contrast** gives **variety**. Repetition gives relaxation. Contrast creates tension.

A well-written piece of music will have a definite **beginning** place, build to a **climax point**, and communicate a definite sense of **conclusion**. Good music will leave the listener satisfied that a "statement" has been made and completed and the artist's intention understood.

Each of the elements of music affects the other elements. Balance in designing the role of each is important as well as balance in combining the elements.

Mathematical precision and order is portrayed in music, too. Acoustically, pitches sounded exactly an octave lower vibrate at half the number of vibrations per second. If you reduce by one half the vibrating element (e.g. the length of a violin string), the resulting pitch is one octave higher than the original pitch. If you double the length of the vibrating column, the resulting pitch is one octave lower.

The notation system for the length of time pitches should be sung or played is worked out by mathematical fractions. The note values in a given measure of music equal the fraction stated at the beginning of the composition as a time signature.

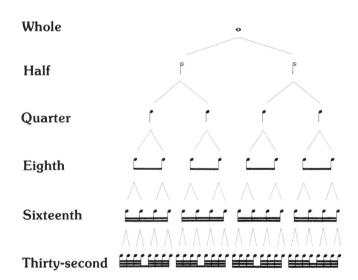

THE MEASUREMENT OF SOUND

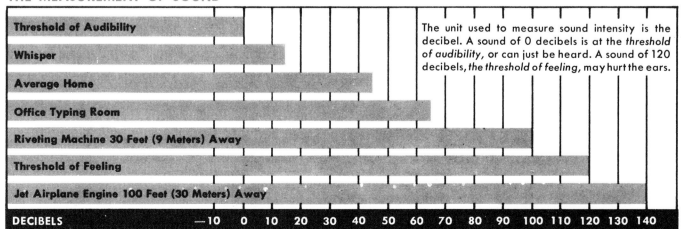

The unit used to measure sound intensity is the decibel. A sound of 0 decibels is at the *threshold of audibility*, or can just be heard. A sound of 120 decibels, *the threshold of feeling*, may hurt the ears.

132

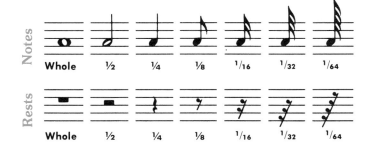

Notes
Whole | ½ | ¼ | ⅛ | ¹/₁₆ | ¹/₃₂ | ¹/₆₄

Rests
Whole | ½ | ¼ | ⅛ | ¹/₁₆ | ¹/₃₂ | ¹/₆₄

The system for measuring the volume of a sound in units of decibels increases in a geometric progression. As one moves up ten decibels, the volume increases ten times, twenty decibels, one hundred times, etc.

In sound and in music, God has provided a great structure of order for mankind.

Why must Godly Christians react to carnal music?

• _____

_____

_____

Sympathetic vibration is an acoustical phenomenon in which the sound from a source is able to set in motion (vibration) any object around it which is compatible with it.

For example, when a violin is played, the vibrating string causes the wood and the air space inside it and around it to vibrate in multiples of the original frequency.

When we allow ourselves to listen to evil music, our entire being must either respond "sympathetically" with it, or we must hinder its effectiveness by rejecting it with an act of the will.

How has carnal music crept into the Church?

• _____

_____

_____

WHAT ARE THE CHARACTERISTICS OF ROCK MUSIC?

While there are many kinds of rock music, they all have in common two basic characteristics: (1) excessive **repetition** of a melodic phrase, harmonic (chordal) pattern, rhythmic pattern, or any combination of these and (2) a **dominant beat**, often driving in nature.

Along with the throbbing beat there is usually a highly accented **backbeat** (a pulse which occurs between the normally accented beats) and even a **breakbeat** (a pulse which occurs between the backbeats.)

For example, in music that is arranged by four-beat measures, normal accents occur on beats one and three; the backbeat accents would occur on beats two and four; and the breakbeat accents would occur anywhere between the four beats.

All rock music is intense, whether performed at a fast or slow tempo. While rock songs are usually performed at high decibel levels, **intensity** and **loudness** are two different things.

The reason for the repetition, dominant beat, and intensity of rock music is that the goal of this style is to dominate and totally consume the listener.

Whether the music claims to be Christian or secular, if these elements are present it is rock music and is the antithesis of what God desires in the life of a Christian.

WHY IS IT DESTRUCTIVE TO HAVE CARNAL MUSICIANS COMPOSING AND SINGING RELIGIOUS MUSIC?

5 _____

_____

_____

Since music is the expression of worship, Christian music must be distinctly different from worldly music. For this reason, the song of the redeemed is described in Scripture as a **new song**.

This phrase occurs nine times in Scripture. Each reference relates to an important theme of salvation, redemption, or deliverance:

A NEW SONG

- *Psalm 33:1, 3*

  "Rejoice in the Lord, O ye righteous. . . . Sing unto Him a new song; play skilfully with a loud noise."

- *Psalm 40:2–3*

  "He brought me up also out of an horrible pit . . . And he hath put a new song in my mouth. . . . many shall see it, and fear, and shall trust in the Lord."

- *Psalm 96:1–2*

  "O sing unto the Lord a new song: sing unto the Lord, all the earth. . . . Show forth his salvation from day to day."

- *Psalm 98:1–2*

  "O sing unto the Lord a new song; for he hath done marvellous things. . . ."

- *Psalm 144:9–10*

  "I will sing a new song unto thee, O God: upon a psaltery and an instrument of ten strings will I sing praises unto thee."

- *Psalm 149:1, 4*

  "Praise ye the Lord. Sing unto the Lord a new song . . . For the Lord taketh pleasure in his people: he will beautify the meek with salvation."

- *Isaiah 42:8–10*

  "I am the Lord . . . my glory will I not give to another. . . . Behold, the former things are come to pass, and new things do I declare. . . . Sing unto the Lord a new song, and his praise from the end of the earth. . . ."

- *Revelation 5:9*

  "And they sung a new song, saying, Thou art worthy to take the book . . . for thou wast slain, and hast redeemed us to God. . . ."

- *Revelation 14:2, 3*

  "And they sung as it were a new song before the throne . . . which were redeemed from the earth."

PERFORMANCE IS THE RENDERING OF A MUSICAL MESSAGE BY SINGING OR PLAYING AN INSTRUMENT.

The message of performance is communicated in several specific ways. First, the actual words of the text must be honest, and all implied ideas must reflect the intent of Scriptural teaching. Many people learn their theology by the subtle messages of the songs they sing. The truths left unsaid also communicate a message by their conspicuous absence. Often this silence speaks louder than any words.

• HUMANISTIC PHILOSOPHY

"Joyful, joyful, we adore thee . . . Thou our Father, Christ our Brother,—all who live in love are Thine . . . Father love is reigning o'er us, Brother love binds man to man" communicates a message of the Fatherhood of God to all men and the brotherhood of man.

• AMBIGUOUS OBJECT OF WORSHIP

"The way that he loves is as fair as the spring that brightens my path each day . . ." While this song implies that the object of the love is the Lord Jesus Christ, the references in it and the harmonies are constructed so that the message could be directed to a romantic love relationship as well.

135

The love of the Lord Jesus should not be brought to the level of romantic familiarity. The delicate balance between "a friend that sticketh closer than a brother" and yet, "fear the Lord your God; worship Him in the beauty of holiness" must be maintained.

Secondly, the musical style must support the theologically correct words without neutralizing the message by worldly associations. Much of the confusion in this evaluation comes from the basic motivation of the musician giving the message.

To justify communicating the message of the Gospel with the world's sound so that it will be more palatable to the lost person or the young Christian is essentially to lie. The lie is that "this way of life that you are challenged to follow is really not that far removed from your own current way of life."

• DOMINANT BEAT OR RHYTHM PATTERN

Music which emphasizes the pulsation or beat appeals to the body and ties the listener to the implications of the rock culture and way of life.

• IMPERTINENT INTIMACY

Music which is sung too close to a microphone so that the breathing and sighing of the singer can be heard recalls a nightclub entertainment style and suggests personal intimacy with the performer.

Singers who manipulate the melody line of the song with sliding and sagging pitches and free-floating rhythms add to the intimate message the suggestion of movements which are sensual.

• WORLDLY ASSOCIATION

Music which imitates the lush sounds of Hollywood entertainment focuses man's mind on amusement. The word **amuse** literally means "without thinking" or "no thought." This music subtly reminds man of his "need" to fulfill materialistic desires and to be entertained.

In each of the preceding examples, the impact of the musical style cited is especially strong in the lives of those who have had extensive experience with that type of performance. The recall of the "old life" is so powerful in these instances that the "new life" in Christ is exceedingly difficult to live.

How can worldly wisdom be distinguished?

* _____

_____

_____

"This wisdom descendeth not from above, but is earthly, sensual, devilish. For where envying and strife is, there is confusion and every evil work. But the wisdom that is from above is first pure, then peaceable, gentle, and easy to be entreated, full of mercy and good fruits, without partiality, and without hypocrisy" (James 3:15–17).

Why do many musicians sing so close to the microphone?

* _____

_____

_____

"For the time will come when they will not endure sound doctrine; but after their own lusts shall they heap to themselves teachers, having itching ears; And they shall turn away their ears from the truth, and shall be turned unto fables" (II Timothy 4:3–4).

Why is sensual music dishonest?

* _____

_____

_____

_____

WHY SHOULD MUSICIANS BE SCREENED FOR SPIRITUAL MATURITY?

6 _____

_____

_____

What qualifications did God have for singers?

● _____

_____

_____

"And David spake to the chief of the Levites to appoint their brethren to be the singers with instruments of music, psalteries and harps and cymbals, sounding, by lifting up the voice with joy" (I Chronicles 15:16).

What is God's attitude toward those who compose or perform sensual music simply because "it sells"?

● _____

_____

"Woe unto them! for they have gone in the way of Cain, and ran greedily after the error of Balaam for reward, and perished in the gainsaying of Core" (Jude 11).

How is carnal music dividing the church?

● _____

_____

_____

"For God is not the author of confusion, but of peace, as in all churches of the saints" (I Corinthians 14:33).

WHAT ABOUT ROCK MUSICIANS WHO CLAIM TO WIN PEOPLE TO CHRIST?

7 _____

_____

If we excuse carnal music on the basis that it brings good results, we are falling into the false philosophy of the world.

What is the basic error of humanistic philosophy?

● _____

_____

This is the philosophy that justifies murder, adultery, stealing, lying, and every other evil.

What if the message of a rock song is good?

● _____

_____

"And Jesus rebuked him, saying, Hold thy peace, and come out of him" (Mark 1:25).
"And devils also came out of many, crying out, and saying, Thou art Christ the Son of God. And he rebuking them suffered them not to speak: for they knew that he was Christ" (Luke 4:41).

What comparison illustrates this point?

● _____

_____

WHY MUST CHRISTIANS NOT LOVE WORLDLY MUSIC?

8 _____

_____

_____

What command are we hindered from obeying when we love worldly music?

● _____

"Let love be without dissimulation. Abhor that which is evil; cleave to that which is good" (Romans 12:9).

How does loving worldly music cause us to lose God's love?

● _____

"Love not the world, neither the things that are in the world. If any man love the world, the love of the Father is not in him. For all that is in the world, the lust of the flesh, and the lust of the eyes, and the pride of life, is not of the Father, but is of the world. And the world passeth away, and the lust thereof: but he that doeth the will of God abideth for ever" (I John 2:15–17).

How does playing any kind of worldly music, including "Christian rock," show that we do not love the Lord?

• _____

"But if thy brother be grieved with thy meat, now walkest thou not charitably. Destroy not him with thy meat, for whom Christ died" (Romans 14:15).

Carnal music does not exist in a vacuum. It comes in a package of four things: drugs, rebellion, immorality, and rock music. Each one is related to the others.

Many Christians who have come out of drugs, immorality, and rebellion are tempted when they hear the music that is associated with this way of life. By damaging them, we sin against Christ, since whatever we do to the least of His brethren, we do to Him.

"WHY ARE YOU PLAYING WITCH DOCTORS' MUSIC?"

"It was in the early 1970s when my sisters arrived in Kalimantan, Karat, Indonesia, where our parents were serving as missionaries. My sisters had brought to the mission field a contemporary Christian record which they said was the 'in' thing back home.

"They were playing the record one evening when an older national Christian came to the door. To my sisters' astonishment, his immediate question was, 'Why are you playing witch doctors' music and calling on Satan?'

"This Christian had left the old heathen practices, which included calling on evil spirits. He recognized the 'Christian music' as the same kind of music that the witch doctors used.

"I was there when this incident happened and am writing now to verify it."

Calgary, Alberta

What is the best way to get rid of wrong music?

• _____

PERSONAL COMMITMENT

Because music is a form of worship, I hereby dedicate all my music to the Lord. I purpose to cleanse my life of all music which violates the principles of His character and gives evidence of loving the world.

May the music of my heart and the songs of my mouth be acceptable in thy sight, O Lord, my Strength and my Redeemer.

Date of commitment _____

THE AWESOME CONSEQUENCES OF ROCK MUSIC— IN ANY FORM

"My husband and I became Christians in our early teenage years and were married in our late teens. From the very beginning, rock music was an important part of our lives. In fact, it would be impossible to describe how much rock music possessed us. My husband played in a Christian rock band, sang, and was a bass guitar player. His group played many Christian songs, but also many secular songs. We loved rock music so much that just thinking about it brings tears to my eyes.

"When we attended the Seminar, we were not aware of what was going to take place during that week. I remember looking through the workbook at the beginning of the Seminar and coming across the topic of rock music to be discussed on Friday afternoon. I thought to myself, 'Oh no, not another one.' It is really a wonder that we did not just get up and walk out. That would have been our normal reaction. I guess the fact that we paid money stopped us.

"The Lord had tried to reach us many times, but our hearts were hard and stubborn. So, as we listened that afternoon, we were prepared to be defensive to what was being said about rock music. That night, as we stood outside the coliseum during the break, for the first time I looked up at my husband and said, 'Honey, what if we have been wrong?' To most people, this probably seems like a very simple thing to say, but it was not. It hurt me tremendously. For the first time ever, there was a small crack in my hard shell. And then, the Lord began to work and to show us just how wrong we had been. By the next day, the conviction of the Holy Spirit was so great that we could hardly bear it. And we had nowhere to run from the Holy Spirit of God!

"We did not know of the satanic battle that lay ahead of us and were not prepared for it. Sunday morning after church as we were driving home, the subject of 'backward masking' came up. In all of our years of involvement in rock music, we had never heard of this technique. We could not understand what the purpose of this would be. Then my husband recalled that there was a song on one of our albums that he had never been able to understand. Being a singer, he had to know every word of each song. He said that he always assumed it was some sort of foreign language and just passed it off. Now we wondered if this could be 'backward masking.'

"When we arrived home, we took that record and placed it on our stereo. We had both listened to this record many times before, but for the first time, the Lord opened our spiritual ears. We now heard the most gross distortion of music that we have ever listened to. We could not believe that we had played that very record and never heard it. Then my husband turned off the amp, placed his finger on the record, and ran the record backwards. We were literally shocked as we heard the most eerie, evil, satanic words spill forth. I still recall the terror that came over us, and would never recommend that anyone mess with this unless they are well prepared.

"What happened as a result of playing that backmasking is hard to understand. But as we stood there and listened to those satanic words spill forth, we were aware that something else had also happened. We had, as a result of our actions, released a power of Satan in our home, a spirit which literally battled against us. We sensed a very real confrontation with the powers of darkness. But as we claimed the Name and Blood of the Lord Jesus Christ through prayer, we saw the power of God be victorious over Satan that day.

"Two years have passed since that eventful day, and the Lord has totally freed me from the love of rock music. He has healed the pain and hurt and has taught me how to be a fearless servant against satanic schemes. Not only has the Lord filled my emptiness with His Holy Spirit, but He has unveiled my eyes to see new meaning in His Word, especially in the book of Romans.

"The Lord has also blessed me with a physical healing. As a result, He has given me the desire of my heart: a miracle baby. He has brought restoration to our marriage that I did not even know was needed. And lastly, He has blessed us financially, all because we have totally yielded to His will and followed the principles of His Word."

Used by permission.

139

NOTES

DIAGRAMS

HOW TO RECOGNIZE "THE LIE" IN OUR CULTURE

One of the most important reasons to reject wrong music is that we are to guard our heart "... *with all diligence; for out of it are the issues of life*" (Proverbs 4:23).

There is a fearful consequence for rejecting God's truth, "... *because they received not the love of the truth, that they might be saved. And for this cause God shall send them strong delusion, that they should believe a [the] lie*" (II Thessalonians 2:10–11).

NOTES

DIAGRAMS

RECOGNIZING "THE LIE"
BUILDING ON THE TRUTH

1 *"The lie" in our vocation:*

- _____
_____

> "And they said, Go to, let us build us a city and a tower, whose top may reach unto heaven; and let us make us a name, lest we be scattered abroad upon the face of the whole earth" (Genesis 11:4).

THE TRUTH

- _____

> "After this manner therefore pray ye: Our Father which art in heaven, Hallowed be thy name" (Matthew 6:9).

Evidences that we believe the lie:

- _____
_____
_____

> "And upon a set day Herod, arrayed in royal apparel, sat upon his throne, and made an oration unto them. And the people gave a shout, saying, It is the voice of a god, and not of a man. And immediately the angel of the Lord smote him, because he gave not God the glory: and he was eaten of worms, and gave up the ghost" (Acts 12:21-23).
>
> "The king spake, and said, Is not this great Babylon, that I have built for the house of the kingdom by the might of my power, and for the honour of my majesty? While the word was in the king's mouth, there fell a voice from heaven, saying, O king Nebuchadnezzar, to thee it is spoken; The kingdom is departed from thee.... The same hour... he was driven from men, and did eat grass as oxen.... And at the end of the days I Nebuchadnezzar lifted up mine eyes unto heaven, and ... Now I Nebuchadnezzar praise and extol and honour the King of heaven, all whose works are truth, and his ways judgment: and those that walk in pride he is able to abase" (Daniel 4:30, 31, 33, 34, 37).

- _____

> "Poverty and shame shall be to him that refuseth instruction: but he that reguardeth reproof shall be honoured" (Proverbs 13:18).

- _____

> "The fear of the Lord is the instruction of wisdom; and before honour is humility" (Proverbs 15:33).

- _____
_____

> "And the men took of their victuals, and asked not counsel at the mouth of the Lord. And Joshua made peace with them ... to let them live: and the princes of the congregation sware unto them" (Joshua 9:14-15).

What is the second evidence that we have believed "the Lie" in education?

- _____
_____
_____

> "And he that doubteth is damned if he eat, because he eateth not of faith: for whatsoever is not of faith is sin" (Romans 14:23).

2 *"The lie" in our education:*

- _____
_____
_____

THE TRUTH

- _____
_____

NOTES

DIAGRAMS

"And he shall turn the heart of the fathers to the children, and the heart of the children to their fathers, lest I come and smite the earth with a curse" (Malachi 4:6).

Evidences that we believe the lie:

* _____

* _____

_____

"And thou shalt teach them diligently unto thy children, and shalt talk of them when thou sittest in thine house, and when thou walkest by the way, and when thou liest down, and when thou risest up" (Deuteronomy 6:7).

* _____

Ewing Galloway

"Now I say, That the heir, as long as he is a child, differeth nothing from a servant, though he be lord of all; But is under tutors and governors until the time appointed of the father" (Galatians 4:1–2).

* _____

_____

"This know also, that in the last days perilous times shall come. For men shall be lovers of their own selves, covetous, boasters, proud, blasphemers, disobedient to parents, unthankful, unholy... Traitors, heady, highminded, lovers of pleasures more than lovers of God" (II Timothy 3:1–2, 4).

What is the second evidence that we have believed "the Lie" in education?

* _____

"That they may teach the young women to be sober, to love their husbands, to love their children, To be discreet, chaste, keepers at home, good, obedient to their own husbands, that the word of God be not blasphemed" (Titus 2:4–5).

". . . Be admonished: of making many books there is no end; and much study is a weariness of the flesh" (Ecclesiastes 12:12).

"From whence come wars and fightings among you? come they not hence, even of your lusts that war in your members?" (James 4:1).

3 *"The lie" in our family:*

* _____

_____

"But were mingled among the heathen, and learned their works.... Yea, they sacrificed their sons and their daughters unto devils." (Psalm 106:35, 37).

THE TRUTH

* _____

"And they shall build the old wastes, they shall raise up the former desolations, and they shall repair the waste cities, the desolations of many generations" (Isaiah 61:4).

Evidences that we believe the lie:

* _____

"Lo, children are an heritage of the Lord: and the fruit of the womb is his reward" (Psalm 127:3).

* _____

"And did not he make one? . . . That he might seek a godly seed. Therefore take heed to your spirit, and let none deal treacherously against the wife of his youth" (Malachi 2:15).

What is the second evidence that we have believed "the Lie" in family size?

* _____

NOTES

DIAGRAMS

HOW TO APPLY PRINCIPLES TO FRIENDSHIP AND ENGAGEMENT

Ewing Galloway

"Be not deceived; God is not mocked: for whatsoever a man soweth, that shall he also reap. For he that soweth to his flesh shall of the flesh reap corruption; but he that soweth to the Spirit shall of the Spirit reap life everlasting" (Galatians 6:7–8).

NOTES

DIAGRAMS

APPLYING LEVELS OF FRIENDSHIP TO DATING

LEVELS	FREEDOMS		RESPONSIBILITIES
ACQUAINTANCE	**1**_____ If questions are: _____ Deeper friendship is ***Not Earned:***	Appropriate questions earn the privilege to deepen friendships.	• _____ _____ _____
CASUAL FRIENDSHIP	**2**_____ If activities are: _____ Deeper friendship is ***Not Earned:***	Proper activities establish the basis to deepen friendships.	• _____ • _____ • _____ • _____ • _____ • _____
CLOSE FRIENDSHIP (FELLOWSHIP)	**3**_____ If standards are: _____ Deeper friendship is ***Not Earned:***	*Godly standards allow deeper friendships.*	• _____ • _____ • _____
INTIMATE FRIENDSHIP	**4**_____ _____ _____ _____		• _____ • _____

FOUR DECISIONS BETWEEN FATHERS AND DAUGHTERS

To ensure the fullest possible success in friendships which could lead to marriage, a father and daughter should discuss and make the following commitments.

1. I WANT GOD'S BEST CONCERNING MARRIAGE.

This commitment means that you are never willing to lower standards, even if it means losing dates. It means you are trusting God for your happiness, whether single or married.

2. I PURPOSE TO SEND POTENTIAL DATES TO FATHER FOR APPROVAL.

There are many important benefits in making this commitment. Here are some of them:

A. You increase his appreciation of you.
What a fellow works for, he appreciates more.

B. You decrease temptation for him to morally mistreat you.

C. You prove that your father loves you.

D. You give a man an opportunity to evaluate the motives of the fellow.

E. You put the fellow in the right relationship with your authority.

3. I PURPOSE TO DIRECT A FELLOW TO FATHER BEFORE DISCUSSING MARRIAGE WITH HIM.

4. I PURPOSE THE FELLOW MUST HAVE 8 ESSENTIAL QUALITIES BEFORE CONSIDERING MARRIAGE.

☐ *Must have genuine salvation*
☐ *Must accept himself*
☐ *Must be a man under authority*
☐ *Must have a clear conscience*
☐ *Must know how to yield rights*
☐ *Must have moral freedom*
☐ *Must know God's purpose for his life*
☐ *Must have financial freedom*

DESIGNING QUESTIONS TO DEEPEN FRIENDSHIPS

The following questions are designed to begin at an acquaintance level and to move forward through the levels of friendship as freedom is given. They are based on the "ten unchangeables" through which God works in a person's life and on the degree to which he has come to self-acceptance.

These are simply suggestions. Other questions should come to your mind as you ask these.

Ewing Galloway

1 PARENTS

• **What are your parents' first names?**

This information will help you properly identify them. (Note: first names of parents should not be used unless given permission.)

• **Do you think your parents know the meaning of their names?**

Take time to look these up; it will give you a basis to talk to them.

• **When is your parents' anniversary?**

If your friendship deepens, it would be appropriate to remember this occassion.

• **Where did your parents (grandparents) grow up?**

Learn about family roots and national heritage.

• **What does your father do for a living?**

Think through questions to ask the father about his job.

• **In what church did your parents grow up?**

Understand the religious background of the family.

• **When did your parents become Christians?**

Learn the spiritual heritage of the parents.

2 TIME IN HISTORY

• **Where were you born?**
Learn about family roots and heritage.

• **How old are you?**
(This is not appropriate to ask of most adults.)

• **When you reach the end of your life, what do you want to look back on and say that you have accomplished?**
Learn your friend's purpose in life.

• **What special interests do you have?**
Learn about hobbies, musical skills, sports interests, and life issues of importance to your friend.

• **When you have free time, how do you enjoy using it?**
Discover how your friend invests leisure time.

• **What is your favorite time of the year?**
Find out whether your friend enjoys indoor or outdoor activities, whether he has accepted his present climate, and what health problems he might have.

• **How did you become a Christian?**
Discern whether he has experienced genuine salvation and whether he has the witness of the Holy Spirit within.

3 GENDER

• **Do you know the meaning of your name?**
Learn and share its cultural and spiritual significance.

• **What was your first childhood ambition?**
Learn the early influences upon your friend.

• **Why do you think God made you the gender He did?**
Find out his understanding of purpose.

• **When you were born, were your parents expecting a boy or a girl?**
Discover the degree of self-acceptance by your friend and his parents.

• **What do you think the special responsibilities and privileges of men are?**

• **What do you think the special responsibilities and privileges of women are?**
Discover whether he understands the purpose for which God made man and woman.

• **What do you think about a mother working outside the home?**
Find out his understanding of the basis of fulfillment in life.

• **What do you react to most in men (women)?**
Learn the level of understanding of the opposite sex and his response to people of the opposite sex.

• **Do you know what your spiritual gift is?**
Discover his basic motivation and visualize spiritual achievement.

• **What has been the most difficult experience that you have had in your life so far?**
Learn how he faces crises and what has been important in shaping his present attitudes and outlook.

• **What do you think of the concept of a "one woman man"?**
Discover his commitment to purity in dating and marriage.

4 BIRTH ORDER

• **What number child are you in the birth order of your family?**
Discover your friend's attitudes toward first-born, second-born, etc.

• **What advantages or disadvantages do you see in your position in the family?**
Learn about his understanding of the responsibilities of the first-born, needs of the second-born, etc.

• **Do you often wish you had older brothers or sisters?**
Learn whether he has accepted his birth order.

5 BROTHERS AND SISTERS

• **How many brothers and sisters do you have?**
Learn about his family heritage.

• **With which brother or sister do you have the closest relationship?**
Learn the scope of harmony in the family.

• **Do you wish that you grew up in a larger or smaller family?**
Find out if he has accepted his family's size.

• **What one thing would you like to see changed in your family?**
Understand family needs and pressures and his response to them.

• **What do you appreciate most about each brother and sister?**
Discern the level of appreciation and commitment to family members.

6 RACIAL BACKGROUND

• **What advantages do you see in being born into your race?**
Discover acceptance of his or her race.

• **How do you view other races?**
Find out his attitudes toward other races.

• **Do you see any special significance in the Jewish race?**
Find out if your friend understands God's program through His people and the special blessing or curse to those who bless or curse the Jews.

• **What different races do you have in your family tree?**
Learn how much your friend knows about his family heritage and the degree to which he accepts it.

7 NATIONAL HERITAGE

• **Where did you grow up?**
Find out the influences of early childhood.

• **How often did you move as you were growing up?**
Find out whether moves were viewed as opportunities or disruptions.

• **What special traditions does your family have?**
Learn the cultural practices of the family.

• **What nationalities are represented among your forefathers?**
Find out the cultural influences in his life.

• **What advantages or disadvantages do you see in your growing up experiences?**
Discover the atmosphere in his home and life as he grew up.

• **If you had your choice, would you want to live in any other country?**
Learn about his patriotism and possible interest in mission work.

8 PHYSICAL FEATURES

• **If you had the power to change anything about the way you look, would you use it?**
Discover whether there is self-rejection.

• **What are some of the physical characteristics that run in your family?**
(If there is an obvious physical handicap, this question should not be asked.)

• **What spiritual significance have you attached to any physical "defect" that you may have?**
Find out the maturity of his self-acceptance.

• **What special physical characteristics have you inherited from your father? mother? grandparents?**
Learn how aware he is of family characteristics.

9 MENTAL ABILITIES

• **What are your special interests in education?**
Find out his achievements and goals.

• **Would you say that you are mechanically inclined?**
Learn what skills he has for home repairs.

• **Do you enjoy reading?**
Learn about his ability in this area.

• **What are some of your favorite books?**
Find out what type of reading has influenced him.

• **What education and training have you had?**
Discover his comprehension of education and his development of specific skills.

• **What job experience have you had?**
Learn what are his marketable skills and whether he has diligently employed them.

• **What Christian activities have you pursued in your life?**
Learn how he is developing and using his spiritual gift.

• **How much Scripture have you been able to memorize?**
Learn how he is developing his mind.

10 AGING AND DEATH

• **What major illnesses have you had?**
Learn about his physical health and strength.

• **What are some of the medical tendencies in your family?**
Identify hereditary conditions.

• **Have you ever had an experience where you almost died?**
Learn whether such an experience has increased his appreciation of the brevity of life and the need to make the best use of his time.

• **Have you experienced the death of a family member or a close friend?**
Discover his response to personal loss.

DEFINITION OF A DATE

When the emotions of a boy and a girl begin to be attached to each other, any activity together becomes a date. This includes a phone call, eating together, going to church together, sitting together in church, and writing to each other.

ADDITIONAL QUESTIONS A FATHER SHOULD ASK A YOUNG MAN WHO WANTS TO DATE HIS DAUGHTER.

The young man must understand that he is dealing with the father and not the daughter on dating arrangements. Thus, questions like the following are appropriate for the father to ask.
• Is this something that we can do as a family?
• How will my daughter's life be benefited by it?
• What time will you have my daughter home?

PREPARATION FOR ENGAGEMENT

Important material is contained in the *Life Notebook* to assist fathers in preparing sons and daughters for engagement.

NOTES

DIAGRAMS

It is essential in any friendship, especially dating and marriage, that each party understand and apply the seven basic principles. Failure to do this will result in a sequence of conflicts such as the following:

CONSEQUENCES OF SELF-REJECTION

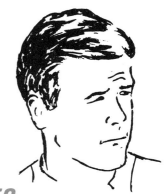

CAUSE-AND-EFFECT SEQUENCES

HER RESPONSES	HIS RESPONSES
1 _____ _____	7 _____ _____
2 _____ _____	8 _____ _____
3 _____ _____	9 _____ _____
4 _____ _____	10 _____ _____
5 _____ _____	11 _____ _____
6 _____ _____	12 _____ _____

From "Preparation for Engagement" in the *Life Notebook.*

REPORTS FROM THOSE WHO HAVE APPLIED THESE CONCEPTS

From a father

"I would just like to say that my daughter and I purposed three years ago here at the IBYC Seminar to apply your four decisions prior to dating. Six months ago, we had our first opportunity to put it into effect. It worked wonderfully, and the relationship has been tremendous! I strongly recommend and encourage others to follow this program."

Atlanta, Georgia

From a daughter

"This is my third Seminar; my first was in 1972, when I was twenty-three years of age and only one year old as a Christian.

"After hearing about the section on dating, I committed myself to wait on God for a mate and to never again engage in a physical relationship until I was married. You see, before I became a Christian I was very immoral.

"Well, here I sit twelve years later, having kept the commitment. Next to me is my husband. We have been married for one year! What a blessing—worth waiting for!

"Because of my commitment, he has confidence knowing that I believe God and keep His commandments and hold the marriage bed in honor. Thank you for teaching God's truths in love.

"P.S. If you can use this information, please feel free to do so. Maybe it will help others."

Harbor City, California

From a son

"I just wanted to write a letter of appreciation for your speaking out on such vital principles in God's Word. Before my wife and I were married, we lived for three-and-a-half years by the dating and friendship principles that you taught. We had a glorious time together while being single.

"We have been married now for almost six years. One thing that I can say about the Word of God: It works!

"The type of unselfish courtship we had has produced a very blessed marriage. God has honored His Word and rewarded us for living by it. These principles have had a great impact on my life, and now I am able to affect the lives of others, especially my two boys.

"Chalk us up as another family that is enjoying the blessings of God in marriage."

Kingsland, Texas

Further notes on dating:

_____

_____

_____

_____

_____

_____

_____

_____

EARNING A POSITION OF RESPECT

SEVEN PHASES OF A GODLY COURTSHIP

World's philosophy: Physical bonding	God's wisdom: Spiritual bonding
The world's approach to dating, courtship, and marriage is just the reverse of God's order. It begins by looking at outward appearances, then promotes physical and emotional involvement, and at some future time possibly considers the spiritual dimensions and responsibilities of marriage. The following sequence has been identified as a normal and acceptable way of establishing physical bonding. Yet, *". . . what they know naturally, as brute beasts, in those things they corrupt themselves" (Jude 10).*	God's order of friendship, courtship, and marriage is first to emphasize spiritual oneness in friendship, then oneness of soul in engagement, and finally physical consumation in marriage. This same order is given by Paul as he prays for our complete sanctification: *". . . I pray God your whole spirit and soul and body be preserved blameless unto the coming of our Lord Jesus Christ. Faithful is he that calleth you, who also will do it" (I Thessalonians 5:23–24).* **Boaz and Ruth** illustrate a Godly courtship.

1

The lust of the eye is one of man's biggest spiritual battles. This fact certainly does not recommend it as the first step for beginning a Godly courtship. In fact, Scripture is filled with examples of men who established wrong moral relationships as they "saw a woman who pleased them well." • _____ *". . . Samson went down . . . and saw a woman. . . . And Samson said unto his father, Get her for me; for she pleaseth me well" (Judges 14:1, 3).* • _____ *"And it came to pass in an eveningtide, that David arose from off his bed, and walked upon the roof of the king's house: and from the roof he saw a woman washing herself; and the woman was very beautiful to look upon" (II Samuel 11:2).* • _____ *"When Judah saw her, he thought her to be an harlot; because she had covered her face" (Genesis 38:15).*	Boaz was attracted to Ruth before he ever saw her. He heard good reports about her character. He was impressed with the loyalty she demonstrated to her widowed mother-in-law and the diligence she demonstrated in unselfishly caring for her needs. • _____ *"A gracious woman retaineth honour: and strong men retain riches" (Proverbs 11:16).* Boaz learned the disciplines of character that go with achieving financial freedom by maintaining a successful farm while others fled the country because of drought. ### MAKE A COVENANT WITH YOUR EYES: A prerequisite for Godly courtship is to purpose not to look lustfully at a woman. This includes not forming sensual pictures in your mind. Job tells his secret in controlling his eyes. *"I made a covenant with mine eyes; why then should I think upon a maid?" (Job 31:1).* • _____

NOTES

DIAGRAMS

2 _____

   • _____

   • _____

     "He that winketh with the eye causeth sorrow . . ." (Proverbs 10:10).

3 _____

   • _____

     To keep thee from the evil woman, from the flattery of the tongue of a strange woman" (Proverbs 6:24).

4 _____

   • _____

     The basic element of lust is "getting for one's self." Lust can never wait to get.

5 _____

     "Now concerning the things whereof ye wrote unto me: It is good for a man not to touch a woman" (I Corinthians 7:1).

     Some have assumed that this verse refers to a total physical relationship; however, the Greek dictionary gives the following definition: "To attach oneself to, i.e., to touch."

6 _____

     Once a relationship is built on lust, the couple quickly moves from one physical expression to the next. Soon they lose the pleasure that God intended for a proper expression of physical love because of burned-out lusts.

7 _____

---

2 _____

   • _____

     The father has the final authority in the marriage decision of his daughter. (See Exodus 22:17 and I Corinthians 7:38.)

3 _____

   • _____

     Praise focuses on character qualities which a woman has already developed in her life, while flattery focuses on features and abilities which were not of her doing.

4 _____

   • _____

     The basic element of love is giving. Love can always wait to give.

5 _____

   • _____

   • _____

6 _____

   • _____

     "Abstain from all appearance of evil" (I Thessalonians 5:22).

7 _____

_____

SEVEN PHASES OF A GODLY COURTSHIP

1   THE RICHNESS OF HIS PREPARATION

Boaz was a *"... mighty man of wealth ..."* (Ruth 2:1).

The discipline of character that produces financial responsibility is an essential prerequisite for a happy marriage and a fruitful wife.

This is precisely the instruction of Proverbs 24:27. *"Prepare thy work without, and make it fit for thyself in the field; and afterwards build thine house."*

The building of a house and the bringing home of a housewife are to be preceded by successful achievement in vocational skills.

"One begins at the wrong end when he begins with the building of his house ..." (F. Delitzsch, Vol. 6, Proverbs).

The lessons that a man learns in wisely handling finances will not only build character essential for a successful marriage, but will also provide the understanding of Scripture that is necessary for his spiritual leadership within the marriage.

"If therefore ye have not been faithful in the unrighteous mammon [money], who will commit to your trust the true riches [the fine gold of Scripture, the ruby of a virtuous wife, and the treasures of Godly children]?" (Luke 16:11).

THE QUIET INFLUENCE OF HER VIRTUE

"And Ruth said [to her mother-in-law], Entreat me not to leave thee, or to return from following after thee: for whither thou goest, I will go; and where thou lodgest, I will lodge: thy people shall be my people, and thy God my God" (Ruth 1:16).

Virtue is the Godly influence which our lives exert on the lives of those around us. This influence is often without our knowledge because it is a by-product of our focus on Christ and His character.

Ruth had already surrendered her expectations for marriage when she made her decision to serve her mother-in-law. Thus, when she went to glean in the field, she was not trying to impress a potential husband.

The Godly influence, however, that she exerted on the reapers and their foreman is obvious from the good report which the foreman gave of Ruth when Boaz asked who she was.

God compares a virtuous woman with the rarest and most valuable of all gems—a translucent ruby.

"Who can find a virtuous woman? for her price is far above rubies" (Proverbs 31:10).

TEST ONE: HIS DESIRE TO LEARN ABOUT HER FAMILY
"Then said Boaz unto his servant ... Whose damsel is this?" (Ruth 2:5).

Note: The violation of any phase will hinder fulfillment and communication in a marriage. In a marriage covenant, the man is to be the initiator and the woman is to be the responder. These phases are seen from Boaz's perspective in the book of Ruth.

2 THE MATURITY OF HIS LEADERSHIP	THE EXAMPLE OF HER DILIGENCE
"And, behold, Boaz came from Beth-lehem, and said unto the reapers, The Lord be with you. And they answered him, The Lord bless thee" (Ruth 2:4). Mature leadership is concerned first of all with the needs of those under his care and secondly with the job to be accomplished. The first statement of Boaz was not "How much have you harvested?" but "May the Lord be with you in all that you do." He understood that if his workers were in right relationship with the Lord they would be in right relationship to him and the job to be done. He also realized that he must be the spiritual example of what he wanted in the lives of his workers. A further mark of Boaz's mature leadership is that he appointed an orderly structure of authority and then consistently worked through it, rather than going around it. *"Then said Boaz unto his servant that was set over the reapers..."* (Ruth 2:5). Mature leadership is essential for a successful marriage.	*"And Ruth the Moabitess said unto Naomi, Let me now go to the field, and glean ears of corn..."* (Ruth 2:2). Gleaning was the occupation of the poor. Ruth's diligence in finding food for her mother-in-law is the same quality that Abraham's servant sought in the bride that he was to select for Isaac. (See Genesis 24:14.) This is also the quality praised of the virtuous woman in Proverbs 31. *"She seeketh wool, and flax, and worketh willingly with her hands.... [She] eateth not the bread of idleness"* (Proverbs 31:13, 27). Ruth's diligence is affirmed by the foreman of Boaz's field. He reported that Ruth worked continually "from the morning until now," and that she only rested a short time in the shelter. A woman's fulfillment will only come as she experiences the purposes for which God made her. Thus, for a woman, fulfillment comes by learning how to be a successful helpmeet. Skill in this area must be developed while single, even though God has given a basic aptitude for it.

TEST TWO: HIS DESIRE TO PROVIDE FOR HER AND PROTECT HER
"Then said Boaz unto Ruth... abide here fast by my maidens.... have I not charged the young men that they shall not touch thee? and when thou art athirst, go unto the vessels, and drink of that which the young men have drawn" (Ruth 2:8-9).

3 HIS COMMITMENT TO GODLY CHARACTER	THE GENUINENESS OF HER GRATEFULNESS
"And Boaz answered and said unto her, It hath fully been shewed me, all that thou hast done unto thy mother in law since the death of thine husband: and how thou hast left thy father and thy mother, and the land of thy nativity, and art come unto a people which thou knewest not heretofore" (Ruth 2:11).	*"Then she fell on her face, and bowed herself to the ground, and said unto him, Why have I found grace in thine eyes, that thou shouldest take knowledge of me, seeing I am a stranger"* (Ruth 2:10). Ruth had a genuine spirit of gratefulness because of a total lack of demands and expectations. She could have very easily said to God,

The character qualities which Boaz recognized and rewarded in Ruth began with loyalty. A mature man knows that if a girl is not loyal to her family, she will not be loyal to him.

Genuine loyalty results in self-sacrifice and a resilience from personal loss.

"You owe me this food because of all that I have suffered and given up."

Genuine gratefulness is one of the most attractive qualities in any woman and one of the most appreciated qualities by any man.

TEST THREE: HIS DESIRE TO BE WITH HER AND TALK TO HER

"And Boaz said unto her, At mealtime come thou hither, and eat of the bread, and dip thy morsel in the vinegar. And she sat beside the reapers: and he reached her parched corn, and she did eat, and was sufficed, and left" (Ruth 2:14).

4 HIS PROPER EXPRESSIONS OF FAVOR

THE CONSISTENCY OF HER SUBMISSION

"The Lord recompense thy work, and a full reward be given thee of the Lord God of Israel, under whose wings thou art come to trust" (Ruth 2:12).

Boaz recognized that anyone whom he would favor should also be one whom God wants to favor.

"And when she was risen up to glean, Boaz commanded his young men, saying, Let her glean even among the sheaves, and reproach her not: And let fall also some of the handfuls of purpose for her, and leave them, that she may glean them, and rebuke her not" (Ruth 2:15–16).

Boaz demonstrated wisdom in the way that he showed favor to Ruth. By doing it quietly through his reapers, he avoided resentment toward him and her.

When favor is properly given to those who deserve it, others share in the joy of it and in the gratefulness for it.

The ultimate test of showing favor is that God is glorified.

". . . Naomi said unto her daughter in law, Blessed be he of the Lord, who hath not left off his kindness to the living and to the dead . . ." (Ruth 2:20).

"And Naomi said unto Ruth her daughter in law, It is good, my daughter, that thou go out with his maidens, that they meet thee not in any other field. So she kept fast by the maidens of Boaz . . ." (Ruth 2:22–23).

Ruth was blessed by God because she remained under the protection of her God-ordained authorities.

Initially she asked her mother-in-law's permission to glean. *". . . Let me now go to the field, and glean ears of corn after him in whose sight I shall find grace. And she [Naomi] said unto her, Go, my daughter"* (Ruth 2:2).

She continued to remain under the protection of her mother-in-law by reviewing with her the instructions that Boaz had given to her.

A woman with true obedience continues to keep her God-given authorities involved in decision-making even when those decisions seem obvious at the moment. This allows the authorities to rejoice in God's blessing and to be well-informed for the next counsel to be given.

Ruth's spirit of obedience was also demonstrated when she came to the field to glean. The law allowed the poor to glean, and she could have simply demanded her legal right. Instead, she asked the foreman for permission to glean.

TEST FOUR: HIS WILLINGNESS TO LET TIME CONFIRM HIS IMPRESSIONS

"So she kept fast by the maidens of Boaz to glean unto the end of barley harvest and of wheat harvest; and dwelt with her mother in law" (Ruth 2:23).

5 HIS DECISIVENESS WITH RIGHT TIMING	THE COURAGE OF HER WILLING RESPONSE

"And now, my daughter, fear not; I will do to thee all that thou requirest . . ." (Ruth 3:11).	"Then Naomi her mother in law said unto her, My daughter, shall I not seek rest for thee, that it may be well with thee? . . . Behold, [Boaz] . . . winnoweth barley to night in the threshingfloor. Wash thy self therefore, and anoint thee, and put thy raiment upon thee, and get thee down to the floor: but make not thyself known unto the man, until he shall have done eating and drinking. . . .
Ruth had just appealed to him to fulfill his kinsman's responsibility following the instructions of her mother-in-law. Accordingly, he would need to redeem Naomi's husband's land and marry Ruth for the purpose of continuing the name of Naomi's husband.	
Boaz was aware of this potential responsibility and had determined that he would become the kinsman-redeemer if Naomi and Ruth requested it.	"And [Ruth] . . . said unto her, All that thou sayest unto me I will do" (Ruth 3:1–3, 5).
He had also determined the hindrance to his becoming the kinsman-redeemer, and he had evaluated the effect of the decision on the entire community. ". . . I will do to thee all that thou requirest: for all the city of my people doth know that thou art a virtuous woman" (Ruth 3:11).	God had blessed Ruth through Boaz, and her mother-in-law had given her precise directions on how to approach Boaz for marriage according to the customs of that day. However, Ruth had to know in her heart that it was right, and she had to be willing to do it.
Boaz's decisiveness was perceived by Naomi when she assured her daughter-in-law the next morning, ". . . Sit still, my daughter, until thou know how the matter will fall: for the man will not be in rest, until he have finished the thing this day" (Ruth 3:18).	God never forces a person to get married through the influence of his or her authorities, because the very nature of love requires a choice.
	Responding to love must also be done with propriety, without giving any appearance of evil.

TEST FIVE: **HIS DESIRE TO ASSUME THE FULL RESPONSIBILITIES OF MARRIAGE**
". . . If he will not do the part of a kinsman to thee, then will I do the part of a kinsman to thee, as the Lord liveth . . ." (Ruth 3:13).

6 HIS PUBLIC THOROUGHNESS ABOVE REPROACH	HER COMMITMENT TO MARRIAGE PURPOSES

"And Boaz said unto the elders, and unto all the people, Ye are witnesses this day, that I have bought all that was Elimelech's. . . . Moreover Ruth the Moabitess, the wife of Mahlon, have I purchased to be my wife, to raise up the name of the dead upon his inheritance. . . . And all the people that were in the gate, and the elders, said, We are witnesses. The Lord make the woman that is come into thine house like Rachel and like Leah . . ." (Ruth 4:9–11).	". . . I am Ruth thine handmaid: spread therefore thy skirt over thine handmaid; for thou art a near kinsman" (Ruth 3:9).
	By asking Boaz to be her kinsman-redeemer, Ruth was demonstrating her commitment to God's purposes in marriage and her devotion to her remaining family.
	Ruth was no longer bound by the marriage vows to her first husband. However, she now had an opportunity to honor her dead hus-

Boaz followed every law, statute, and custom in the legal and social setting of the city gate. He made sure that there were ample witnesses who would not only give him and Ruth their blessing but would spread the good news to everyone else in the city.

Boaz had already earned the respect of all the people in the city, and Ruth was admired because of her dedication to Naomi and her reputation as a virtuous woman.

Now everyone was able to rejoice when they saw the Godly motives toward their marriage and the spiritual potential which their union could have for the Lord's people.

"And let thy house be like the house of Pharez, whom Tamar bare unto Judah, of the seed which the Lord shall give thee of this young woman" (Ruth 4:12).

band's name, protect his property, and fulfill one of the goals of their marriage by marrying the kinsman and raising up a child to inherit her first husband's land.

Boaz was deeply impressed with her willingness to overlook more attractive offers for marriage in order to fulfill the spirit of her original vows.

"And he said, Blessed be thou of the Lord, my daughter: for thou hast shewed more kindness in the latter end than at the beginning, inasmuch as thou followedst not young men, whether poor or rich" (Ruth 3:10).

TEST SIX: HIS WILLINGNESS TO LET GOD STOP THE MARRIAGE AS HE PLACED IT IN THE HANDS OF THEIR AUTHORITIES

". . . There is a kinsman nearer than I. . . . If he will perform unto thee the part of a kinsman, well; let him do the kinsman's part: but if he will not do the part of a kinsman to thee, then will I do the part of a kinsman to thee . . ." (Ruth 3:12–13).

7 GOD'S BLESSING UPON THE MARRIAGE, FAMILIES, AND WORLD WHEN HIS ORDER OF COURTSHIP HAS BEEN FOLLOWED

"So Boaz took Ruth, and she was his wife: and when he went in unto her, the Lord gave her conception, and she bare a son.

"And the women said unto Naomi, Blessed be the Lord, which hath not left thee this day without a kinsman, that his name may be famous in Israel.

"And he shall be unto thee a restorer of thy life, and a nourisher of thine old age: for thy

daughter in law, which loveth thee, which is better to thee than seven sons, hath borne him.

"And Naomi took the child, and laid it in her bosom, and became nurse unto it.

"And the women her neighbours gave it a name, saying, There is a son born to Naomi; and they called his name Obed: he is the father of Jesse, the father of David" (Ruth 4:13–17).

TEST SEVEN: THEIR OBEDIENCE IN RAISING UP THE FOUNDATIONS OF MANY GODLY GENERATIONS

"The book of the generation of Jesus Christ, the son of David, the son of Abraham. . . . And Salmon begat Booz [Boaz] of Rachab; and Booz [Boaz] begat Obed of Ruth; and Obed begat Jesse; And Jesse begat David . . ." (Matthew 1:1–6; see also Luke 3:31–32).

Development of an Immoral Woman

INWARD MOTIVATION	VISIBLE RESPONSES	RELATED SCRIPTURE
1 _____ _____	_____	"Whose adorning...even the ornament of a meek and quiet spirit, which is in the sight of God of great price" (I Peter 3:3–4).
2 _____ _____	_____	"Only by pride cometh contention: but with the well advised is wisdom" (Proverbs 13:10).
3 _____ _____	_____	"For of this sort are they which creep into houses, and lead captive silly women laden with sins, led away with divers lusts" (II Timothy 3:6).
4 _____ _____	_____	"The eye that mocketh at his father, and despiseth to obey his mother, the ravens of the valley shall pick it out, and the young eagles shall eat it" (Proverbs 30:17).
5 _____ _____	_____	"Reprove not a scorner, lest he hate thee: rebuke a wise man, and he will love thee" (Proverbs 9:8).
6 _____ _____	_____	"For the lips of a strange woman drop as an honeycomb, and her mouth is smoother than oil" (Proverbs 5:3).
7 _____ _____	_____	"Having eyes full of adultery, and that cannot cease from sin; beguiling unstable souls: an heart they have exercised with covetous practices; cursed children" (II Peter 2:14).

NOTES   **DIAGRAMS**

SIX PURPOSES
OF MARRIAGE

"... Blessed is the man that feareth the Lord, that delighteth greatly in his commandments. His seed shall be mighty upon earth ..." (Psalm 112:1-2).

"Throwing rice" (seed) is a symbol of fruitfulness.

NOTES

DIAGRAMS

SIX PURPOSES AND PRINCIPLES IN THE MARRIAGE RELATIONSHIP

psychological oneness, they still have less than half of what God intended for the marriage.

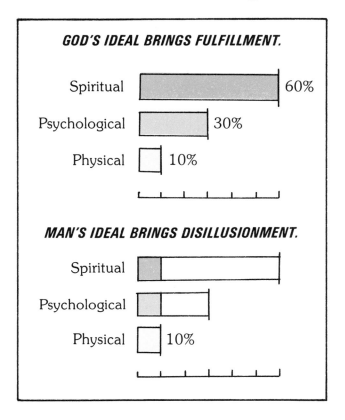

MARRIAGE PURPOSE:

1 COMPANIONSHIP

"Can two walk together, except they be agreed?" (Amos 3:3).

The companionship of marriage is the enjoyment of the fourth level of friendship. It involves intimate fellowship. Companionship in marriage occurs when both can say, "My partner is my best friend."

The word *companion* finds its origin in the Latin words meaning "with bread;" hence, it is someone with whom you break bread. This word origin is significant since the breaking of the bread in Scripture always symbolizes a covenant relationship.

PRINCIPLE:

• *Marriage oneness Gen. 2:24*

God's design of marriage is the complete unity of man and wife. This design includes oneness of spirit, oneness of soul, and oneness in the physical relationship. In order to achieve oneness on the physical level, each partner must recognize that the predominant factor of unity in the marriage comes first by oneness of spirit and then by oneness of soul.

If one were to describe the order of emphasis in the marriage relationship, the spirit must be pictured as representing 60%, the soul as 30%, and the physical representing 10%. With these proportions, the spirit of the marriage will remain strong even if the soul and the body become incompatible.

If a couple achieves the best possible physical relationship, they only experience 10% of marriage companionship. If they enjoy the best physical and

On the other hand, if a couple comes together in a oneness of spirit, they are already enjoying over half of the potential of the marriage. Then if for some medical reasons they are not able to enjoy the physical aspects of marriage, they only lose 10% of marriage happiness.

HOW IS THE SPIRIT OF A MARRIAGE DEVELOPED?

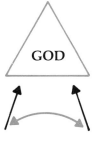

As the partners come closer to the Lord, they come closer to the spirit of each other. For this reason, it is essential that each partner maintain an intimate fellowship and communion with the Lord and also that they come together in daily times of fellowship in the Word.

As *Wisdom Searches* are conducted in the morning and evening, and as there are regular times of prayer, intercession, and thanksgiving, the couple will experience a growing oneness of spirit. They will be given the right desires of the heart for marriage and have them fulfilled by God.

In this way the couple is "seeking first the kingdom of God and His righteousness" and everything else will be added unto them. (See Matthew 6:33.) "*. . . No good thing will he withhold from them that walk uprightly*" (Psalm 84:11).

GOD'S "HIDDEN" DESIGN:

Key: *Living in harmony with wife's cycle Lev. 15:28*

"*Likewise, ye husbands, dwell with them according to knowledge, giving honour unto the wife, as unto the weaker vessel, and as being heirs together of the grace of life; that your prayers be not hindered*" (I Peter 3:7).

How is Satan attacking the "hidden" design of marriage companionship?

SATAN'S GOAL: *Promote insensitivity to wife's cycle*

WHAT SPECIAL PURPOSES DOES GOD HAVE FOR THE WIFE'S CYCLE?

1 *A sign of promise between God and the woman. I Tim 2:15*

"*Unto the woman he said, I will greatly multiply thy sorrow and thy conception; in sorrow thou shalt bring forth children . . .*" (Genesis 3:16).

There is little doubt that the normal reproductive functions in a woman were in place before Adam and Eve sinned. God's first command to them as a couple was to bear children. Labor in childbirth was a consequence of the fall, but was given to the woman for her spiritual benefit, not for her physical destruction.

"*Notwithstanding she shall be saved in childbearing, if they continue in faith and charity and holiness with sobriety*" (I Timothy 2:15).

2 *A monthly warning to the wife of the danger of beguilement.*

"*But I fear, lest by any means, as the serpent beguiled Eve through his subtilty, so your minds should be corrupted from the simplicity that is in Christ*" (II Corinthians 11:3).

3 *A monthly reminder to the husband of his need for self control and her need for protection & cleansing.*

"*That he might sanctify and cleanse it with the washing of water by the word*" (Ephesians 5:26).

4 *The presence of blood pictures Christ's redemption*

"*And almost all things are by the law purged with blood; and without shedding of blood is no remission*" (Hebrews 9:22).

Doré Bible Illustrations

How should a husband view his wife's cycle?

A MONTHLY REMINDER THAT:

"*Surely he hath borne our griefs, and carried our sorrows: yet we did esteem him stricken, smitten of God, and afflicted. But he was wounded for our transgressions, he was bruised for our iniquities: the chastisement of our peace was upon him; and with his stripes we are healed*" (Isaiah 53:4–5).

170

How can a new outlook transform the cycle?

• The trials of a wife's cycle must be welcomed as a "friend" not an "intruder".

The basic message of James 1:2-4 is that whenever trials push their way into our lives we should not react to them as unwelcomed guests but recognize that they are allowed by God to build His character within us. For this reason we are to "... *Let patience have her perfect work, that ye may be perfect and entire, wanting nothing.*"

IMPORTANT NOTE TO HUSBANDS:

In order for you to fulfill Scripture and "dwell with your wife according to knowledge" you must make it your responsibility to keep track of your wife's cycle and to know what special needs she has at various times of the month. During the menses, most women need verbal reassurance of your love for them and much more sensitivity and patience.

When you recognize the character benefits that will come to you during this time, you can view her cycle as a blessing rather than a curse.

A wife expressed her gratefulness for her husband's alertness in this area in the following testimony:

"When my husband first began keeping track of my monthly cycles, I felt cherished for the first time in our marriage. Then each month as he gave me a gentle reminder, I felt protected and accepted."
A wife from Oklahoma.

What are the consequences of resenting the cycle?

• Resentment communicates rejection of God's design. It results in self-rejection, frustration and bitterness

"*Looking diligently lest any man fail of the grace of God; lest any root of bitterness springing up trouble you, and thereby many be defiled*" (Hebrews 12:15).

"*Woe unto him that striveth with his Maker! Let the potsherd strive with the potsherds of the earth. Shall the clay say to him that fashioneth it, What makest thou? or thy work, He hath no hands?*" (Isaiah 45:9).

MARRIAGE PURPOSE:

2 ENJOYMENT

It is important to distinguish enjoyment from pleasure. Enjoyment is a more forceful term denoting a sustained condition of the spirit, whereas pleasure is a weaker term suggesting superficial and transitory emotions.

Enjoyment is the exultation of our spirit that comes from genuine harmony with both God and others. Pleasure is the temporary emotion that comes from the conscious pursuit of happiness. Joy is a giving and sharing expression; pleasure is a self-gratifying desire.

PRINCIPLE:

• Self-control

Any wholesome activity can be turned from enjoyment into drudgery by excessive indulgence. It is enjoyable to participate in recreation; however, if we were required to do it everyday, it would lose its function of joy and become a labor.

GOD'S "HIDDEN" DESIGN:

Key: Abstinence during specific times.

How is Satan attacking the "hidden" design of marriage enjoyment?

SATAN'S GOAL: *Self-gratification*

How can marriage enjoyment be maintained?

- *God designed periods of physical abstinence for the spiritual, mental, emotional, and physical health of the couple*

During the wife's monthly period and after the birth of a child, a husband is to abstain from a physical relationship with her. God identified these times in His instructions to the nation of Israel so that they could be healthier, wealthier, and wiser than any other nation. If further times of abstinence are desired, these should be by mutual consent and for spiritual purposes.

"Defraud ye not one the other, except it be with consent for a time, that ye may give yourselves to fasting and prayer; and come together again, that Satan tempt you not for your incontinency" (I Corinthians 7:5).

- *Observing these periods increases physical enjoyment, just as fasting increases food enjoyment.*

How does self-gratification damage the marriage?

- *Self-control in marriage is required to keep the marriage bed holy. Heb. 13:4*

Many Christian couples have accepted the erroneous philosophy that "within the context of marriage virtually nothing is immoral as long as both partners are comfortable with it and neither is harmed by it."

The error of such a conclusion should be obvious to any observer of human nature, to say nothing of a student of Scripture.

First, we live in an "adulterous generation" and a morally corrupt society. Many Christians have learned to be comfortable with the world's immoral standards.

Even when a wife says she is comfortable with an unnatural act, she often experiences a deep sense of revulsion at what she is asked to do and guilt after doing it.

Many couples are not aware of the legal definition of "sodomy." Sodomy is a crime of unnatural physical intimacy. From early times, sodomy has been referred to in statutes and court cases as the "crime against nature," by a man with a man or in an unnatural manner by a man with a woman.

Dictionaries also define sodomy in this way and also go on to list specific acts which would constitute sodomy within a marriage. (See The New College Edition of the *American Heritage Dictionary of the English Language* ©1976), page 1161.)

These definitions should leave no question in the mind of a Christian that certain acts in marriage are violations of purity and therefore defile the marriage bed.

God condemns sodomy as abomination (I Kings 14:24), vile affections (Romans 1:26), burning with lust, (Romans 1:27), dishonoring the body, (Romans 1:24), lusting after strange flesh, (Jude 7), filthy dreamers, (Jude 8), abusers of themselves, (I Corinthians 6:9), defilers of themselves, (I Timothy 1:9-10), violating nature, (Romans 1:26-27), and wickedness, (Genesis 13:13).

Based on the above list, these activities are "leaving the natural use of the woman." Therefore, it defiles the marriage bed and makes it a place of perversion. Perversion can be defined as taking members of our body which God designed for one function and using them for an adverse function.

This is precisely the warning of Hebrews 13:4. A reading of the Greek text would be as follows. "Hold marriage honorable in every way and do not defile the marriage bed. For God will judge and punish all those who are unchaste and guilty of sexual vice."

Second, God has given guidelines and limitations within marriage. Even though we may not see a direct cause-and-effect relationship by violating them, we cannot conclude that no harm occurs.

For example, a couple may believe they can engage in a physical relationship any day of the month and see no harm in it. However, a growing number of women with chronic yeast infection are finding dramatic relief by abstaining from physical relationships during the menstrual period as prescribed by Leviticus 15:19.

The preceding information allows only one conclusion regarding marriage standards.

Partners cannot set their own marriage standards.

If God's moral standards have been violated in your marriage, it would be very important to confess this to the Lord and to ask Him and your partner for forgiveness.

Only *"by humility and the fear of the Lord are riches, and honour, and life" (Proverbs 22:4).*

"If we confess our sins, he is faithful and just to forgive us our sins, and to cleanse us from all unrighteousness" (I John 1:9).

What is God's source of power for self-control?

Self-control is a fruit of the Holy Spirit.

"But the fruit of the Spirit is love, joy, peace, longsuffering, gentleness, goodness, faith, meekness, temperance [self-control]: against such there is no law" (Galatians 5:22–23).

In what way is the Christian under God's Law?

The Old Testament Law is described by Paul as a "schoolmaster to bring us to Christ" (see Galatians 3:24). The Law reveals to us how far short we have fallen of God's holy standards. (See Romans 7:8.) It brings us to the point of repentance. However, once we receive forgiveness for our sin through the shed blood of the Lord Jesus Christ, we enter into our position in Christ.

Christ fulfilled *every* demand of the Law. Thus, when we enter into Christ, we enter into His fulfillment of the law. We are no longer under its curse.

Those who don't understand the good news of salvation often try to keep the law with their own human efforts in order to be saved. This goal could be described as "legalism."

A further expression of legalism takes place when a Christian thinks he has to keep the law in order to maintain his salvation or that he has to fulfill the righteousness of the law by his own human efforts.

The Christian can never keep the standards of the law by his own efforts. It is only as he is obedient to the Holy Spirit living within him that the principles of the law can be lived out in his life.

A believer who is being led by God's Spirit is subject to the laws of sowing and reaping, which are described in Galatians 6:7–8:

> *"Be not deceived; God is not mocked: for whatsoever a man soweth, that shall he also reap. For he that soweth to his flesh shall of the flesh reap corruption; but he that soweth to the Spirit shall of the Spirit reap life everlasting."*

HOW DO WE KNOW WHEN WE ARE SOWING TO THE FLESH?

This question is answered in amazing detail in the Old Testament Law. *". . . The commandment of the Lord is pure, enlightening the eyes" (Psalm 19:8).* We don't keep the law in order to gain or maintain salvation, but we should apply the principles of the law to avoid sowing to the flesh and reaping corruption.

The laws and commandments throughout Scripture constitute a single unity. In light of this concept, Scripture explains, *"Whosoever shall offend in one point, he is guilty of all" (James 2:10).* The claim that the Old Testament Law has no application for us today not only violates the unity of Scripture, but also the clear instruction of II Timothy 3:16: *"All scripture is given by inspiration of God, and is profitable for doctrine, for reproof, for correction, for instruction in righteousness: That the man of God may be perfect, throughly furnished unto all good works."*

Furthermore, the entire law is summed up by Christ in two commands: *". . . Thou shalt love the Lord thy God with all thy heart, and with all thy soul, and with all thy mind. . . . Thou shalt love thy neighbour as thyself" (Matthew 22:37–39).*

A person may think he is a loving partner by things he says or does, but God's law is much more precise and accurate in defining what is loving and unloving.

marital Fast

1. Extend self-control that increases spiritual alertness.

2. Minimizes routine and boredom.

3. Lets both rest without feelings of guilt or inferiority

4. Gives consideration of emotional feelings.

How is "uncleanness" related to the menstrual cycle?

"And if a woman have an issue, and her issue in her flesh be blood, she shall be put apart seven days: and whosoever toucheth her shall be unclean until the even. And every thing that she lieth upon in her separation shall be unclean: every thing also that she sitteth upon shall be unclean" (Leviticus 15:19-20).

How does the New Testament confirm the need for abstinence during the wife's cycle?

- NT warnings on uncleanness include OT commands on abstinence

"Wherefore God also gave them up to uncleanness through the lusts of their own hearts, to dishonour their own bodies between themselves" (Romans 1:24).

". . . For as ye have yielded your members servants to uncleanness and to iniquity unto iniquity . . ." (Romans 6:19).

". . . And have not repented of the uncleanness and fornication and lasciviousness which they have committed" (II Corinthians 12:21).

"Now the works of the flesh are manifest, which are these; Adultery, fornication, uncleanness, lasciviousness" (Galatians 5:19).

"Who being past feeling have given themselves over unto lasciviousness, to work all uncleanness with greediness" (Ephesians 4:19).

"But fornication, and all uncleanness, or covetousness, let it not be once named among you, as becometh saints" (Ephesians 5:3).

"Mortify therefore your members which are upon the earth; fornication, uncleanness, inordinate affection, evil concupiscence, and covetousness, which is idolatry" (Colossians 3:5).

"For God hath not called us unto uncleanness, but unto holiness" (I Thessalonians 4:7).

Why is a Christian free to gain the benefits of applying God's laws on abstinence?

- God's laws on abstinence are not legalism

1 Legalism is trying to earn salvation

"For by grace are ye saved through faith; and that not of yourselves: it is the gift of God: Not of works, lest any man should boast" (Ephesians 2:8-9).

2 Trying to live the christian life in the energy of the soul

"For that which I do I allow not: for what I would, that do I not; but what I hate, that do I" (Romans 7:15).

3 Legalism is following the letter of the law—not the Spirit of the Law.

"Who also hath made us able ministers of the new testament; not of the letter, but of the spirit: for the letter killeth, but the spirit giveth life" (II Corinthians 3:6).

By what power does a Christian carry out abstinence?

- Christ in us overcomes the weakness of the flesh

"That the righteousness of the law might be fulfilled in us, who walk not after the flesh, but after the Spirit" (Romans 8:4).

WHAT ARE GOD'S GUIDELINES FOR TIMES OF ABSTINENCE?

1 During the menstrual cycle.

"But if a man be just, and do that which is lawful and right, And hath not eaten upon the mountains, neither hath lifted up his eyes to the idols of the house of Israel, neither hath defiled his neighbour's wife, **neither hath come near to a menstruous woman**" (Ezekiel 18:5-6).

NOTES

DIAGRAMS

If there is an unusual flow or a need for healing such as chronic yeast infection, then the following should also be observed:

2 *7 days after menstrual cycle*
Ezek. 18:6

"But if she be cleansed of her issue, then she shall number to herself seven days, and after that she shall be clean" (Leviticus 15:28).

Many couples have discovered deeper levels of communication by observing fourteen days of abstinence when needed. There is also benefit in having stronger seed by waiting until the wife's time of ovulation.

3 *40 days after the birth of a son.*

"... If a woman have conceived seed, and born a man child: then she shall be unclean seven days; according to the days of the separation for her infirmity shall she be unclean. And in the eighth day the flesh of his foreskin shall be circumcised. And she shall then continue in the blood of her purifying three and thirty days..." (Leviticus 12:2-4).

4 *80 days after birth of a daughter.*

"But if she bear a maid child, then she shall be unclean two weeks, as in her separation: and she shall continue in the blood of her purifying threescore and six days" (Leviticus 12:5).

Ewing Galloway

5. *The evening before worship. Lev. 15:8, 31*

WHAT ARE THE BENEFITS OF ABSTINENCE?

1 *It builds self-control.*

When sex drives are misused, they become self-consuming and can never be satisfied. Burned-out lusts call for new forms of perversion, which become even greater tyrants of unfulfillment.

The relationship between sexual drives and creative energy has been observed by many. However, the principles of God's working through self-control can be illustrated in the following diagram.

SEXUAL DRIVES
under control

CREATIVE POWER
outflowing

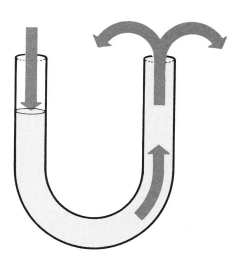

"He that believeth on me, as the scripture hath said, out of his belly shall flow rivers of living water" (John 7:38).

As physical drives are brought under the control of the Holy Spirit, greater spiritual power is experienced. This potential can also be reversed, however. Thus, a man like David who had great spiritual creativity was subject to greater sexual temptations when he allowed his physical drives to get out of control.

Those who complain that they have stronger sexual desires than normal need to realize what this means: They have greater potential of creative power. Elijah was such a man. The tremendous spiritual power which he possessed is documented in the book of Kings; however, he is also described as a man of passions: "Elias was a man subject to like passions as we are ..." (James 5:17).

177

HOW A COMMITMENT TO ABSTINENCE TRANSFORMED A MARRIAGE

"I am writing to report what has happened in our marriage since our decision to follow God's guidelines for abstinence. To be honest, I was waiting to see if the changes in our lives were short-lived or permanent. Now after a third of a year and five menstrual cycles, I am encouraged that our decision was correct, Biblically-based, and that the Lord is blessing our marriage more than ever before.

"Let me start at the beginning. Our dating relationship was based on the physical, not the spiritual. It ended in pregnancy and then marriage. She was sixteen, and I was twenty.

"After we married, our sex life became a shambles. My physical drives were impossible for her to satisfy, and even with a daily physical relationship, I became involved in pornography and other impure habits.

"After ten years of marriage we attended our first Basic Youth Seminar. When you went over the consequences of defrauding in dating, I suddenly realized my problem and our marriage problem. I asked God and my wife to forgive me for defrauding her before marriage, and for the first time in my life, I began exercising self-control.

"Also for the first time in ten years of married life, we began to experience true sexual intimacy. Our relationship continued to improve, but my wife still felt forced to submit to me, and she worried daily about whether or not she would have to 'make love' that night.

"I began having difficulty exercising self-control. Then we attended your Corporate Leaders Seminar and learned about abstinence during the menstrual period and for seven days after the period. I knew immediately that this is what God wanted me to commit to, and it scared me to death! I couldn't picture myself being committed to anything like that!

"However, God gave me the strength and encouragement to talk to my wife. We discussed it and that day, with her permission, I made a commitment to follow that principle. The relief within my wife was almost visible. The "fear" is gone from our marriage.

"We now have a freedom we never experienced before. We are blessed to the point that we almost feel guilty when we are around our Christian friends who are completely loaded down with problems. Our lives have been transformed by applying this and other principles from God's Word."

From Oklahoma City

A CONFIRMING REPORT FROM THE WIFE:

"I cannot tell you how much the material on abstinence has meant to me and our marriage. I have *never* experienced what has been happening in our marriage since we began following the principle of abstinence.

"It is indeed a miracle!!!! Through the power of the Holy Spirit, my husband has exercised real self-control in the area of our sex life. I feel *so* loved, cherished, and protected! I have been able to respond to him as seldom before. The difference in our relationship is difficult to describe, but very wonderful to experience. Thank you again for motivating us to choose God's best."

If you give your minds to Christ,
YOU WILL BE AN INTELLIGENT COUPLE;

If you give your emotions to Christ,
YOU WILL BE A DEVOTIONAL COUPLE;

If you give your wills to Christ,
YOU WILL BE A FORCEFUL COUPLE;

If you give your sex life to Christ,
YOU WILL BE A DYNAMIC COUPLE;

> If you give your minds to Christ
> but withhold your sex life,
>
> > YOU WILL BE A PSUEDO-INTELLECTUAL
> > COUPLE;
>
> If you give your emotions to Christ
> but withhold your sex life,
>
> > YOU WILL BE A GUSHY, SENTIMENTAL
> > COUPLE;
>
> If you give your wills to Christ
> but withhold your sex life,
>
> > YOU WILL BE AN IMPETUOUS, FRUSTRATED
> > COUPLE.

2 minimizes marital boredom + keeps tenderness and expectations alive.

"The divorce rate among Orthodox Jews is astonishingly low. One estimate was under three percent. This statistic is significantly lower than the divorce rate among Christians!

When one Orthodox Jew was asked why their divorce rate was so low, he explained, "We follow the abstinence laws, and each month I look forward to the time when we can come together. It's like being on a continuous honeymoon. The relationship never becomes routine."

This same response is echoed in the following testimonies:

HOW A "DITCHED IDEA" BROUGHT DELIGHT TO A COUPLE

"Last year I came home from your Seminar with the "Jewish fast" idea. We really pondered that one! Decided to give it a try for a couple months. Then we ditched it! Poor idea, we thought.

"Then my husband came home from another one of your seminars re-emphasizing this crazy idea. So we determined since April 1984 to make this part of our marriage if it was something the Lord wanted.

"I can't express to you what it has done for our marriage! We get so excited and thrilled with

one another in those two weeks of being "Jewish." It is better than any courting or honeymoon existence. We have reached a sharing level that is so special, and I truly feel cherished and adored. I'm so glad you shared this with the women as well as the men."

A wife from Oregon

HOW ABSTINENCE DEEPENED RESPECT AND JOY IN A MARRIAGE

"We wish to thank you for the Advanced Seminar that has changed our lives dramatically *again*. We took to heart your teaching on marriage. The abstinence provision has deepened the respect and genuine love we have for each other.

"We are learning to meditate more and more, and as a result have real joy."

A couple from Washington

HOW A COUPLE USED ABSTINENCE EVEN AFTER THE CYCLE STOPPED

"When you were discussing the topic of abstinence during a wife's period, it came to my remembrance that my wife has had a hysterectomy, and, therefore, no more periods. However, she still feels the physical changes within her and even though she has no periods, she has the need for a time of abstinence.

"After discussing it together, we agreed to continue as we had done before. I want the very best for my wife, and therefore, I consider the recurring physical needs in her as God saying, 'Now is the time for this [abstinence].' This discipline has deepened our love and affection for each other.

A pastor

HOW ABSTINENCE PREPARED A COUPLE FOR A CRISIS

"Because of following the abstinence principle for the last ten of our twenty-three years of marriage, my wife and I have been able to establish a level of intimate communication that before that time was never known.

"This communication was a major factor in allowing us to go through a serious surgery. As a result of the surgery, she would no longer have a

179

period or any other physical difficulties. When she opened her eyes after the operation, one of the first things she said to me was, 'Honey, how are we going to count our days now that I won't be having a period?'

"When I assured her that we would continue to carry out a time of abstinence on a regular basis, she expressed gratefulness and a deep sense of peace.

"In the years that have transpired since her operation, I have come to see more clearly than ever before the benefits which a time of abstinence has brought to our marriage. It has allowed me to give to her physical, emotional, and spiritual needs and maintain moral freedom with joy and fulfillment."

A couple from Illinois

3 *Items at the peak of the wife's enjoyment of sex.*

In order to obey the injunction of I Peter 3:7 to live with your wife "according to knowledge," it is important to know the precise time of your wife's ovulation. The easiest way to determine past times of ovulation is to count fourteen days back from the beginning of a new cycle. By charting this over several months, the approximate time of ovulation will become clear. Other factors may cause this time to vary.

It is significant that God designed this point in the wife's cycle for greatest enjoyment of the physical relationship. Couples who wait until this time are given an added blessing, which is described in the following section:

HOW HEALTHIER AND STRONGER CHILDREN COME FROM PROPER ABSTINENCE.

God gives a special promise regarding children to those who love and obey His commandments. "... *Blessed is the man that feareth the Lord, that delighteth greatly in His commandments. His seed shall be mighty upon earth ...*" (Psalm 112:1–2).

Couples who are observing proper abstinence are having children who are stronger and healthier than they expected. Doctors have expressed surprise and delight as APGAR tests show the highest possible scores.

One medical doctor explained that when a couple practices Biblical abstinence, they come together at the optimum time of her fertility, shortly before or at the time of her ovulation. This timing does not give any opportunity for deterioration of the ovum.

Presumptive support of this hypothesis has come from countries where a majority of the population practice the rhythm method of birth control. In several studies it has been demonstrated that there is a higher incidence of genetic abnormalities than would be expected in these countries. The rhythm method is exactly opposite the schedule taught in Scripture.

HOW ABSTINENCE ALLOWS "BARREN" COUPLES TO HAVE CHILDREN

A young couple was informed that due to the inadequacy of the husband's seed they could not have children. They began following the abstinence principle so that they came together when his seed was the strongest. They also applied several other guidelines which were explained at the Seminar. The result was conception and the gift of a treasured child. Here is their firsthand account:

"Two years ago I heard you explain some principles on how a husband ought to treat his wife in their most intimate relationship through Six Scriptural Principles of Marriage.

"We had been trying to have a child for some months without success. . . . When I heard you give the principles of the time of uncleanness, I went home and told my wife what you said, and we agreed to try it. (We had always abstained during her period, but only during the four or five days of flow.) So, we decided to wait the seven days. Nothing happened.

"Then the next year I returned to the Pastor's Seminar, and you mentioned it again. I had forgotten that the waiting period might extend seven days beyond the end of the flow. I went home and shared this with my wife. We committed this to the Lord and waited the fourteen days. As I was in the midst of an extended fast with the Lord, we abstained on all but the fifteenth day after the cycle began.

"My wife then became pregnant, and the Lord has blessed us with a baby girl. When we took her to the pediatrician at two days of age, he commented that she was one of the most perfect two-day-olds that he had ever seen."

A pastor from Washington

4 *It sets the couple free from guilt and inadequacy*

By following Scripturally-based guidelines which have proven physical, mental, emotional, and spiritual benefits, the focus of the relationship of a couple changes from "getting" to "giving." Problems that may have been present as the result of concupiscence are removed, because new self-control and new self-respect is achieved through the disciplines of this procedure.

Many husbands who had deeply damaged their wives by promiscuity prior to marriage have been able to restore the spirit of their marriage by following the abstinence guidelines. They have given testimony that even if there were no other benefits, this restoration was worth all the discipline that was required to carry out the time of abstinence.

The enjoyment of the physical relationship is often stifled by an unhealthy and unscriptural fear of pregnancy. There may be times when a couple would determine that they should postpone having more children; however, the alternative must then be abstinence rather than any other method of conception control.

It is important for couples to be informed about the consequences of using any unnatural methods of preventing conception.

GUILT COMES BY CALLING GOD'S BLESSINGS "CURSES" AND GOD'S CURSE "A BLESSING."

Throughout Scripture, God consistently teaches us that children are His blessing. He also cursed several women by closing their wombs.

"Lo, children are an heritage of the Lord: and the fruit of the womb is his reward" (Psalm 127:3).

When God brought judgment upon Abimelech and his household, He closed up the wombs of all the women. (See Judges 20:18.)

God assigns a special woe to those who reverse His pronouncements. Any couple who calls that which God loves "evil," receive to themselves a special woe: *"Woe unto them that call evil good, and good evil; that put darkness for light, and light for darkness; that put bitter for sweet, and sweet for bitter!" (Isaiah 5:20).*

Children are good, not evil; they bring light into a home, not darkness; they are a sweet experience, not a bitter one. The woe continues upon *"... them that are wise in their own eyes, and prudent in their own sight!" (Isaiah 5:21).*

Some of the woes include the physical, psychological, and spiritual destruction of modern birth control methods. *from the use of*

GUILT COMES BY DISCOVERING THAT ABORTIONS WERE UNKNOWINGLY COMMITTED

There is no question that many birth control methods and devices simply kill the conceived child. Chief among these is the IUD. It comes as a shock to many couples, however, that taking the pill also results in aborting a conceived child.

The following quote is from the director of the Food and Drug Administration in the United States, "Fundamentally, these pills [birth control pills containing estrogen and progestrin] take over the menstrual cycle from the normal endocrine mechanisms, and in so doing they inhibit ovulation and change the characteristics of the uterus so that it is not receptive to a fertilized egg."

In medical studies it has been discovered that

"breakthrough ovulation" has occured in two to ten percent of cycles.

A statement was given on this by a medical researcher from the University of Southern California School of Medicine, "Furthermore they [the combined pills] alter the endometrium so that glandular production of glycogen is diminished and less energy is available for the [developing new life] to survive in the uterine cavity."

GUILT IS INTENSIFIED FROM HEALTH COMPLICATIONS

The pill has been proven to produce blood-clotting defects. These have resulted in thrombophlebitis, pulmonary embolisms (blood clots which lodge in the lung and may be fatal), strokes, heart attacks, and blindness.

Eighteen other diseases or health problems have been associated with the pill, including cancer. These have been listed in the FDA's patent warning brochure published in April, 1978.

According to the British Medical Journal, September 15, 1979, pages 632–634, the mortality risks for women taking the pill are higher than those who go through pregnancy.

GUILT COMES FROM ENGAGING IN UNNATURAL PHYSICAL RELATIONSHIPS TO AVOID CONCEPTION.

When a couple uses unnatural ways of engaging in physical relations in an attempt to avoid conception, they only open up a new set of problems which go deeper than the health consequences. They strike at the core of the spirit of the marriage and the relationship of each partner with the Lord.

The following letter clearly describes the problem:

"Please, Please, Please, emphasize the importance of men *not* introducing certain 'sexual techniques' in marriage.

"Some of these are things I believe God never intended for us to get involved in. For example, there is one practice which my husband and I engaged in over a period of time. All of a sudden my husband stopped doing it but didn't tell me why. I had come to enjoy the pleasure of it. One day I finally asked him why he had stopped. He said he didn't know, just that 'something' told him to stop.

"The guilt that I had pushed away over doing this activity came flooding in. If only I had not been introduced to this, I would never have suffered the frustration and confusion that I did. I asked God's forgiveness for engaging in it in the first place. Then I asked God to deliver me from the further desire for doing it. God has mercifully answered these prayers. Now I am praying for deliverance from the memory of it.

"At the Seminar this year you mentioned what the forbidden fruit was — certain knowledge of evil. This definition certainly applies to our situation. Curiosity can be a real snare."

A wife from Texas

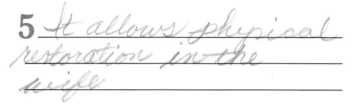

5 It allows physical restoration in the wife

God promised that none of the diseases of Egypt would be on His people if they obeyed His commandments. This same promise is being experienced by couples who are applying the principles of the commandments that God gave to His own nation of Israel.

A significant number of health benefits are being reported by couples who have begun following the Scriptural guidelines of abstinence. The following are only examples:

HOW INFECTION AND IRREGULAR CYCLES CLEARED UP AFTER PROPER ABSTINENCE

"In November 1982, the owner of a company called to ask whether we would advise him to have a vasectomy done. He had already been counseled by others that there was nothing wrong with this, but he felt somewhat uneasy about it.

"He was asked whether or not he had violated moral standards prior to marriage. He acknowledged that this had occurred and that his marriage communication was now at the bottom of the chart. ("Communication Breakdown in Marriage" as given at the Basic Seminar.)

"The principle of abstinence during the wife's monthly period and seven days afterward was explained to him, and he agreed to try it.

"Two months later he called again to explain

that a miracle had taken place in his marriage. There was a new level of communication. The only word to describe what they now experienced was "beautiful."

"Six months later he called again to give a further report. The communication in their marriage was continuing to deepen. His wife told him that she finally felt cherished. Two other rewards were also experienced. A yeast infection that his wife had had for several years in spite of treatment by many doctors had cleared up, and for the first time in twenty-eight years her monthly cycle had become regular."

A business man in Nebraska

HOW A PERSISTENT BLADDER INFECTION STOPPED WHEN ABSTINENCE BEGAN

"At my ninth Basic Seminar you mentioned something that I had not heard before—abstaining from physical relationship during the menstrual period. My husband and I decided that we would try that.

"For many years I had been having recurring bladder infections. In fact, I went to the doctor regularly for medication, and he assured me that I would have to continue taking medication for years to come.

"We started our times of abstinence in November of 1983, and the infection cleared up within the month. To this day I have been free from any trouble whatsoever from bladder infection.

"Abstinence has not only helped in my medical problems, but we were beginning to have pressures in our marriage because I couldn't satisfy my husband's sexual desires. You will never know the freedom I received since applying this powerful information on having self-control.

"Both of us are free, and God has truly come through where I didn't think there were any solutions."

A wife in Wisconsin

P.S. This wife sent us sixteen years of medical records to document her report.

The following material is a series of exerpts from the report of a medical doctor on the benefits on Biblical abstinence.

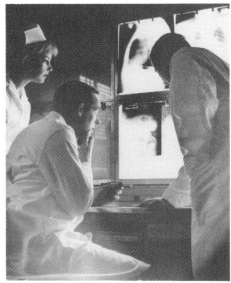

Ewing Galloway

AVOIDING THE POTENTIAL OF INFECTION

"In regard to the negative consequences of ignoring the abstinence laws, the medical data is clear. The potential for spreading disease to the fallopian tubes and to the peritoneal cavity of the female is at a maximum during and immediately after the menstrual period. There are conflicting reports as to whether subsequent to the menstrual cycle a mucous plug forms in the cervical os which eliminates that danger and that that plug is formed 7–14 days after the onset of the cycle."

DECREASING THE DANGER OF GENETIC ABNORMALITIES

"It is in the area of the negative or detrimental effects upon the children of those ignoring the abstinence laws that we find the strongest evidence presently available which supports this hypothesis. It is here that this hypothesis is most clearly supported by scientific data.

"While advancing maternal age has long been associated with genetic abnormalities, fewer than 6% of the births of those with genetic abnormalities occur to women who are 35 years of age and older. This means that 94% of genetic abnormalities occur in births to women in the 'normal reproductive years.' This staggering statistic has caused much inquiry into the question of etiology. There are many potential explanations, but one of the most fruitful has been that of delayed fertilization.

James L. Holly, MD., PA.

NOTES

DIAGRAMS

What are the continuing consequences of the lack of self control?

• *Lack of self-control is passed on to children*

"Thou shalt not bow down thyself to them, nor serve them: for I the Lord thy God am a jealous God, visiting the iniquity of the fathers upon the children unto the third and fourth generation of them that hate me" (Exodus 20:5).

HOW CAN PHYSICAL DRIVES BE BROUGHT UNDER CONTROL?

In order for couples to follow Biblical guidelines of abstinence, they must have moral freedom and the ability to keep their desires under the control of the Holy Spirit.

One couple made the accurate observation, "When you abstain for the glory of God, He gives you the grace to maintain self-control."

The grace of God is appropriated when we humble ourselves and consistently follow the Biblical steps to transform drives.

God's way to transform drives

1 *Engraft Rom. 6 and 8 in your soul.*

2 *Personalize and name temptation as you recite the verses.*

3 *Compare the law of sin to the law of gravity.*

4 *Picture yourself dead to sin.*

5 *Make no provision for the flesh* Rom 13:14

6 *Be accountable to partner for victory.*

7 *Yield physical members to God.*

"I speak after the manner of men because of the infirmity of your flesh: for as ye have yielded your members servants to uncleanness and to iniquity unto iniquity; even so now yield your members servants to righteousness unto holiness" (Romans 6:19).

Each of these seven points is further explained and illustrated in the *Eagle Story*.

185

NOTES

DIAGRAMS

MARRIAGE PURPOSE:

3 COMPLETENESS

Completeness is bringing together in marriage what God divided in creation. He took part of Adam to make Eve, then brought her to him as his completion. When Adam saw Eve, he immediately recognized this purpose and said, *". . . This is now bone of my bones, and flesh of my flesh: she shall be called Woman, because she was taken out of Man" (Genesis 2:23).*

The word *complete* is an absolute term and cannot be qualified by further adjectives such as more or most. This rules out the adding of another wife to the marriage and rules out the potential of greater fulfillment in extramarital relationships.

PRINCIPLE:

- *Spiritual power*

"That he would grant you, according to the riches of his glory, to be strengthened with might by his Spirit in the inner man" (Ephesians 3:16).

When two come together in spiritual oneness, they multiply their potential and power in the Lord. They will be able to accomplish great spiritual achievements through prayer since God promised *". . . if two of you shall agree on earth as touching any thing that they shall ask, it shall be done for them of my Father which is in heaven" (Matthew 18:19).*

GOD'S "HIDDEN" DESIGN

Key: *Oneness in Spirit*

"Likewise, ye husbands, dwell with them according to knowledge, giving honour unto the wife, as unto the weaker vessel, and as being heirs together of the grace of life; that your prayers be not hindered" (I Peter 3:7).

How is Satan attacking the "hidden" design of marriage completeness?

SATAN'S GOAL: *Damage to the spirit of the marriage*

How does concupiscence damage the spirit of a marriage?

- *marriage spirit is damaged when either party flees used.*

The husband is to view his wife as an extension of himself and to protect her as he would protect himself.

"For no man ever yet hated his own flesh; but nourisheth and cherisheth it, even as the Lord the church" (Ephesians 5:29).

How is the spirit of the marriage deepened?

- *marriage spirit is deepened through the word and prayer*

"That he might sanctify and cleanse it with the washing of water by the word" (Ephesians 5:26)

Why is oneness essential for prayer? ✳

- *Tremendous power is available when two agree in prayer*

"Again I say unto you, That if two of you shall agree on earth as touching any thing that they shall ask, it shall be done for them of my Father which is in heaven" (Matthew 18:19).

How can abstinence strengthen oneness?

- *times of abstinence is to be used for prayer and fasting*

"Defraud ye not one the other, except it be with consent for a time, that ye may give yourselves to fasting and prayer; and come together again, that Satan tempt you not for your incontinency" (I Corinthians 7:5).

FURTHER INSIGHTS ON COMPLETENESS

- Completeness is promoted by a servant's spirit—working to make the partner successful.
- An important resource for completeness is deepened by helping each other identify and develop spiritual gifts.
- Completeness is rewarded when major decisions are not made until both partners are in oneness of Spirit.

NOTES   **DIAGRAMS**

MARRIAGE PURPOSE:

4 FRUITFULNESS

Throughout Scripture, the blessing of God and the purpose of God were explained and understood in terms of fruitfulness. God's promise to Abraham was to multiply his descendants as the stars of the heavens and the sands of the seashore. (See Genesis 22:17.)

Christ taught His disciples that the purpose of pruning in their lives was to cause them to bear "much fruit." This would be a sign that they were His disciples and a means by which they would glorify God. (See John 15:8.)

PRINCIPLE

Life multiplication

"And God blessed them, and God said unto them, Be fruitful, and multiply, and replenish the earth, and subdue it . . ." (Genesis 1:28).

In order for God's purpose to be accomplished in the world, we need to think in terms of multiplication, not just addition. The early Church had an impact in the world because the number of disciples was "multiplied greatly." (See Acts 6:7.)

The nation of Israel became a mighty force in Egypt because they "grew and multiplied" (Acts 7:17).

The very nature and character of God is to multiply life, whereas the nature and character of Satan is to multiply death.

GOD'S "HIDDEN DESIGN"

Key: *Viewing children as God's blessing.*

"Lo, children are an heritage of the Lord: and the fruit of the womb is his reward." The next verses are equally significant: "As arrows are in the hand of a mighty man; so are children of the youth. Happy is the man that hath his quiver full of them: they shall not be ashamed, but they shall speak with the enemies in the gate" (Psalm 127:3–5).

The Hebrew word for *speak* means "to subdue or to destroy." Thus, the strength of the church and the nation depends upon the fruitfulness of its families.

How is Satan attacking the "hidden design" of marriage fruitfulness?

SATAN'S GOAL: *Pleasure without responsibility.*

What is God's command for fruitfulness?

- *Be fruitful and multiply Gen. 1:28 also repeated after flood. Gen 9:1*

"... And God said unto them, Be fruitful, and multiply ..." (Genesis 1:28).

"And God blessed Noah and his sons, and said unto them, Be fruitful, and multiply, and replenish the earth" (Genesis 9:1).

The actual Hebrew words contained in this command leave no question about God's will in the matter of family size.

- **Be fruitful:** *pârâh,* meaning "to increase"

- **And multiply:** *râbâh,* meaning "to increase exceedingly"

- **And replenish the earth:** *mâlâ* meaning "to fill up the world to overflowing"

Few couples have stopped to consider how great an impact they could make on the world by obeying this first commandment. In the process of discovering their potential, however, many couples would be horrified to realize the damage which has already occurred in our churches and nation by the acceptance of humanistic philosophies.

The hidden agenda of secular humanism is to reduce the size and strength of the family. A strong family that understands and lives by Biblical principles is the single greatest threat to the ultimate control of humanistic forces.

In Scripture, Egypt is a type of the world's system. When God's people began to multiply in the land of Egypt, Pharoah and his officers became alarmed.

"And the children of Israel were fruitful, and increased abundantly, and multiplied, and waxed exceeding mighty. . . .And he [Pharaoh] said unto *his people, Behold, the people of the children of Israel are more and mightier than we: Come on, let us deal wisely with them; lest they multiply . . ." (Exodus 1:7, 9-10).*

Pharoah's first program to control the Israelites' population was to work through the medical community of the day. The midwives were instructed to kill the male children. However, they refused, and God blessed them by giving them large families.

Pharoah's attempts to discourage God's chosen people failed because of the commitment of the Hebrews to have large, God-fearing families.

When Pharoah's attempts to reduce the family size of the Israelites failed, he tried to dissipate and destroy them through hard labor. However, this only served to strengthen their ranks and prepare them to be a victorious and powerful nation that was to influence the world.

The impact that one couple following God's first commandment could have on a nation and the world is staggering. If this couple had just six children and each of their descendants has six children and each one was trained in the ways of the Lord to be mighty in Spirit, there would be in only five generations 19,666 descendants and spouses.

If the same couple were to have twelve children and each of their descendants were to have twelve children, the total number in five generations would be 271,455! The seed of this couple would certainly be mighty upon the earth!

If large families sound unusual or inappropriate to us, it is only because we have been influenced by the deceptive philosophies of humanism. Humanists have carried on a persistent propaganda campaign to convince nations that the world is overpopulated and has dwindling natural resources.

These assertions are total myths and are very destructive since they provide the rationalization for abortion, sterilization, infanticide, euthanasia, and suicide.

IS THE WORLD FACING THE THREAT OF OVERPOPULATION?

NO. Actually, the world is comparatively empty. There are 52.5 million square miles of land area in the world, not including Antarctica.

If all the people in the world were brought together into one place, they could stand, without touching anyone else, in less than 200 square miles.

• The city limits of Jacksonville, Florida contain 841 square miles. Each square mile contains 27,878,400 square feet. The total number of square feet in the city is 23,445,734,400. The world population is four and a half billion people. By allowing an average of 2.6 square feet for each person from babies to adults, every person in the world could stand shoulder to shoulder in just one-half of the city.

A further fallacy in the population explosion myth is the assumption that the greater the population, the lower the standard of living. This is not true.

Japan has a population density of 798 people per square mile, yet they have a higher per capita gross national product ($4,450) than India, which has 511 people per square mile ($140).[1]

China has a population density of 232 persons per square mile. West Germany has 636 per square mile. The United Kingdom has 593 per square mile, and the United States has only 60 people per square mile.[2]

The 1973 *Handbook on Population,* Third Edition, by Robert L. Sassone, reports the following considerations about population and the available land area to support it:

"If you look at a population density map, you would find that most square miles of land in the world have less than one family living in them. Many Americans crowd into cities and assume the whole United States and the whole world are like their city.

"If the Pentagon Building were a little bit over a mile high, you could put everybody in the world in it. If you had ten buildings the width of the Pentagon and the height of the Empire State Building, you could put everybody who had lived or died during the past hundred years in them.

"When we add together all of man's artificial artifacts such as homes, paving, buildings, etc., they take up less than 75,000 square miles. This is one sixth of one percent of the land area of the world.

"The United Nations lists total farmland of far less then 1.5 billion hectares or far less than six million square miles. In the average year, most of this land is not harvested, but if you assume it all is farmed and add to it the 75,000 square miles of man's artifacts, you would find that man is using about three percent of the earth's surface or ten percent of the earth's land surface.

"If present trends continue, Europe is going to be depopulated. If you assume everyone is going to live to be sixty, a nation needs a birth rate of 16.8 to grow. In Europe, according to the 1970 United

Nations Statistical Yearbook, pages 93-94, 15 of 26 nations had a birth rate lower than 16.8.

"Total birth rates in the United States dropped four percent since 1970, even though the number of potential mothers in the population increased.

"Census Bureau analysts estimate that these figures would translate into a total fertility rate of 2.284 children per mother. That would be the lowest since the mid-1930's, when it dropped to 2.235. The rate needed to replace the population is 2.110. United States vital statistics show the U.S. birth rate in recent years to be the lowest in history.

"The United States has already gone below the point of population stagnation and has entered an era of population decline." [In 1980, the birth rate had declined still further to 1.8 children per mother.]

IS THE WORLD RUNNING OUT OF VITAL NATURAL RESOURCES?

NO. Projections of running out of energy or food sources are totally misleading. God gave to man the command and ability to fill up the world with people and to subdue the earth for their own needs.

Shortages of one product have always been a motivation to create a new product from existing and often overlooked resources.

Significant progress has been made in reclaiming, through irrigation, areas of land around the world which previously have been considered infertile. The vast potential of food resources in the oceans has as yet been unexplored, and many essential components of a balanced diet are now being synthesized in the laboratory.

Civilizations such as those of the Mayas and Incas were not destroyed through lack of natural resources but by moral decadence which came by

1. Pat Gilliland, ed., *Our Magnificent Earth,* (Chicago: Rand McNally and Co., 1979), p.168.
2. Brian P. Price, *Rand McNally Pictorial World Atlas,* (Chicago: Rand McNally and Co., 1980), pp. 24, 78, 159.

rejecting Biblical truth and devoting themselves to the passions and dissipations of perverted pleasure.

Joseph was considered an expendable human being by his jealous brothers. However, God gave him the understanding which preserved his brothers during a time of famine.

How many of the 55 million babies that the world has considered expendable and has aborted in the last ten years would have been destined to discover amazing new sources for food and energy?

DOES INDIA HAVE WIDESPREAD HUNGER BECAUSE OF LACK OF FOOD?

NO. India does not have a hunger problem because of a lack of food. It has a hunger problem because of religious beliefs which are contrary to the Word of God.

The Hindu religion teaches that people who die are reincarnated in the form of animals; thus it is against their laws and religion to kill rats, mice, cows, or other animals.

Every cow eats enough food to feed seven people, and there are two hundred million "sacred cows" in India.

If the people of India would just stop feeding these cows, they would have enough food to feed one billion, four hundred million people. That is more than one fourth of the entire world's population![1]

God promises adequate provision for those who serve Him and obey His laws. On the other hand, He warns that those who reject His Word will experience destructive hunger and famine.

It is for this reason that in both the Old and the New Testaments God warns us "... that man doth not live by bread only, but by every word that proceedeth out of the mouth of the Lord doth man live." [2]

1. Sassone, op. cit., pp. 53–54.
2. Deuteronomy 8:3; see Matthew 4:4.

In the last census count, the United Nations determined that India had roughly four hundred people per square mile. That is fewer people than live on a square mile in Italy, and far fewer than the six hundred people per square mile in England.

The Netherlands has one thousand people per square mile, yet the Dutch government pays farmers not to grow food. Taiwan has more than twelve hundred people per square mile. Both the Netherlands and Taiwan export food and have two to three times the population density of India.

The alarmists who use statistics to try to prove that there is a population problem fail to account for God's judgment on nations that violate His principles.

They also overlook the tendency among decadent civilizations to kill their own children. Because the wicked have little regard for their offspring, God warns His people to avoid contact with them and commands His people not to learn their ways.

Because the Israelites *"were mingled among the heathen, and learned their works. And they served their idols: which were a snare unto them. Yea, they sacrificed their sons and their daughters unto devils, And shed innocent blood, even the blood of their sons and of their daughters. . . . Therefore was the wrath of the Lord kindled against his people. . . . And he gave them into the hand of the heathen; and they that hated them ruled over them"* (Psalm 106:35–38, 40–41).

Why is the decision to limit family size contrary to the grace given by God for marriage?

When a couple prohibits the God-ordained result of the marriage act, they are in a very real sense defrauding each other and denying the Lord, Who designed marriage. Because God ordained the functions of marriage and because God is present and a part of the blood covenant of marriage, it is a very serious matter to withhold that which was publicly promised.

Onan went through the act of marriage, but withdrew himself before it was completed. His actions displeased the Lord, and he was killed. (See Genesis 38:9.) The same violation of integrity and honesty in giving was judged in the New Testament by the lives of Ananias and Sapphira. (See Acts 5:1–11.)

192

In both of these cases the individuals gave to another individual, but their gift was evaluated by the Lord. Each time a couple engages in a physical relationship, they are reaffirming their marriage covenant and the vows which accompanied it. It is, therefore, totally inconsistent to promise complete commitment and then prohibit the physical results which that commitment will bring.

The purpose of the knowledge which a husband is to have about his wife is that they might more fully enter into being "heirs together of the grace of life." This grace which is given to a married couple is the desire and the power to reproduce themselves physically.

"Likewise, ye husbands, dwell with them according to knowledge, giving honour unto the wife, as unto the weaker vessel, and as being heirs together of the grace of life; that your prayers be not hindered" (I Peter 3:7).

How does "family planning" interfere with God's planning?

• <u>God opens and closes the womb.</u>

"But unto Hannah he gave a worthy portion; for he loved Hannah: but the Lord had shut up her womb" (I Samuel 1:5).

"And God remembered Rachel, and God hearkened to her, and opened her womb" (Genesis 30:22).

WHAT ARE THE CONSEQUENCES OF STERILIZATION?

There is growing medical evidence that long-term effects on the immunological system are caused by vasectomies. After a vasectomy the sperm production is the same as before: around fifty thousand spermatozoa every minute.

Since there is not a normal passage for the sperm, they are either consumed by destroyer cells within the body or degenerate and produce antigens. These antigens cause antibodies, which will frequently infiltrate the bloodstream. When this happens, other cells begin to manufacture antibodies against the sperm.[1]

When the body generates defenses to ward off cells of its own making, it becomes auto-immune, or allergic to itself. Several studies have found such antibodies generated in fifty-five to seventy-five percent of patients within two years after vasectomies.[2]

One of the nation's foremost surgeons who performs reversals of vasectomies and tubal ligations has reported that "blowouts" occur in the body and a pathological condition exists because of vasectomies.[3]

The physical and emotional consequences of tubal ligation are equally serious. There are reports of increased gynecological problems in women who have had tubal ligations.

In one study, forty-three percent of women experienced such conditions as heavy menstrual bleeding, menstrual disturbances requiring hormonal treatments, cervical erosion, ovarian tumors, and recanalization of the fallopian tubes requiring a second operation.[4]

Of even greater seriousness is the fact that there is an increased incidence of hysterectomies among women who have had tubal ligations.[5]

1. H.J. Roberts *Is Vasectomy Safe?* (West Palm Beach, Florida: Sunshine Academic Press, 1979), 90.

2. K.S.K. Tung. "Human sperm antigens and antisperm antibodies," *Clinical Experiences in Immunology.* (1975). 20. 93–104. R. Ansbacher, et al. "Sperm antibodies in vasectomized men," *Fertility and Sterility.* 23:640. R. Ansbacher. "Sperm-agglutinating and sperm-immobilizing antibodies in vasectomized men," *Fertility and Sterility.* 22:629. Rudi Ansbacher. "Vasectomy. sperm antibodies." *Fertility and Sterility.* 24:788–792. Nancy J. Alexander. B.J. Wilson. and G.D. Patterson. "Vasectomy: Immunologic effects in rhesus monkeys and men." *Fertility and Sterility.* 25:149. S. Shulman, E. Zappi. U. Ahmed. and J.E. Davis, *"Immunologic consequences of vasectomy." Contraception.* 5(4) 269–278 (April, 1972)

3. Dr. Sherman J. Silber, M.D., F.A.C.S., St. Luke's Hospital - West, 224 Woods Mill Road, Suite 730, St. Louis, Missouri 63017.

4. M.J. Muldoon, "Gynaecological illness after sterilization," *British Medical Journal.* (January 8, 1972). 84–85. Table III.

5. James G. Tappan, *American Journal of Obstetrics and Gynecology.* 115:8, 1056.

WHAT ARE THE BENEFITS OF REVERSING STERILIZATION?

The following testimonies give firsthand documentation of victories won in lives by reevaluating and reversing the world's philosophy on birth control.

HOW A FAMILY REVERSED THE REGRET OF A TUBAL LIGATION

"My husband and I had our last child five years ago when I was thirty-two years old. My physician at that time advised us to have a tubal ligation performed due to my age. We reluctantly agreed and followed through with the surgery at the time of her birth. Although neither of us was saved at the time, we regretted it!

"Then a year later, by the grace of God, we were saved. I began to have physical problems which I believe all stemmed from a hormone imbalance.

"I went to another physician in my hometown and he, without hesitation, said hysterectomy! We began to pray and once again reluctantly agreed. Surgery was to be three weeks before attending our first Seminar. We had no peace, so we decided to postpone it until after the Seminar.

"We then began to pray and believed that God would show us during the Seminar what He would have us to do. We attended the Seminar with excitement and enthusiasm. I don't remember exactly which night, but I do remember that God answered.

"You began to talk about God's army dwindling and Satan's army growing larger—about how we Christians listen to the humanists. Without realizing it, we have done just that. My husband almost broke my ribs that night punching me with everything you'd say! We went home, got down together and asked God to forgive us.

"We then decided on the reversal surgery. We knew that God had forgiven us, but if possible, we wanted to rectify our sin. Of course, Satan's

army is on the ball. Our insurance would not cover the surgery, and we were told it would cost in the area of seven thousand dollars. Our insurance would, however, cover abortion one hundred percent.

"That's when we decided to apply the principle from God's Word that you had taught at the Seminar on appealing to those in authority. We began to pray and ask God to turn the hearts and minds of those who had the power to change this policy.

"My husband, a welder by trade, attended a union meeting and brought our problem to the attention of the president of his local. This took place in November of 1984, and we were notified in December that we would be the case study for this surgery before a final decision was made on whether the insurance policy would be changed.*

"I had the surgery January 8, 1985. It's been seven weeks, and I feel great! We are leaving it all up to the Lord now. We just praise him for answering prayer. We praise God for using you as He does. May God bless you."

A wife from Illinois

* It would be wise in such an appeal to point out to the insurance company that a hysterectomy would probably cost more than the reversal, and that there are usually continuing expenses after a hysterectomy with the need of treating hormonal imbalances.

HOW A FAMILY PUT THE PLANNING BACK IN GOD'S HANDS

"We especially wish to thank you for speaking out on vasectomy reversals. Last November after hearing that particular session, my husband and I repented for taking that part of our lives into our own hands four years before as non-Christians. We pursued God's promptings and leadings, and in February the operation was reversed at the University of Minnesota.

"We told our doctor the reason was to get back in God's will, and if He then blessed us with children—wonderful! But if no children, it would still be a success to us just to give that area of our marriage back to God. The doctor said he had never heard that reason before. He also said, 'If you conceive, it would be six to twelve months.'

"But that wasn't God's plan. The first month a

new life was formed in my womb. And our due date is Christmas! I couldn't think of a more wonderful time. My husband, our five-year-old daughter and I have no doubt that this baby is a miracle and a blessing for God! We are so thankful."

A couple from Minnesota

WHAT STEPS CAN A "BARREN" COUPLE TAKE TO HAVE CHILDREN?

An increasing number of couples are desiring to have children, but are being told by their doctors that it is medically impossible for them to do so.

Based on the fact that God is the One Who opens and closes the womb, and based on the principle that He desires to multiply fruitfulness, the following four steps are recommended:

1 FULLY DEDICATE TO THE LORD YOUR DESIRE TO HAVE CHILDREN.

Inward tensions and anxieties may have an effect upon the ability to conceive. When Hannah resolved her bitterness of soul and anxiety over not having children by fully yielding her rights to the Lord, God gave her five children. (See I Samuel 2.)

Bible Art Series, Standard Publishing, Cincinnati

Her emotional release came when she told the Lord that she would give the child back to Him if He gave one to her.

2 MAKE SURE THAT THE MUSIC IN YOUR HOME FOLLOWS BIBLICAL PRINCIPLES.

The imbalance of rock and various kinds of contemporary music produces tensions and also spiritual warfare in the home which can have a significant effect in preventing conception. Good music contributes to a sense of inner rest, which is important for conception to take place.

3 FOLLOW THE GUIDELINES OF BIBLICAL ABSTINENCE.

By observing the full fourteen days of abstinence (unless the wife's cycle is shorter), the seed of the husband is the strongest and there is the greatest possibility for conception and giving birth to healthy children.

4 CALL FOR THE ELDERS OF THE CHURCH.

Many couples are experiencing conception after recognizing that the inability to have a child is a physical infirmity and thus, following the guidelines given in James 5:14–16:

"Is any sick among you? let him call for the elders of the church; and let them pray over him, anointing him with oil in the name of the Lord: And the prayer of faith shall save the sick, and the Lord shall raise him up; and if he have committed sins, they shall be forgiven him. Confess your faults one to another and pray one for another, that ye may be healed. The effectual fervent prayer of a righteous man availeth much."

Why should Christians delight in having a large family if God allows it?

• *Children are God's gift and heritage*

"Lo, children are an heritage of the Lord: and the fruit of the womb is his reward" (Psalm 127:3).

• *Large families are a foundation of human*

ness

"Happy is the man that hath his quiver full of them: they shall not be ashamed, but they shall speak with the enemies in the gate" (Psalm 127:5).

THE HIDDEN MESSAGE OF THE LOST PEARL

"When I was eleven years old, my family took a vacation in Florida. One morning my brother and I went swimming. The shallow water revealed an oyster bed, so we began digging up oysters. It was great fun. During the morning we accumulated quite a collection.

"Our greatest finds were not the live oysters, but dead oysters which still had both halves of the shell joined together. Many were closed shut, and we didn't know until we had pried them open whether they were alive or not.

"The live ones we threw back. The empty ones usually did not reclose, but remained partly open. These we set aside as our most prized treasures.

"Toward the end of the morning, I dug up a very nice, complete oyster shell which was in perfect condition. It was obviously dead because it was already open about an eighth of an inch and seemed empty. It was definitely one that I wanted to keep, except for one flaw—it had some kind of object trapped inside that rattled. I thought it detracted from the quality of my shell.

"The halves of the shell were still very tight and were hard to budge with just my fingers. It took all of five minutes to remove this rather large, round, perfectly smooth object. Having successfully removed it, and being pleased with my now empty and unblemished shell, I threw the object toward the end of the pier.

"At about the midpoint of its flight, a horrifying light dawned in my mind. I was old enough to have known, but young enough to have overlooked the value of what I had just thrown away. I had treasured what was secondary and had lost what was real. My focus had been wrong.

"I visually marked the location of the splash. With great care I slowly approached the spot, trying not to disturb the bottom. For the next half hour I searched diligently.

"Finally, when it was time to leave, I told my parents what I had done. Then we all looked for it. Our efforts were useless and our time was up. Our schedule demanded that we leave.

"When I was twenty-five years old, I got married. For some undefined reason I rejected for seven years the suggestion that we have children. I thought I had valid reasons, but no one had ever talked to me about it. I had received no counsel or teaching from either family, friends, or church. No one seemed to consider it to be a critical issue. In addition, the world had all kinds of new medical methods for preventing pregnancy.

"As I look back, I don't remember hearing one dissenting voice. Down deep I always knew that I wanted children someday. I didn't really want to be childless all of my life. Eventually, I decided that I wanted five children. So, after seven years of some very difficult decision making, we had our first child—a girl.

"To my great amazement, I found that I actually liked having children. In fact, having a child is one of the greatest things that has happened in our lives.

"The fears which had prevented conception for so long proved to be mostly imaginary. This new member of our family changed our lives. We discovered a multitude of rewards that we had not known we were missing.

"My wife and I have just been told that it now looks medically impossible for us to have any more children! Suddenly, all our newly established family dreams have been erased. All the excitement and anticipation of a newly discovered future have vanished. It seems like there is a void in our lives— like four of our five children have just been killed.

"What makes the burden so heavy is that we had the treasure within our grasp and we threw it away. We saw the outer shell and mistakenly overlooked the treasure within. With our hands we plucked it out and cast it away. We tried to take God's timing into our own hands."

A couple from Iowa

196

HOW A COUPLE DISCOVERED THAT GOD'S FAMILY PLANNING INCLUDED A MONTHLY HONEYMOON

"When we first heard you talk about God's design for the size of the family at the 1984 Advanced Seminar, we were very happy with our two children. Before we were married, we had talked of having a large family, but after the two children were born, we decided to stop having any more.

"We had always rejected sterilization procedures, however, based on a spiritual feeling of closing off God. We find this interesting since we had never heard the topic mentioned before. Perhaps this is part of God's Law 'written on our hearts.' Preferring to do things naturally also played a part in our decision.

"The idea of abstinence for the purpose of birth control was not new to us, however, since we had tried it for a short while with a 'natural family planning' method. We failed in that miserably.

"After many months of studying the matter, we found that God's way of abstinence is at a different time in the cycle than natural family planning and for a longer period, too. And we found that when you abstain for the glory of God, God gives the grace to maintain control.

"At the end of our first fourteen days of abstinence, my husband's comment was, 'God has given us a romantic experience with all the excitement of courtship and with the satisfaction and fulfillment of a mature marriage.'

"Each month at the close of the fourteen days of abstinence, we have taken turns planning a big celebration evening. It is like going on a honeymoon every month!

"In addition to the enrichment of our physical union, we have experienced a rich development in the fruit of the Spirit. We see each aspect of the fruit more greatly manifested in our marriage as well as other areas of our lives.

"Thank you for being open to God's instruction in sharing this principle."

A couple from California

What would we have lost if Jesse had had a smaller family?

- *David would not have been born.*

Jesse had eight sons. If he would have decided that seven sons were enough, we would be deprived of the Psalms and key portions of the Old Testament. Jesse's eighth son was David.

How would we have been affected if Jacob had had a smaller family?

- *no Paul the apostle*

Jacob had twelve sons. If he would have decided that his family was complete after eleven sons, the apostle Paul would not have been born. Paul was a descendant of Jacob's twelfth son, Benjamin.

What reasons do Christians give in support of smaller families?

1. *We will lose our freedom*

Couples with larger families have experienced more freedom than others have imagined. As the first children grow older and are properly trained, they assume many responsibilities in assisting the parents to care for the younger ones. Susannah Wesley, for example, was able to have two hours a day of undistracted time in private devotions while the older children taught and cared for the younger.

2. *We can't afford them.*

God pays for the things He orders, and He delights to hear the prayers of children for their daily needs. The testimony of God's faithfulness in providing for any size family is given in Psalm

197

Train up a child
in the best of his gift.

37:25: *"I have been young, and now am old; yet have I not seen the righteous forsaken, nor his seed begging bread."*

As children get older, the potential for home industry is significant, especially in our computer age. Many sons and daughters have more than earned their own way by developing productive skills.

3 *Wife will lose her physical attractiveness*

When God's guidelines of proper nutrition, Biblical fasting and abstinence, and other proper health measures are followed, God renews our youth like the eagle's. (See Psalm 103:5.)

4 *They might rebel against us*

By training up sons and daughters to be mighty in spirit and by removing them from the destructive influence of peer dependence through home education, parents are able not only to avoid rebellion, but to enjoy the fellowship of their children as they grow spiritually.

5 *They will grow up in an evil world!*

Our world will become as evil as it was in the days of Noah. (See I Peter 3:20.) Yet Noah had a family and through the help of his three sons, he was able to escape the judgment of God upon the wickedness of his day.

6 *The world is overpopulated*

This destructive myth has already been discussed and refuted.

7 *There may be medical complications*

It is not wise to make decisions on the basis of probability. God deals with us as individuals, and He delights to show His power to those who obey His commandments. *"... No good thing will he withhold from them that walk uprightly"* (Psalm 84:11).

If complications do come, God will give grace for them. However, many complications can be avoided by proper knowledge and careful discipline.

How should we respond if the doctor tells us that it is medically impossible to have a child?

• *medical "impossibilities" have been God's opportunities to demonstrate His supernatural power. (Isaac, Samuel)*

It would be important to follow the guidelines listed on page 156 if this is your situation.

How can a couple determine the size of their family?

• *Size of family, including adopted children, must be based on the faith of the couple*

"Hast thou faith? have it to thyself before God. Happy is he that condemneth not himself in that thing which he alloweth. And he that doubteth is damned if he eat, because he eateth not of faith: for whatsoever is not of faith is sin" (Romans 14:22–23).

Faith is discerning what God intends to do through the marriage and then claiming His grace and the power of His Spirit to carry it out.

Faith comes by hearing, and hearing by the Word of God. Faith is a deep confidence in the will of God revealed by the principles of His Word. It is not a blind "leaping in the dark" or a reliance upon our own inclinations.

MARRIAGE PURPOSE:

5 *Protection*

When a man enters into the marriage covenant, he is thereby pledging his strength, resources, and life to his wife. When the couple gives themselves to each other and God blesses that union with

NOTES

DIAGRAMS

children, it is a rewarding responsibility for parents to give whatever sacrifices are necessary to protect those children.

For this purpose God has placed within men a strong protective drive. It is because of this motivation that a man will go off to war and lay down his life to defend his family.

PRINCIPLE

• *A Godly seed*

Since the fall of Adam and Eve, it has been God's desire to raise up a Godly seed. At each step of history, Satan has sought to destroy this seed, since he knows that through it God will accomplish His program in the world.

The severe discipline of unfaithfulness in marriage under Old Testament Law and the public shame attached to remarriage in New Testament teaching are strong confirmations of the need for life-long commitment in marriage. (See Romans 7:1-3.)

"And did not he make one? Yet had he the residue of the spirit. And wherefore one? That he might seek a godly seed. Therefore take heed to your spirit, and let none deal treacherously against the wife of his youth" (Malachi 2:15). 13

What is God's "hidden design" for protection?

KEY: *Life long commitment to marriage.*

After God judged Israel by scattering its families throughout the Babylonian Empire, He sent a prophet to exhort them to raise up a Godly seed so that this remnant could be used of Him in the further program which He had planned for them.

"Thus saith the Lord of hosts, the God of Israel, unto all that are carried away captives, whom I have caused to be carried away from Jerusalem unto Babylon; Build ye houses, and dwell in them; and plant gardens, and eat the fruit of them;

"Take ye wives, and beget sons and daughters; and take wives for your sons, and give your daughters to husbands, that they may bear sons and daughters; that ye may be increased there, and not diminished" (Jeremiah 29:4-6).

How does Satan attack God's design of protection?
SATAN'S GOAL: *Scatter the families*

"And it shall come to pass, that as the Lord rejoiced over you to do you good, and to multiply you; so the Lord will rejoice over you to destroy you, and to bring you to nought; and ye shall be plucked from off the land whither thou goest to possess it. And the Lord shall scatter thee among all people, from the one end of the earth even unto the other . . ." (Deuteronomy 28:63-64).

Today families are being scattered by divorce, by job relocation, by higher education, by retirement centers and nursing homes, and by rebellion.

Why is a Godly seed essential?
God's kingdom on earth requires a Godly seed.

"Thy kingdom come. Thy will be done in earth, as it is in heaven" (Matthew 6:10).

Susanna Wesley was the twenty-fifth child of Dr. and Mrs. Annesley. Susannah's fifteenth child was John Wesley, a leader of the Great Awakening in England and America and the founder of the Methodist movement.

John Wesley
1703-1791

Charles Wesley was the eighteenth child of Susannah Wesley. Charles was also a leader in the Methodist movement. He wrote six thousand hymns, many of which we still sing today.

Wesley, His Own Biographer

Charles Wesley
1708-1771

How has a Godly seed enriched the world?
God promises to make the seed of those who fear Him, mighty upon the earth.

NOTES

DIAGRAMS

"Praise ye the Lord. Blessed is the man that feareth the Lord, that delighteth greatly in his commandments. His seed shall be mighty upon earth: the generation of the upright shall be blessed" (Psalm 112:1-2).

Jonathan Edwards
1703-1758

Jonathan Edwards was the only son among eleven children. He was the recognized leader of the Great Awakening in America (1740-1742). His Godly life and writings helped to usher in the great missionary movement of the nineteenth century.

THE FAR-REACHING INFLUENCE OF A GODLY FAMILY

One thousand four hundred direct descendants of Jonathan Edwards were traced to determine their influence in shaping early American history. Among those descendants were the following: three college presidents, sixty-five college professors, one hundred lawyers, thirty judges, sixty-six medical doctors, and eighty holders of public office, including three senators, three governors, and one Vice-president of the United States!

Whatever the size of your family, God wants fathers to train up their children and their grand-children in the wisdom of His Word, *"that the generation to come might know them, even the children which should be born; who should arise and declare them to their children"* (Psalm 78:6).

Why does God hate divorce?

• *It decreases the potential of Godly seed.*

"... And wherefore one? That he might seek a godly seed. Therefore take heed to your spirit, and let none deal treacherously against the wife of his youth. For the Lord, the God of Israel, saith that he hateth putting away: for one covereth violence with his garment, saith the Lord of hosts: therefore take heed to your spirit, that ye deal not treacherously" (Malachi 2:15-16).

How does God protect children if a parent is not a Christian?

• *God promises to protect*

"For the unbelieving husband is sanctified by the wife, and the unbelieving wife is sanctified by the husband: else were your children unclean; but now are they holy" (I Corinthians 7:14). ✓

MARRIAGE PURPOSE: *TYPE OF CHRIST*

6 ILLUSTRATION *Eph 5:32*

Marriage is a human object lesson of several basic divine relationships: God's relationship with Israel, God's redemption of mankind, Christ's relationship to the Church, and the believer's relationship to the law.[1]

A married couple has a unique opportunity and responsibility to be a living epistle of God's truth by demonstrating these relationships in their marriage.

On the other hand, when a couple does not build their marriage around the principles of Scripture and maintain the harmony that God planned, they do damage to the basic teachings of Scripture and cause others to be led astray.

PRINCIPLE

• *Self-denial*

A clear witness for Christ requires self-sacrifice. It is for this reason that Christ gave the call He did to His disciples.

"Then Jesus said unto his disciples, If any man will come after me, let him deny himself, and take up his cross, and follow me" (Matthew 16:24).

What is God's "hidden design" for illustration?

KEY: *The wife's submission and the husband's sacrifice*

How does Satan attack God's marriage illustration?

SATAN'S GOAL: *Equal authority*

How is the husband to illustrate Christ?

The husband is to lay down his life for the wife

203

"Husbands, love your wives, even as Christ also loved the church, and gave himself for it" (Ephesians 5:25).

"For even hereunto were ye called: because Christ also suffered for us, leaving us an example, that ye should follow his steps: Who did no sin, neither was guile found in his mouth: Who, when he was reviled, reviled not again; when he suffered, he threatened not; but committed himself to him that judgeth righteously:

"Who his own self bare our sins in his own body on the tree, that we, being dead to sins, should live unto righteousness: by whose stripes ye were healed. For ye were as sheep going astray; but are now returned unto the Shepherd and Bishop of your souls" (I Peter 2:21-25).

Why must the wife submit to her husband?

The wife is to submit to the husband in order not to blaspheme God's word.

"To be discreet, chaste, keepers at home, good, obedient to their own husbands, that the word of God be not blasphemed" (Titus 2:5).

"Let this mind be in you, which was also in Christ Jesus: Who, being in the form of God, thought it not robbery to be equal with God: But made himself of no reputation, and took upon him the form of a servant, and was made in the likeness of men" (Philippians 2:5-7).

How do parents illustrate Christ's love?

Parents are to lay down their lives for the children.

". . . for the children ought not to lay up for the parents, but the parents for the children" (II Corinthians 12:14).

HOW TO DISCOVER THE TRUE SIGNIFICANCE OF WEDDING TRADITIONS

Like everything else in life, a wedding ceremony that is not directly related to the Lord Jesus Christ loses its real significance.

The traditions of a Christian wedding grow out of God's covenant relationship with Israel and Christ's relationship with the believer.

Further insights on wedding traditions are gained from the Jewish wedding ceremonies in the day of Christ. The correctness of interpretation can be confirmed, because God also uses the Jewish wedding to illustrate redemption and Christ's relationship with the Church.

1 THE JEWISH WEDDING

The prospective bridegroom took the initiative and traveled from his father's house to the home of the prospective bride.

RELATIONSHIP TO SALVATION

Christ left His Father's house and came to earth to gain a bride for Himself. (See Ephesians 5:25-28.)

2 THE JEWISH WEDDING

The father of the woman then negotiated with the prospective bridegroom the price that must be paid to secure his bride.

Christ had to pay the price with His own blood. (See I Corinthians 6:19–20.)

3 THE JEWISH WEDDING

When the bridegroom paid the purchase price, the marriage covenant was thereby established. At that point, the man and woman were regarded to be husband and wife, even though no physical union had taken place.

RELATIONSHIP TO SALVATION

The believer has been declared to be sanctified or set apart exclusively for Christ. (See Ephesians 5:25–27.)

4 THE JEWISH WEDDING

The moment the covenant was established, the bride was declared to be set apart exclusively for the bridegroom. The groom and the bride then drank from a cup over which the betrothal benediction had been pronounced. This symbolized that the covenant relationship had been established.

RELATIONSHIP TO SALVATION

Christ symbolized this marriage covenant through communion at the Last Supper. (See I Corinthians 11:25.)

5 THE JEWISH WEDDING

After the marriage covenant was in effect, the groom left the home of the bride and returned to his father's house. He remained there for a period of twelve months separated from his bride.

RELATIONSHIP TO SALVATION

Christ returned to His Father's house following the payment of His purchase price. (See John 6:62.)

6 THE JEWISH WEDDING

During this period of separation, the bride gathered her wardrobe and prepared for married life. The groom prepared living accommodations in his father's house for his bride.

RELATIONSHIP TO SALVATION

Christ is preparing a place for His bride and is also sending pastors and teachers to perfect the bride for the coming wedding. (See John 14:2; Ephesians 4:11–13.)

7 THE JEWISH WEDDING

After this period of separation, the groom, best man, and other male escorts left the house of the groom's father, usually at night, and conducted a torch-light procession to the house of the bride.

RELATIONSHIP TO SALVATION

Christ will soon come from His Father's house in heaven accompanied by an angelic host. (See John 14:3.)

8 THE JEWISH WEDDING

The bride was expecting her groom to come for her; however, she did not know the exact time. Thus, the groom's arrival was preceded by a shout.

RELATIONSHIP TO SALVATION

Christ's return will be preceded by a shout. (See I Thessalonians 4:16.) We expect His return, but we do not know the day or the hour.

9 THE JEWISH WEDDING

The groom received the bride with her female attendants and returned to his father's house.

RELATIONSHIP TO SALVATION

The bride will be caught up with the Lord to be with Him. (See I Thessalonians 4:14–17.)

10 THE JEWISH WEDDING

The bride and groom then entered the bridal chamber and, in the privacy of that place, entered into physical union for the first time, thereby consummating the marriage.

RELATIONSHIP TO SALVATION

Christ's union with the Church will take place in heaven for all eternity. (See I Thessalonians 4:17.)

Christ, the bride-groom, will return for true believers who make up His bride.

NOTES

DIAGRAMS

HOW TO BUILD
THE SPIRIT OF A MARRIAGE

Ewing Galloway

If you are single, this material will give you valuable direction in one of the most important ministries that you can have: strengthening the marriages of others. As you accomplish this important objective in the lives of others, you will also strengthen the potential of having a successful marriage yourself as God leads you to it.

If you are married, this material is vital to experiencing the happiness and the fruitfulness which God planned for your marriage.

NOTES

DIAGRAMS

THE SPIRIT OF A MARRIAGE

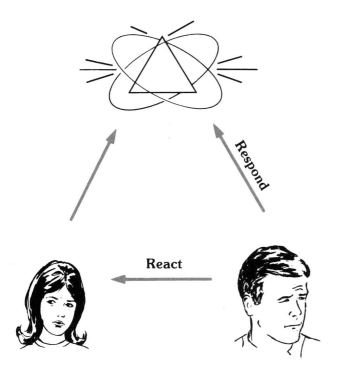

WHAT CAUSES THE SPIRIT OF A HUSBAND TO REACT TO HIS WIFE?

1 *When she rehearses "forgiven failures"*

When a husband humbles himself by acknowledging that he was wrong and asks the Lord and his wife to forgive him, the offense should be forgotten. The lessons that grew out of the failure, however, should be learned and remembered. It is a wise and skillful wife who can bring these to her husband's mind without communicating the spirit of "don't forget how you failed in the past."

Often just a cautious nod will bring to the husband's mind the lessons learned. Sometimes there is a need for her to ask if they could spend time praying about an idea or decision. Still another way she can help is to ask what the results will be from this decision in areas that the husband may not have considered.

A wife can assist her husband to avoid failures by encouraging and supporting him in memorizing and meditating on Scripture and carrying out *Wisdom Searches* in Psalms and Proverbs.

One of the most destructive ways a wife can damage the spirit of her marriage is to correct her husband in public.

2 *When she neglects home responsibilities.*

Wives are to be "keepers at home." (See Titus 2:5). This instruction involves keeping the home neat and clean and providing an atmosphere which is conducive to the goals and needs of the family. Her husband will usually have a preference of areas that he would like to have kept neat. The more confused his "working world," the more necessary it is to have order in his home.

If the wife does not have the natural abilities to be organized, it would be wise for her to get counsel from another woman who has the spiritual motivation of organization.

There is, however, another side to this problem: What should a wife do if a husband has messy areas that are an irritation to her? The testimony of the "Messy Table" provides direction for this problem.

HOW A MESSY TABLE REBUILT THE SPIRIT OF A MARRIAGE

"The battlefield of our home and marriage was a messy dining room table. My husband used it as a 'catch-all' for his papers and belongings and refused to keep it neat. I could keep the rest of the house clean, but he wouldn't let me touch 'his' table.

"After years of trying to overlook this irritation, I found that it had produced deep feelings of anger, frustration, and bitterness toward my husband.

"I was humiliated whenever guests would arrive. I just knew they were judging me by the appearance of all that clutter. In desperation, I sought help. Another Seminar alumnus reminded me of what we heard on Thursday evening about responding to sources of irritation.

"I was willing to thank God for the table, but I couldn't see any reason for His allowing the irritation to be there in the first place. My friend gave me a project that I thought totally impossible, but it proved to be the turning point in rebuilding the spirit of our marriage.

"The project was simply to list all the spiritual benefits for the messy table. I assured my friend that I wouldn't be able to think of any, but I agreed to write down any that might come to my mind.

"After a few weeks I still couldn't think of any, but I asked God to show me some, if there were any.

NOTES

DIAGRAMS

"By the end of four months, I was amazed and excited at a list of ten attitudes which God was beginning to build in my life because of that messy table. Humility was the first one. Every time a guest looked at that table I learned a little more humility and remembered God's promise in James 4:6, *'. . . God resisteth the proud, but giveth grace unto the humble.'* With all that grace, I found the desire and power to develop the nine qualities of Galatians 5:22–23.

"**Love**, by overlooking the table as a proof that I love my husband; **Joy**, resulting from building character in my life; **Peace**, by not being troubled by temporal concerns; **Patience**, by not giving God a deadline to remove the problem; **Gentleness**, in my responses to my husband and family; **Faith**, in visualizing how God is using the table for my spiritual growth; **Meekness**, by giving up my rights to a clean table; **Godliness**, by learning God's responses to situations resulting from the condition of the table; and **Self-control**, by quickly obeying the promptings of the Holy Spirit whenever I see the messy table.

"Without realizing what was happening, that table had taken on a whole new meaning for me. I can honestly say that I am thankful for it. In fact, if my husband were ever to clean it up, I would want to retain in my mind a picture of a messy table."

3 *When she has undefined expectations.*
- *He can never please her.*
- *He receives no admiration*

Very often things that are perfectly clear and obvious to the wife go undetected by the husband. On the other hand, the strongest motivation in a man is his protective instinct. A wise wife will clearly explain to her husband how he can meet her physical, mental, emotional, and spiritual needs.

A wife could say to her husband, "You could protect me from a spirit of jealousy by not delighting in other women" or "I feel overwhelmed in the things that I have to do today; could you decide which is the most important?"

4 *When she resists his leadership*

Most men are very fragile when it comes to being the spiritual leader of their families. One criticism or sarcastic remark can cause a husband to give up his God-given spiritual responsibilities. For this reason, it is essential that the wife look for ways to reassure her husband in this area. When a wife is aware that she has wounded her husband's spirit in this area, she must quickly ask his forgiveness and assure him that she wants him to take the spiritual leadership in the family.

Many wives unknowingly discourage their husbands in spiritual leadership by looking to other spiritual leaders for their counsel. The following testimony illustrates the importance of wives working through their husbands to find Scriptural answers.

HOW A PASTOR AVOIDED A SPIRITUAL CASUALTY BY HAVING A WIFE ASK HER HUSBAND A QUESTION

Ewing Galloway

"Three years ago I received a phone call that was to change the emphasis of my ministry and the lives of those in my church. The phone call was from the wife of one of my elders. She didn't understand a difficult section of Scripture.

"Until then, I had always tried to answer any question any person asked me about the Bible. I believed that this was one of my responsibilities as a pastor, but that day, God prompted me not to answer her question. Here is the reason why.

"I believe that a husband is to assume the leadership of his family, and a wife is to be submissive to that leadership. No husband can be a leader unless he has a follower. It is not a matter of

211

abilities, it is a matter of leadership. The wife who has more ability should work to make her husband more successful. I have preached this message from the pulpit, and I have counseled couples to do this, but God showed me that my practice was not consistent with my belief.

"So I didn't explain the passage of Scripture to her. Instead, I asked her, 'Have you asked your husband about this?' She replied, 'No. He wouldn't understand it either.'

"I told her that I had been meditating on I Timothy 2. I explained how her question was a special opportunity for her. She could use it to illustrate to her husband a genuine humility and a learner's spirit.

"She hesitated, so I gave her the wording. 'Honey, I'm having a difficult time understanding this section of Scripture. Would you help me with it?' I waited as she gave serious thought to this new idea. Eventually she asked, 'What if he says no?'

"I told her what to do if that happened. I reminded her that her husband's 'no' would be another opportunity for her to demonstrate confidence in God and in her husband. She was to say, 'If you aren't sure of the answer, would you ask someone else for me? I really do want help, and it would mean a lot to me if you explained the answer to me.'

"Again there was silence at the other end of the phone. Then she said, 'I've never thought about asking my husband to help me understand Scripture, but it makes sense. I'll go to him for help and trust God for the outcome.'

"Before she hung up, I explained five things she would accomplish by doing this:

1 She would be looking to her husband and not to the pastor for primary spiritual guidance.

2 She would encourage other women to do the same as they saw that her husband was her spiritual leader.

3 She would motivate her husband to be her spiritual leader. She would help him gain the confidence to become what God intended him to be by saying, 'I'm counting on you and no one else for my spiritual leadership.'

4 She would strengthen her marriage rather than weaken it.

5 She would prevent herself from becoming spiritually proud of her own Bible knowledge.

"I didn't hear from her again, but a few weeks later I saw her husband. He told me the following:

"'You will never know how much your advice to my wife has changed my relationship with her. She didn't know it, but I was within an inch of giving up the Christian life.

"'My work is very demanding. I don't have large slots of time when I can study the Bible and memorize Scripture. At least, I don't have as much time as my wife does. Our children are gone now. My wife can spend the entire day reading the Bible, leading a prayer group, or attending a Bible study. I resented her knowing more about the Bible than I did. She was so far ahead of me that I knew I could never catch up with her.

"'I didn't want to be an elder in the church anymore. I didn't want to hear another sermon about being the spiritual leader. I had decided that the competition was too great. I was going to give up and let my wife be the spiritual leader in our family. I thought she wanted it to be that way anyway.

"'I couldn't believe the difference in her after she talked to you. I was absolutely amazed! For the first time, I sensed my wife wanted me to help her understand the Bible. She didn't want to be my teacher anymore.

"'God used her question and her submissive spirit to put the right kind of pressure on me. Now it's a pressure that motivates me rather than defeats me. My wife still knows more about the Bible than I do, but I'm learning fast. I'm concentrating on those passages which will help me be a better leader. I'm very happy. My wife needs me now in a way that she has never needed me before.'

"This experience has given me, as a pastor, a new appreciation for the teaching of I Corinthians 14:35—that if a woman has a question in church, she should go home and ask her husband for the answer."

A Pastor from Wisconsin

5 <u>*When she shows lack of confidence in his decisions.*</u>

When a wife expresses quick disapproval over her husband's decisions, he will probably take it as a personal attack upon himself. This strikes at the very basis of his manliness and his judgment. On the other hand, when she responds with an eagerness to carry out his wishes, he will be open to questions which she may have about them.

If a husband gives direction that is contrary to God's Word, His wife must appeal, and if her appeal fails, she must refuse to do evil. In some cases, the husband finds direction for his own life by the wife's commitment to the moral standards of God's Word as confirmed by her own conscience. When a wife takes a stand for not doing evil, her life must be totally consistent in the area involved.

For example, a wife cannot socially drink on one occasion and refuse to go with her husband to a bar on another occasion.

SEEING DECISIONS FROM YOUR OWN VIEWPOINT

HER PERSPECTIVE	HIS PERSPECTIVE
• A wife tends to view a decision from the perspective of immediate needs: daily routine, welfare of children, home improvements, or personal limitations.	• A husband tends to respond to a decision by relating it to such future goals as job advancement, financial gain, or future security.
• A wife may not be able to clearly define these immediate needs and often she expects her husband to be aware of them and understand them.	• A husband is usually not able to explain his larger frame of reference and expects his wife to trust him and to be patient. He needs, however, to communicate his goals to his wife.
• If a husband focuses only on immediate needs, his wife may try to get him to think ahead by worrying and nagging him about the future.	• If a wife focuses on future objectives, her husband will tend to react to her leadership and put pressure on her to fulfill immediate needs.

SEEING DECISIONS FROM YOUR PARTNER'S VIEWPOINT

Before a wife explains her immediate needs, she must draw out of her husband his future goals so that she can relate her needs to helping him reach his needs and goals.

Before a husband shares his goals, he must draw out of his wife her immediate needs and the consequences which his decision will have on meeting them.

6 _When she lacks a grateful spirit._

An ungrateful wife is a public rebuke to her husband. By her spirit she communicates the message, "My husband does not know how to make me happy." Ungratefulness usually indicates that a wife has many expectations.

Many husbands feel that they are either not able to meet these expectations or that even if they do meet them, there will only be more demands to take their place. In any event, an ungrateful spirit in a wife tends to cause her husband to feel like a prisoner of her expectations.

A wise wife will give all of her expectations to the Lord and then demonstrate sincere appreciation to the Lord and to her husband for the things that are done for her. She is then able to say with the Psalmist, _"My soul, wait thou only upon God; for my expectation is from him"_ (Psalm 62:5).

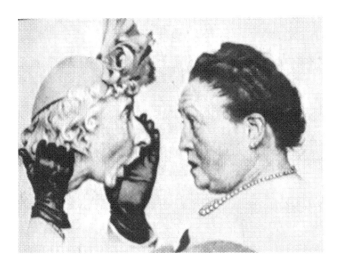

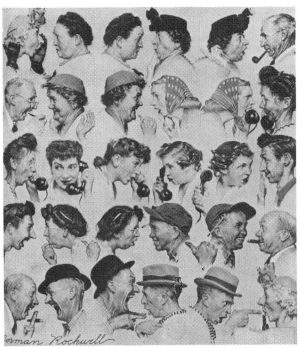

7 _When she fails to build loyalty for him in their children_

Children are quick to sense their mother's true feelings toward their father. They are also able to detect many symptoms of disloyalty that their mother has toward their father. Such statements as "Don't tell your father what happened," or "Your father has no right to expect us to do this" not only communicate disloyalty, they breed it.

When one parent encourages disloyalty toward the other parent, children are usually quick to capitalize on the situation by playing one against the other in order to get permission to do what they want.

If a parent breeds disloyalty in the children, the other parent will tend either to show favoritism to regain loyalty or to communicate rejection.

8 _When she exposes their marriage problems to outsiders_

When a wife finds a fault in her husband, it is extremely difficult for her to share it first with the Lord and then at the right time with her husband. It is much easier to discuss it with a friend, tell her mother, or ask counsel from her pastor.

The Gossips, which appeared on the cover of "The Saturday Evening Post" ©1948, courtesy of Norman Rockwell Estate

There are consequences whenever a wife fails to follow Scriptural guidelines in discussing a marriage problem. If she tells her friend, word will often get back to her husband. If she tells her mother, her parents will take up an offense against her husband. If she tells the pastor, her husband will feel that the pastor has taken his wife's side and has prejudged him.

If after talking to the Lord and her husband, the fault persists and is seriously damaging the marriage, the wife should then appeal to her father and together they should talk to the husband. (The father is the one who gave her to her husband in good faith.) Only if this fails should the matter be brought to the pastor and the church.

One of Satan's most effective ways of damaging marriages is to cut off communication with the individuals through whom God has ordained to give counsel.

9 *When she is unfaithful to his priorities.*

God's purpose for a wife is to be a helpmeet for her husband, not the reverse. A wife will, therefore, only find her identity and fulfillment as she functions in harmony with God's design.

The priorities of a wife usually involve the many details which are necessary to maintain efficiency in the home. When a husband suggests a change in plans which will be difficult to achieve, it is important for the wife to ask his counsel on rearranging her priorities rather than simply saying, "I can't do it."

10 *When she repeatedly misunderstands what he is trying to say.*

One of the most frustrating experiences for a husband is to explain something to his wife and not to have her understand what he is trying to say. Some men will feel that their wife's inability to understand comes from their own inadequacy to explain a situation; others will divert responsibility from themselves by blaming their wives.

When the spirit is damaged, it is very difficult to mentally comprehend what the partner is trying to say. When explanations are difficult to understand, a mature wife will claim the promise of James 1:5:

"If any [wife] . . . lack wisdom, let [her] . . . ask of God . . . and it shall be given [her] . . ."

THE FOUR LEVELS OF COMMUNICATION A HUSBAND MUST LEARN IN ORDER TO UNDERSTAND HIS WIFE

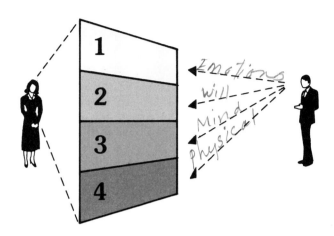

Most men are not aware of the fact that their wives respond to information on four different levels and that they are able to switch from one level to the other without letting the husband know. The significance of this fact is that the wife's response on each level is different.

Thus, the husband may become frustrated and conclude that his wife is totally inconsistent. This is not true. She is consistent within each level of response. It is up to him to figure out with which level he is dealing. The following illustration demonstrates the challenge:

1 *Emotions:* "I'm hurt when you don't pay attention to me in public."

2 *Will:* "I don't want you to pay attention to me in public."

3 *Mind:* "I wish you would pay attention to me in public."

4 *Physical* "I don't expect you to pay attention to me."

INTERPRETING HER REAL MESSAGE

1 *I want you to love me.*
2 *I don't want you to embarrass me.*
3 *I want others to know you love me.*
4 *I want you to be sincere.*

WHY DO WIVES REACT?

CAUSE	EFFECT
☐ When a husband fails to be a spiritual leader . . .	His wife feels insecure.
☐ When a husband allows problems to continue and even get worse . . .	His wife feels helpless and finally takes matters into her own hands.
☐ When a husband does not support his wife in disciplining the children . . .	His wife blames him for rebellious children.
☐ When a husband spends extra money on things which he enjoys . . .	His wife resents the financial pressure under which they must live.
☐ When a husband does not accept himself . . .	His wife feels the same rejection.
☐ When a husband praises or admires other women . . .	His wife feels inferior and jealous.
☐ When a husband verbalizes love only when he wants a physical relationship with his wife . . .	His wife feels degraded and used and finds it hard to love him.
☐ When a husband forgets anniversaries and other special occasions . . .	His wife feels that she is unimportant and not cherished by him.
☐ When a husband does not praise his wife for specific things . . .	His wife feels frustrated in not knowing how to please him.
☐ When a husband makes bad judgments and unwise business decisions . . .	His wife resists his will in future decisions.
☐ When a husband is not alert to dangers which his wife faces . . .	His wife feels unprotected.
☐ When a husband neglects needed home repairs . . .	His wife builds up resentment and impatience.
☐ When a husband does not have good manners or consistent manners . . .	His wife loses self-worth and feels isolated from her husband's real world.
☐ When a husband lusts after other women . . .	His wife feels inadequate in trying to meet her husband's physical needs.
☐ When a husband loses his temper and does not ask for forgiveness . . .	His wife reacts to his pride.

Taken from *Men's Manual*, Volume I, page 12.

NOTES

DIAGRAMS

SPECIAL STEPS IN SELECTING A SECRETARY

One of the greatest dangers to the spirit of a marriage is the unwise selection of a secretary or an improper working relationship with her. The factors involved in the decision to hire a secretary are of such importance that special time and attention must be given to them.

Each of the following guidelines has been confirmed by both husbands and wives as being vitally important in selecting and working with a secretary:

1 Make sure that the secretary you hire is not likely to look to you to meet her emotional needs.

Attempting to meet the emotional needs of a secretary is sure to produce insecurity in your wife, if not jealousy and resentment. A secretary's basic emotional needs must be met by her parents if she is single, by her husband if she is married, and by God if she is widowed.

2 Make sure your wife meets, interviews, and approves of the secretary before you hire her.

Technically, a secretary is working for your wife, since she is doing things to assist you that your wife is not able to do.

3 Keep your relationship w/ your secretary on a business level at all times.

Do not become involved in the personal life of your secretary. If she has serious problems, refer her to her husband, her parents, her minister, or other sources of help.

4 Make sure that your wife can call you without going thru your secretary.

If you do not have a private phone, instruct the secretary to always put your wife through without asking questions. If you are busy, have her tell your wife what you are doing and let your wife make the decision of whether or not to disturb you.

5 Make sure that you never ask your secretary to meet personal needs or perform special tasks that your wife normally does.

Do not ask a secretary to sew a button on your coat or bake you a special pie. Do not allow her to bake a cake to celebrate your birthday.

6 Make sure that your secretary is committed to the success of your marriage.

Your secretary must help you to make your wife and home your priority by shielding you from unnecessary interruptions, helping you keep appointments with your wife, and guarding you from temptations of moral impurity.

7 Make sure that you praise your wife to your secretary and never discuss problems in your marriage w/ her.

Appreciate your secretary's abilities without praising her to your wife, especially if your wife does not have equal abilities in that area.

TEN WAYS A HUSBAND DAMAGES THE SPIRIT OF HIS MARRIAGE

Many husbands are unaware of the "little" offenses that cause an ever-widening separation in the spirit of their marriages. Let us assume that a couple begins with an ideal relationship, but during the years, the husband damages the spirit of the wife in ten ways which are to follow.

Marriage begins in oneness of spirit

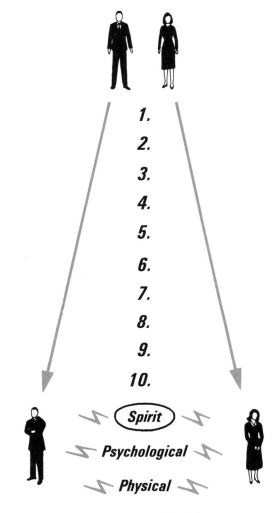

1.
2.
3.
4.
5.
6.
7.
8.
9.
10.

Spirit

Psychological

Physical

Marriage ends in divorce
(actual or psychological)

The first important lesson to learn in any relationship is that a very delicate and accurate cause-and-effect sequence exists. A man may assume that a little offense here or there will soon be forgotten. What he does not realize is that every offense is a seed of destruction to the relationship of his marriage. It must be Scripturally dealt with, or it will grow up into a harvest of devastation.

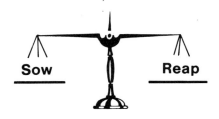

Galatians 6:7

"Be not deceived; God is not mocked: for whatsoever a man soweth, that shall he also reap" (Galatians 6:7).

WHAT CAUSES THE SPIRIT OF A WIFE TO REACT TO THE SPIRIT OF HER HUSBAND?

1. *Awareness that she is not first place in your life.*

"But I would have you without carefulness. He that is unmarried careth for the things that belong to the Lord, how he may please the Lord: But he that is married careth for the things that are of the world, how he may please his wife" (I Corinthians 7:32–33).

"Husbands, love your wives, even as Christ also loved the church, and gave himself for it" (Ephesians 5:25).

Sow: *He is preoccupied with people, possessions or activities*

Reap: *She doubts his love and becomes insecure.*

HOW TO MAKE YOUR WIFE "FIRST PLACE"

• *Establish a weekly date night*

Genuineness of a priority is judged by what it takes to "bump" it.

This time is necessary throughout the years of marriage; however, it is especially important when little children are making demands on the wife throughout the week. Keeping this time a priority will be a difficult, yet a convincing way to show your wife that she has "first place" in your life.

Find out the places and activities that your wife enjoys. Also make a note of potential distractions which would hinder intimate conversation when you are together. Purpose ahead of time to avoid or correct them.

☐ *Having your mind on other things*

☐ *Phone calls*

☐ *Being late for your appointment*

☐ *Talking to friends you meet*

☐ *Looking at other women*

☐ *Lack of manners*

☐ *Improper dress or grooming*

☐ *Distracting music or surroundings*

☐ *Bringing up unpleasant subjects*

Know what topics your wife enjoys discussing with you and ask her about them.

☐ *Events of her day*
☐ *Needs and activities of the children*
☐ *Her ideas on home improvements*
☐ *Enjoyable past memories*
☐ *Spiritual lessons and insights*
☐ *Clothes she is making or buying*
☐ *How she really feels about certain things*

make surprise appointments for lunch
Give occasional calls during the day.
Help with the dishes.

Allow direct access to her phone calls
Prepare for the most exciting moment of Friday.
Meet their deepest need. (intimate fellowship)

Intimate conversation takes place when a wife is able to trust her husband with the secrets of her deepest emotions. Very often a wife will have fears, guilt, or other anxieties which she needs to discuss. She may, however, be hesitant to share them for one or more of the following reasons:

1. *Feeling guilty for having them*
2. *Hoping they will pass*
3. *Fearing rejection from you*
4. *Desiring to reduce your burdens*
5. *Knowing you don't have answers*

Your wife finds out how you will respond to her fears and whether or not you have answers by telling you about "another woman" who has the same problem. She then watches to see if you have compassion, understanding, patience, and practical help.

The fears in your wife are a test of your love because "perfect love casts out fear." It is your responsibility to lovingly and patiently assist your wife to identify and verbalize her fears and to gain wisdom from God in resolving them.

☐ *Insecurity if the husband dies*

☐ *Getting old*

☐ *Becoming unattractive to husband*

☐ *Ill health due to past sins*

☐ *Failing as a wife or mother*

☐ *Husband losing his job*

☐ *Having a mental breakdown*

☐ *Social awkwardness*

☐ *Educational deficiency*

☐ *Physical safety when alone*

☐ *Future of children*

☐ *Being displaced by another*

NOTES

DIAGRAMS

Take each fear your wife expresses and ask God for wisdom in resolving it:

What Scripture deals with that fear? Study and memorize it.

What steps of action can you take? Begin taking them.

What steps of action can she take? Encourage her to take them.

- *purpose to have good manners.*

"Love has good manners." (See I Corinthians 13:5.) Discuss the following manners with your wife, and ask her to indicate which ones are most important to her. Then ask her to assist you in consistently practicing them. She can do this by waiting for you to open the door, standing by a chair, handing you her coat, etc.

☐ **Helping her on and off with her coat**

☐ **Seating her at the table**

☐ **Opening doors for her—especially the car door**

☐ **Lifting heavy objects**

☐ **Ordering for her at restaurants**

☐ **Knowing and using table manners**

☐ **Picking up after yourself at home**

☐ **Punctuality**

☐ **Properly introducing your wife**

☐ **Telling her your schedule**

☐ **Refraining from crude language, criticism, and improper subjects**

☐ **Personal cleanliness, neatness, and grooming**

Having good manners is an excellent way to demonstrate to your wife how valuable she is to you, that you cherish her, and you enjoy being in her presence. Your wife unconsciously "measures" your awareness of her presence every day. Attention to the details of good manners tells her she is an important part of your life.

2 *Lack of spiritual leadership Eph 5:23*

Every woman has certain needs which will only be met by strong spiritual leadership. Spiritual leadership is not only where a man is spiritually, but it is what direction he is going.

There are two major marks of a spiritual leader: first, a man who seeks the Lord; and second, a man who lives by Scriptural convictions.

Sow: *He shows lack of spiritual interest in his family*

Reap: *She feels insecure; unable to place full confidence in him; seeks spiritual leadership from others*

EVIDENCES OF A SPIRITUAL LEADER:

- *Teaching God's Principles to family*

"And thou shalt teach them diligently unto thy children, and shalt talk of them when thou sittest in thine house, and when thou walkest by the way, and when thou liest down, and when thou risest up" (Deuteronomy 6:7).

- *Leading in prayer times*

"Likewise, ye husbands, dwell with them according to knowledge, giving honour unto the wife, as unto the weaker vessel, and as being heirs together of the grace of life; that your prayers be not hindered" (I Peter 3:7).

- *Having regular quiet times*

"I love them that love me; and those that seek me early shall find me" (Proverbs 8:17).

NOTES

DIAGRAMS

- *memorizing scripture consistently*

"Thy word have I hid in mine heart, that I might not sin against thee" (Psalm 119:11).

- *Sharing Christ w/ others*

"The fruit of the righteous is a tree of life; and he that winneth souls is wise" (Proverbs 11:30).

- *Refusing to compromise scriptural convictions*

"And I sought for a man among them, that should make up the hedge, and stand in the gap before me for the land, that I should not destroy it: but I found none" (Ezekiel 22:30).

3 *Inadequate preparation for changes*

If a wife is going to make a major change, such as moving to a new location, she usually needs to mentally move before she physically moves. This means that she needs to see the new location and visualize how she will carry out her daily responsibilities within that context.

Sow: *He does not give her time to rearrange her frame of reference for major readjustments.*

Reap: *She becomes insecure, apprehensive, and little.*

4 *Unfavorable comparison with other women.*

"For we dare not make ourselves of the number, or compare ourselves with some that commend themselves: but they measuring themselves by themselves, and comparing themselves among themselves, are not wise" (II Corinthians 10:12).

Sow: *He openly admires the appearance, abilities of other women (which she lacks)*

Reap: *She is deeply hurt; becomes jealous and begins to reject herself.*

Comparisons can be made in many areas: cooking, housekeeping, dressing, gardening, responding to pressure, etc. When a husband compares his wife to another woman in any of these ways, it not only destroys her sense of self-worth, but it causes her to have a wrong focus on the individuals with whom she is being compared.

On the other hand, when a husband favorably compares his wife's character with that of the Lord, he encourages her to delight in inward qualities and to grow in her relationship with the Lord.

When a man delights in inward character, it frees his wife to respond to physical difficulties that would normally devastate a woman. The following testimony illustrates this important point:

HOW A HUSBAND'S FOCUS TURNED THE LOSS OF HIS WIFE'S HAIR INTO A CROWN OF GLORY.

Ewing Galloway

"Four years ago God saw fit to take from me a very beautiful head of hair. A year later He removed the eyebrows and eyelashes.

"I have been His child for thirty-one years, and He has been pleased to give me a strong faith in Him. I do not doubt anything He does, but I was grieved and almost sick when I would wash my hair and see it lie in the sink by the handful! I prayed earnestly that He would prevent it from continuing, but in the course of three months, I had lost it all.

225

NOTES

DIAGRAMS

"Two years and seven doctors later, an internist discovered I was low in thyroid output. This diagnosis confirmed anew to me that this was God's plan and will. The first doctor I had gone to was a dermatologist, and in the course of treatment he said it might be due to thyroid, but he felt it was due to fatigue. Consequently, he never checked the thyroid. Had he done so, it might have been prevented. But I just smiled in my heart because I knew for a fact that this was God's will. By this time I had submitted it to the Lord and was able to thank Him. However, at that point I did not know all that would result from my 'defect' and my willingness to say 'thank you.'

"I am sure that while my hair was coming out, God was preparing my husband with an extra measure of grace! I have a precious husband, who even though it was my hair that first made him notice me, found he loved me for myself, not for my hair. He had delighted in seeing our relationship deepen and become more beautiful in the Lord! And that was great because we already were one of the five percent who experience a really happy marriage! Because of his love, devotion, and concern for me, my defect has slipped so far in the background that we only discuss it when friends ask about how I'm doing. I'm doing GREAT—in the Lord."

5 _Lack of inner discipline_

"For the ways of man are before the eyes of the Lord, and he pondereth all his goings.

"His own iniquities shall take the wicked himself, and he shall be holden with the cords of his sins.

"He shall die without instruction; and in the greatness of his folly he shall go astray" (Proverbs 5:21–23).

"If I regard iniquity in my heart, the Lord will not hear me" (Psalm 66:18).

A **soft** answer turneth away wrath: but grievous words stir up anger" (Proverbs 15:1).

"I made a covenant with mine eyes; why then should I think upon a maid?" (Job 31:1).

Sow: _He lacks discipline in anger and displays moral weakness; refuses to discuss it_

Reap: _Her admiration and respect for him are greatly damaged._

When a husband admires skills in other women, it is destructive to the sense of self-worth of his wife. However, these may be abilities which she can learn or improve. But when a man admires the physical appearance of other women, he compares his wife to something she cannot change. This often produces devastating emotions within her. For this reason, it is crucial that every husband make a commitment to be a "one-woman man," and based on this commitment, gain victory over his heart and his eyes daily.

The sequence of *The Eagle Story* vividly illustrates how a man becomes trapped by the lust of his eyes. This volume also explains how a man can gain victory over the lust of the eyes.

6 _Failure to recognize and express appreciation for special "little" attempts to please him._

"Her children arise up, and call her blessed; her husband also, and he praiseth her. Many daughters have done virtuously, but thou excellest them all. Favour is deceitful, and beauty is vain: but

NOTES

DIAGRAMS

a woman that feareth the Lord, she shall be praised. Give her of the fruit of her hands; and let her own works praise her in the gates" (Proverbs 31:28-31).

Sow: He is insensitive to special little things she does to please him

Reap: She seeks admiration and praise from others; loses creativity; seeks outside interests.

Many men fail to realize or remember that a woman tends to be much more attentive to details than a man. She notices little things, and she responds to little things. She needs to have her husband do the same. The "little things" that she does to brighten the life of her husband and family are really "big things." They represent her commitment, thought, time, and energy in making him and the family successful.

7 Attempts to correct in public. Pet. 3:7 (honor wives)

"Husbands, love your wives, and be not bitter against them" (Colossians 3:19).

Sow: He uses jokes or cutting remarks in public to emphasize something he has been trying to change in her.

Reap: She feels her self-worth is damaged; reacts with desire to retaliate in public

The folly of a husband correcting his wife in public is that he is criticizing himself. God holds the husband responsible to purify the wife by the Word, and the wife is actually part of the husband and reflection of his care, wisdom, and leadership.

Rather than trying to correct in public, a wise husband will cry out to the Lord in his wife's behalf with times of fasting, prayer, study of the Word, and self-examination.

8 Rejection of her opinions as unimportant

"When he [Pilate] was set down on the judgment seat, his wife sent unto him, saying, Have thou nothing to do with that just man: for I have suffered many things this day in a dream because of him" (Matthew 27:19).

Sow: He evaluates her opinions from his larger frame of reference vs. her immediate frame

Reap: She is hurt and hindered from sharing cautions concerning his judgment or character

There are several rewards that come to a man when he listens to the cautions of his wife. First of all, he strengthens the spirit of his marriage. Second, he avoids many financial losses and emotional drains that would have come from unwise decisions, especially in the area of business.

Since God has given the wife the calling of being a helpmeet and since God wants to let each partner know how much the other partner is needed, He will often give special promptings of danger to the wife that He will not give to the husband. The following testimonies illustrate the importance of listening to these promptings:

HOW A HUSBAND LOST SEVERAL THOUSAND DOLLARS BY NOT LISTENING TO THE CAUTIONS OF HIS WIFE

"One day a friend said to me, 'I've got a great investment. Why don't we go into it together?'

"It looked good, so I agreed and gave him several thousand dollars. That evening I told my wife about it.

" 'Oh, I wish you hadn't done that,' she said. 'I sense that he is not as Godly as he appears on the outside.'

"I reacted, 'Now that's not right! This guy has been the chairman of the deacon board.'

"My wife replied, 'Well, there's just something that a woman knows about a man, and one of those things is that he does not have moral freedom. I can tell by the way he looks at women.'

"So I said, 'Well, I don't think you're right. But even if you are right, and even if he does have a problem, that doesn't have anything to do with investments.'

" 'But how can God bless a man like that?' my wife asked. 'And if you are in a partnership with him, how can He bless that partnership?'

"Well, I just ignored her cautions. There was no way this deal could miss.

"A few months later this man called up and said, 'I've got bad news. The deal fell through and you lost your money. I can't understand why it didn't work.' "

HOW A LIFE WAS SAVED BECAUSE A MAN LISTENED TO THE CAUTIONS OF HIS WIFE

"I hired a man for my company but soon discovered that he was an alcoholic. Every once in a while he would disappear for three or four days after first calling in sick.

"One day I said to him, 'If you miss work like this again, you will have fired yourself.' He agreed.

"Several weeks later he didn't show up again. On Monday I came home and said to my wife, 'Honey, he's doing it again! I'll bet he's on another drinking spree.' Tuesday night I told my wife, 'That guy is just an alcoholic. He's a bum. He's no good. I've just got to get him out of the office.' While eating dinner on Wednesday night I said, 'Honey, that does it. He has fired himself. I'm through with him.'

"My wife gently asked, 'Have you called him?'

" 'No,' I replied. 'I'm not going to call him. I told him if he did it, he's through. I don't need to call him. I mean it's over, period.'

" 'Why don't you go call him?' my wife asked.

" 'I'm not going to call him,' I insisted. 'I wouldn't call him for anything. He's through, and that's it.'

"We ate a little more, and pretty soon she said, 'I really feel that you ought to call him.'

"I got all worked up and excited and said, 'I'm not going to call him. Will you leave it alone? The subject is dead!'

"My three-year-old daughter started crying. 'Daddy, you are talking so ugly to Mommy. You need to ask Mommy to forgive you.'

"So I smiled and looked across the table and said, 'Honey I'm sorry I talked so roughly to you. Would you forgive me?'

"She said, 'Yes, I will.'

"Then under my breath, I hissed, 'And would you leave it alone?'

"We continued eating. A minute later my wife bravely persisted, 'I've just got to ask you—what if he's going to commit suicide?'

" 'Commit suicide? That's never been in the picture. It's never been talked about. He just loves alcohol.' I got up and stormed over to the phone. 'All right, I'm going to call him just for you.' I dialed and let it ring. It rang about seven times. On the eighth ring, just to 'rub it in,' I yelled into the kitchen, 'There's eight rings. There's nine. There's ten. See, he's out buying some more booze. I told you.'

"All of a sudden he answered the phone. In a deep voice that I could hardly recognize, he said, 'Hello.'

" 'What are you doing, drinking again?' I asked.

"In a low, gutteral voice he answered, 'Yes, I am.'

" 'That's what I thought,' I sneered. 'That's what you deserve.'

" 'Oh, please!' he cried, 'I just put a bullet in my gun and cocked it. I was waiting for the phone to quit ringing so I could kill myself, but it just wouldn't quit ringing.'

"Chills went up and down my spine! 'Put the gun down! I'm coming right over!' As I ran past my wife, I shouted, 'How did you know?'

"She said, 'I don't know. It was just something inside of me. Something kept saying, "What if he's going to kill himself?" '

"I raced to his home with my pastor. We were able to help sober him up. Later, he received Christ as his personal Savior. Today he is a different person, living with his family, and doing very well."

HOW A COMPANY PRESIDENT LISTENED TO HIS WIFE AND SAVED HIS GOOD NAME BY "LOSING" A SALE

A very happy smile greeted the president of a small company when one of his salesmen announced that he had just lined up a sale that would bring a commission of $100,000. A few years earlier, the staff of this company had attended a Seminar in

Basic Youth Conflicts and many of them had become Christians. Business was good that year; but by the following year, the changing economy had reduced their profits drastically. This sale was badly needed.

That evening the company president excitedly told his wife about the deal they were making with an investment group. He explained that a large number of prominent Christians in their town were involved in it.

Later on that evening his wife asked, "Honey, would you explain again how that deal is going to be worked out?"

With a tinge of irritation he answered, "I explained it to you once."

"Honey, why are you angry?" she asked.

"I don't know why I'm angry," he replied, and then he thought, "Maybe I'd better check this whole thing out again."

The following day he approached his salesman and explained that he was not free to go ahead with the deal. Would the salesman be willing to drop it, even though each of them would lose $50,000 of the commission? The president explained his wife's cautions; and then to his surprise, the salesman reported that his mother and girlfriend also had expressed cautions about the deal. Both men agreed that they would not move ahead until they felt free to do so.

Together they approached the director of the investment group and explained that they were not able to proceed with the deal. They told him that they wanted to return the $100,000 note in exchange for a letter of release. The investment director scornfully laughed and assured them that they were making a big mistake.

About six months later that investment group, which was composed of Christian leaders and businessmen of the community, discovered that they had been swindled.

Lawyers were hired and a complete investigation was made. Every company and person involved in the business deal became liable and had lawsuits filed against them. One lawyer told this company president, "It looks like everyone is going to be sued, except you. We are absolutely amazed that you got out of this when you did. How did you know to get out?"

The law firm which conducted the investigation was so impressed by the honesty of this company president that they began giving him their business and referring others to him. Not only did he avoid a costly lawsuit, but he made more money on commissions from these references than he had lost in the other commission.

9 _Inconsistent in discipline_

"He that spareth his rod hateth his son: but he that loveth him chasteneth him betimes" (Proverbs 13:24).

Sow: _He defends or takes sides with children against her._

Reap: _She feels he is being disloyal to her; she blames him for rebellious children._

Isaac's inconsistent discipline not only damaged the spirit of his marriage but brought destruction to his family and his descendants.

10 _Unwillingness to ask forgiveness Lk 18:14_

". . . War a good warfare; Holding faith, and a good conscience; which some having put away concerning faith have made shipwreck" (I Timothy 1:18–19).

Sow: _He tends not to want to admit failures._

Reap: _She reacts to his pride and loses respect for him._

Further direction on rebuilding or strengthening the spirit of your marriage is contained the Rebuilder's Guide.

NOTES

DIAGRAMS

HOW TO PREPARE FOR
EFFECTIVE SPIRITUAL WARFARE

"For though we walk in the flesh, we do not war after the flesh; (For the weapons of our warfare are not carnal, but mighty through God to the pulling down of strongholds;)" (II Corinthians 10:3-4).

". . . Endure hardness, as a good soldier of Jesus Christ" (II Timothy 2:3).

BEING MIGHTY IN (GOD'S) SPIRIT

The chart "Being Mighty in Spirit" (see page 39) is based on the larger perspective of the following charts. These charts provide the overall structure of integrating all learning around the five basic responsibilities in life:

- Being a mature man or woman
- Being a successful businessman or home manager
- Being a loving husband or wife
- Being a wise father or mother
- Being a dynamic leader or teacher of good things

The overall charts were designed by asking such questions as: "What training does a young man need at age five to be a successful father when he is married? What character does a girl need to develop at ten to be a successful home manager when she is a wife and mother? What information does a boy need at twelve to be a dynamic spiritual leader when he is mature?"

When all character, knowledge, and skill development has this kind of objective, it takes on exciting meaning for both parents and sons and daughters.

BUILDING CURRICULUM AROUND LIFE GOALS

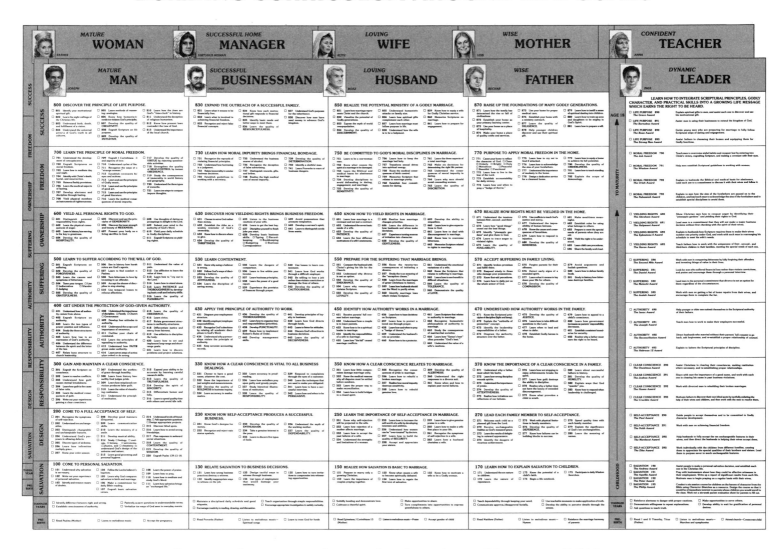

Scope and sequence charts relate learning to life responsibilities.

HOW TO FIND TREASURES IN WISDOM SEARCHES

California State Library

"If thou seekest her [wisdom] as silver, and searchest for her as for hid treasures" (Proverbs 2:4).

God assures us that there is a wealth of wisdom and practical instruction in His Word. It has direct application to every area of our lives. However, He establishes an important prerequisite for receiving it. It must be searched out as silver or hidden treasures. Daily *Wisdom Searches* are designed to do just that.

How can I prepare my family for Wisdom Searches?

1 _____

_____

_____

Why is a Wisdom Search essential for my life?

• _____

"Thy word have I hid in mine heart, that I might not sin against thee" (Psalm 119:11).

Why is a Wisdom Search necessary for my wife?

• _____

"That he might sanctify and cleanse it with the washing of water by the word, That he might present it to himself a glorious church, not having spot, or wrinkle, or any such thing; but that it should be holy and without blemish" (Ephesians 5:26–27).

Why are Wisdom Searches vital for my children?

• _____

"And thou shalt teach them diligently unto thy children, and shalt talk of them when thou sittest in thine house, and when thou walkest by the way, and when thou liest down, and when thou risest up" (Deuteronomy 6:7).

In order to be successful, a father has to establish God's Word as the number one priority in his life and his family.

HOW CHILDREN ARE DISCOVERING INSIGHTS FROM WISDOM SEARCHES

"We are enjoying so much the adventure of learning together as a family. It seems that each day we are discovering more about how absolutely *wonderful* God is and more about how we can actually train our eyes to see what is important to Him.

"*Wisdom Search* times have been *so rich.* Often, insights shared by the children have prompted exciting discussions and sometimes have led to the discovery of rich nuggets of truth.

"During our first study session together while discussing the 'power of the pen,' our six-year-old son remarked that a pen in the hand of our Holy God is more powerful than a sword in the hand of a human man."

A father from Virginia

HOW A FATHER LENGTHENED HIS DAY BY GIVING TIME TO WISDOM SEARCHES

"The biggest struggle for me in establishing daily *Wisdom Searches* has been dealing with the demands made on my time. However, I have been amazed that as I have given time to *Wisdom Searches,* I have gotten more done, and God has removed unnecessary pressures. My children are beginnning to use Psalms and Proverbs to meet everyday situations with wise responses and praise to God. This time in the Word has been the most rewarding venture that we have had as a family."

A father from Washington

HOW A FAMILY ESTABLISHED WISDOM SEARCHES WITH YOUNG CHILDREN

"We started the morning *Wisdom Searches* the day we arrived home and haven't missed a day in nine months. This discipline has helped our

NOTES

DIAGRAMS

younger children to sit still. It has united the family at a deeper level and has given us many spiritual insights.

"Our six-year-old and eight-year-old have also used this as a time of learning to read. I hold our seventeen-month-old baby, and this gives me the added benefit of a half hour of closeness which I wouldn't have otherwise."

A father from New Hampshire

HOW A HUSBAND GAINED TRUE ADMIRATION BY ESTABLISHING DAILY WISDOM SEARCHES

"I want to give a word of praise for my husband's involvement in *Wisdom Searches*. My respect and admiration for him has absolutely sky-rocketed as a result of sensing his deep commitment to nurturing and ministering to 'all' of us.

"He works some all-night shifts now and then, but he has re-arranged his whole schedule at the shop in order to put himself into the teaching position at home. To say that we're 'flourishing' under his leadership would be putting it mildly. His dedicated efforts already in the one and a half hours of *Wisdom Searches* each day make us feel so blessed!"

A wife from Virginia

Would you purpose now to make God's Word the number one priority of your daily schedule?
□ Yes

Date _____

Once I am committed to having Wisdom Searches, what is the next step?

2 _____

_____

What will your wife be looking for in you?

● _____

_____

What freedom should you give your wife?

● _____

_____

_____

As you and your wife discuss *Wisdom Searches*, it would be important to review the material on pages 19–22.

This material amplifies Proverbs 6:23 and emphasizes that your responsibility is to give the command while your wife's responsibility is to work out guidelines in order to institute them in the family.

HOW ACADEMIC SKILLS INCREASE THROUGH WISDOM SEARCHES

"Our daughter has excelled in verbal skills, but I really do believe her reading skill has developed *most* as a result of our taking turns reading Scripture every morning in our *Wisdom Search* time. I guess what is exciting to me is to see how as we honor God's Word, He does bless our lives!

"Because our daughter is growing in her ability to read Scripture herself, her love for it is growing too."

How can a family get started?

3 _____

_____

● _____

_____

_____

_____

A practical way to establish accountability for rising early is to have someone call you on the telephone or for you to agree to call someone when you are up. You might also plan to meet someone for a time of devotions.

GOD'S WARNINGS ABOUT TOO MUCH SLEEP

A proper amount of sleep is essential for good health. Lack of sleep is one of the consequences of business problems or of doing evil. However, God's primary concern for sleep is not that we get too little, but that we get too much.

● BEWARE OF THE BONDAGE OF SLEEP

"As the door turneth upon his hinges, so doth the slothful upon his bed" (Proverbs 26:14).

- ### *BEWARE OF SLEEP THAT DISABLES*

"*Slothfulness casteth into a deep sleep; and an idle soul shall suffer hunger*" (Proverbs 19:15).

- ### *BEWARE OF LOVING SLEEP*

"*Love not sleep, lest thou come to poverty . . .*" (Proverbs 20:13).

- ### *BEWARE OF SLEEP THAT ROBS*

"*Yet a little sleep, a little slumber, a little folding of the hands to sleep: So shall thy poverty come as one that travelleth; and thy want as an armed man*" (Proverbs 24:33–34).

- ### *BEWARE OF SLEEP THAT DISAPPOINTS GOD*

"*How long wilt thou sleep, O sluggard? when wilt thou arise out of thy sleep?*" (Proverbs 6:9).

- ### *BEWARE OF A LITTLE EXTRA SLEEP*

"*Yet a little sleep, a little slumber, a little folding of the hands to sleep: So shall thy poverty come as one that travelleth, and thy want as an armed man*" (Proverbs 6:10–11).

- ### *BEWARE OF INAPPROPRIATE SLEEP*

"*He that gathereth in summer is a wise son: but he that sleepeth in harvest is a son that causeth shame*" (Proverbs 10:5).

HOW TO CONQUER SLOTHFULNESS

1. *COUNTERACT SLOTHFULNESS WITH HUNGER*

God's primary cure for slothfulness is hunger. "*. . . If any would not work, neither should he eat*" (II Thessalonians 3:10).

This is consistent with the requirement which God established after Adam and Eve sinned. "*In the sweat of thy face shalt thou eat bread, till thou return unto the ground . . .*" (Genesis 3:19).

There is value in every person's experiencing hunger, especially in one who tends to be slothful. A beginning point in conquering slothfulness would be a three-day fast, for the purpose of studying God's principles and examples of diligence. (See Matthew 6:16–18.)

2. *LEARN THE PRINCIPLES OF DILIGENCE*

The ultimate goal of a slothful person must be to develop diligence. This is precisely the instruction of God. "*Go to the ant, thou sluggard; consider her ways, and be wise*" (Proverbs 6:6).

The ant illustrates the basic characteristics which are lacking in those who are slothful—initiative, self-direction, respect for seasons, the ability to finish jobs, and the foresight that is necessary in planning for the future.

After studying the ant, it would be wise to read the biographies of great Christians in order to learn how their diligence was developed by obedience to God's Word.

3. *REALIZE THAT SLOTHFULNESS DEVELOPS IN STAGES*

Slothfulness is not confined to just a few or a certain type of persons. Anyone can become its victim. Its gradual development begins unnoticed; and if left unchecked, slothfulness will disable those who obey its promptings.

- ### *LATENT SLOTHFULNESS*
  Latent slothfulness is the inward tendency to reject God's requirement for diligent labor. This tendency requires instant obedience to the promptings of the Holy Spirit.
- ### *INITIAL SLOTHFULNESS*
  Initial slothfulness is selecting the soft

choices in daily decisions. This type of slothfulness requires accountability to others for the completion of projects.

- **DISABLING SLOTHFULNESS**

Disabling slothfulness is allowing little surrenders each day to become a habitual way of life. This slothfulness requires the discipline of going without food in order to clarify goals and reach objectives.

4. LEARN THE DISCIPLINE OF RISING EARLY

The definition of the Hebrew word translated *diligently* is "being up early at a task."

This discipline strikes at the very heart of slothfulness. *"How long wilt thou sleep, O sluggard? when wilt thou arise out of thy sleep?" (Proverbs 6:9).*

If necessary, be accountable to others for getting up at a given time. Resist the temptation to get just a little more sleep. Do not even learn how to use the "doze" button on your alarm clock. When you wake up, get up!

5. LEARN TO RESPECT TIME

Life is a race against time. We will only win the race if we realize the following:

- Time is limited.
- Death is certain.
- The second coming of Christ is even more certain.
- The maximum number of productive years is established by God.

"The days of our years are threescore years and ten; and if by reason of strength they be fourscore years, yet is their strength labour and sorrow; for it is soon cut off, and we fly away" (Psalm 90:10).

- Days must be counted.

"So teach us to number our days, that we may apply our hearts unto wisdom" (Psalm 90:12).

- Time requires accountability.
- Time is entrusted for God's work.

". . . The night cometh, when no man can work" (John 9:4).

- Time is unrecoverable.

There are several practical projects that will reinforce our respect for time and guard us from wasting it.

For one week, keep a detailed record of what you do every fifteen minutes. At the end of the week, go back and evaluate how many of the 168 hours were used for sleeping, eating, resting, entertainment, and conversations, and how many hours were used for productive work and achievement. The results may shock you. Thereafter, keep a daily journal of goals and achievements.

TIME

. . . is no respecter of persons: No one receives more hours in a day than another.

. . . is not recoverable: Every hour that is lost is gone forever.

Further information about detecting and conquering slothfulness is contained in *Men's Manual*, Volume II, pages 218–233.

The sequence of reading Scripture *before* eating breakfast is important to follow. If properly planned, the morning schedule can include both. However, if a choice must be made, it is better to start the day without physical food than without spiritual food.

This was Job's attitude, a man of whom God said, *". . . there is none like him in the earth . . ." (Job 1:8).* Job said, *". . . I have esteemed the words of his mouth more than my necessary food" (Job 23:12).*

In order to confine breakfast to half an hour and have it after a family *Wisdom Search*, wise preplanning must be made. The breakfast should be simple to prepare, and everyone should eat the same menu.

NOTES

DIAGRAMS

• _____
_____

A setting that is the most conducive to conversation and interaction should be chosen for the *Wisdom Search*. If possible, the Bibles, notebooks, and other necessary materials should be left there from day to day. A markerboard should be available as well for diagrams, key words, and special insights.

A television should not be in sight and preferably not even in the home.

• _____
_____
_____

Additional resources would be a valuable asset to *Wisdom Searches*. These would include a concordance (such as *Strong's*), Bible maps, an expository dictionary (such as *Vine's*), a Bible dictionary, and an English dictionary.

• _____
_____
_____

The individual appointed to answer the phone should give the following message, "Our family is conducting a *Wisdom Search* right now. Unless it's urgent, could we call you back when we are finished [in half an hour]?"

An effective way to maintain the attentiveness of toddlers is to allow them to color if they are restless during the *Wisdom Search* time. The babies should be held.

By making the *Wisdom Search* a routine part of your day, your close friends will know when to avoid calling, and guests will feel comfortable in becoming part of your *Wisdom Search* when they are visiting.

• _____
_____

The key to making *Wisdom Searches* successful is establishing them as a regular part of every day. Once the pattern is broken, it is very difficult to re-establish it. For this reason, only the most unusual circumstances should be allowed to interfere with this time.

The particular time of the *Wisdom Search* may vary depending on the schedule of the father. However, once the hour is set, other activities should be built around it.

What schedule should be followed for morning Wisdom Searches?

4 _____
_____

• _____

The true test of manliness is leading your family in disciplines that will strengthen and build godliness. The first and often most difficult discipline of the day is putting yourself to sleep quoting Scripture (since the day begins in the evening).

The second most important discipline of the day is rising before your family does and spiritually preparing for the day. Some men get up half an hour before the family to spend time alone with the Lord. Their example pays tremendous spiritual dividends.

• _____
_____

It would be excellent for the father to awaken the family with bright, cheerful music or triumphant marching music.

• _____
_____

The Psalms could be consecutive (one to five, six to ten, etc.) or they can be every thirtieth Psalm (1, 31, 61, 91, 121). By reading five Psalms and one chapter of Proverbs each day, you will be able to complete both books each month.

By following the *Wisdom Search* approach, each time you read them, they will be like new books.

• _____
_____

This point is actually what makes *Wisdom Searches* so excitingly different. You go to the Scripture looking for particular spiritual nuggets just like a prospector would go to a mine looking for silver, gold, or diamonds.

NOTES

DIAGRAMS

Historical Pictures Service

You may wish to search out one topic throughout a whole month or consider a different topic each week. Always be ready, however, to relate a *Wisdom Search* to a special problem, question, or general attitude which comes up in the course of daily living.

HOW TO FIND TREASURE IN A WISDOM SEARCH

1 IDENTIFY THE TYPE OF WISDOM FOR WHICH YOU ARE SEARCHING.

What do you need from God's Word today? Do you have a decision to make? Do you need a question answered? Is there conflict in your life or home? Do you need to understand how to apply a principle? Are you seeking to define or apply a character quality?

Without focus, your Bible reading time will become a ritual of routine rarely yielding new insights which motivate spiritual growth.

☐ *Topic—wisdom, dress, dating, money* _____

☐ *Character—obedience, gratefulness* _____

☐ *Principle—design, authority, morality* _____

☐ *People—wise, scorner, slothful* _____

☐ *Needs—decisions, questions, counsel* _____

2 LIST KEY WORDS RELATING TO THE TOPIC FOR WHICH YOU ARE LOOKING.

If you are seeking to develop your understanding of marriage and the family, write down key words such as father, husband, wife, mother, children, house, family, and baby.

As you are reading the Scriptures, these words will be your signals to stop and dig for treasures.

3 CRY OUT TO GOD FOR WISDOM IN YOUR SEARCHING.

*"My son, if thou wilt receive my words, and hide my commandments with thee; So that thou incline thine ear unto wisdom, and apply thine heart to understanding; Yea, if thou **criest** after knowledge, and **liftest up thy voice** for understanding; If thou **seekest** her as silver, and **searchest** for her as for hid treasures; Then shalt thou understand the fear of the Lord, and find the knowledge of God. For the Lord giveth wisdom: out of his mouth cometh knowledge and understanding"* (Proverbs 2:1–6).

Allow the Word of God to be the commentary on the Word of God; study the cross references indicated in the passage.

HOW A NEWSPAPER DESCRIBED THE WISDOM SEARCH OF ONE FAMILY

". . . The four older children rise at 6:15 a.m. each weekday with their father. They have about thirty minutes to tidy their rooms and get dressed. Then they join their father to sing a hymn or song.

"Prayer follows. Then a 'Wisdom Search.' This means reading selections from the books of Proverbs and Psalms in the Bible. If there is a problem one of the children or parents is experiencing, 'we see what the Word of God has to say about it that day,' the father reported.

NOTES

DIAGRAMS

"They look for characteristics in these Scriptures such as diligence or wisdom and think of examples of these traits.

"Breakfast comes after their *Wisdom Search*. Then dad takes off for work. He travels back and forth from the capital each day the Legislature is in session so he can spend the learning time with his family . . ." (*Greenville Piedmont*, February 4, 1985)

Frank Pearce

Katie, 6, Ricky, 5, and Rebecca, 3 learn with their parents.

A family from South Carolina

HOW A FAMILY'S WISDOM SEARCH CHANGED THE ATTITUDE OF A GRANDPARENT

"Morning *Wisdom Searches* have been such a blessing to us. We have especially enjoyed the blessing of character focus while reading through the Psalms.

"Last week our maternal grandparents were with us. One day was not good, and grandma had a questioning, skeptical attitude about what we were doing as a family.

"The next morning in our *Wisdom Search* we read Psalm 60, and verse 4 jumped out at us, 'Thou hast given a *banner* to them that fear thee, that it may be displayed because of the truth.'

"After a good discussion on specific applications of this verse, we turned the Psalm into our personal aspiration and prayer.

"That night at the supper table, grandma told how she was in the living room while the boys were being taught. The material was so interesting and the discussion so intriguing that she never did finish her devotions.

"She then related all that she had learned and expressed amazement at the attentiveness of the boys."

A family from Connecticut

• _____

_____

_____

If children are able to read, it is better to have them read one verse or a whole chapter rather than a certain number of verses. By assigning a number of verses, their concentration is focused on counting the verses instead of thinking about the content of the verses and proper inflection.

• _____

_____

After a complete chapter has been read, stop and share any special insights that were discovered in it. If this method produces too much discussion, have each family member make a note of the insight they see and discuss it when all five Psalms and a chapter of Proverbs have been read.

• _____

_____

_____

Young children are learning to read simply by listening to older members of the family read during the *Wisdom Searches*.

• _____

_____

After insights are shared, pick out the key ideas and turn them into expressions of prayer. For example, if you have discovered rich insights about music, ask God to put a song in your heart throughout the day, allowing you to live out those insights.

Before your time of prayer, write out a specific prayer request from each family member for the day. In the evening, allow a time to report on any answers to their prayers. It is important to have one family member assigned to writing out the prayer requests and their answers in a family prayer journal.

5 _____

_____

_____

245

HOW TO LEAD YOUR FAMILY IN EVENING WISDOM SEARCHES

As a follow-up to the morning *Wisdom Search*, we would urge you to schedule half an hour after the evening meal for a different kind of *Wisdom Search*.

SURVEY THE ENTIRE BIBLE

The first goal of the evening *Wisdom Search* is to read through the entire Bible. Several reading programs have been designed which will allow you to accomplish this in one year.

However, we recommend that you extend the schedule through several years so that you can discuss insights that you find and add further resources to your search, such as *Character Sketches, Men's Manuals,* and biographies of great Christians.

USE MEN'S MANUALS AND QUIZ PLACEMATS

Each volume of the *Men's Manual* contains a supplementary packet of quiz placemats. These are designed to create curiosity for the material in the chapter as well as to survey its contents. Follow the instructions on pages 10–11 in *Men's Manual,* Volume I for using the placemats.

Men's Manual, Volume I contains thirty concept questions and material designed to teach your sons and daughters how to be mighty in spirit.

Men's Manual, Volume II contains twenty chapters on financial freedom. Each chapter gives practical direction on a vital aspect of reaching and maintaining this goal.

246

USE CHARACTER SKETCHES

Character Sketches, Volumes I and II have been designed to place in the hands of fathers basic concepts of Scripture and interesting facts of nature which his family has not yet heard. For this purpose it is suggested that the books remain under the supervision of the father until all the concepts are discussed with all the family. Pages 11 through 15 of Volume I explain the objectives of this approach to learning, and pages 16 through 21 give a detailed description of how the volumes can be used.

A SAMPLE CHARACTER SKETCH PRESENTATION

Loyalty is adjusting my schedule to meet the needs of those I am serving (Volume I, pp. 28–39).

You may need to plan to present the Biblical aspect one night and the animal study another night. If you were to have a character sketch study once a week, this would give you two weeks to deal with a particular character quality with related projects and applications.

FIRST SESSION—

- Put the character quality and its definition on a board or chart so that your whole family can see it. Repeat the definition several times, emphasizing different words each time.

- Read the concept question on page 17. You may wish to personalize the concept question for your family to help them to identify with the problem. "If you were told by Mom and Dad to do the dishes all by yourself and you knew that in a couple of hours your brothers and sisters would be home and could help you, what would you do?"

- Allow each member of the family to contribute an answer to the discussion, but do not yet give the correct answer yourself. Encourage each one to be honest. Affirm them in the discussion.

- Ask additional related questions which you have previously prepared. "What does it mean to have a servant's heart?" Discuss how you can make others successful. "What can we do to make Mother successful? She spends so much time teaching us; how can we show our loyalty to her?"

- Read from page 29 the introduction to the Scripture portion of the lesson. Then read the italicized paragraph on page 37 to introduce the story. Ask, "Who was this man?"

- Read the story to the family, highlighting the points you have prepared to emphasize. Feel free to emphasize points other than the written narrative if you feel your family has other needs than are pointed out. It is helpful in your preparation to have read the actual Scripture passage involved.

- Present the material which is developed on pages 38–39 to study the character of Amasa.

- Emphasize a key concept. "Loyalty must first be learned in our family." Emphasize the principle of self-acceptance. (See Proverbs 1:8; 30:17; Ephesians 6:1.) Present the chart explaining the family relationships in Amasa's background. Discuss how David's failure to clear his conscience hindered him from dealing with Amnon. What effect did this have on Absalom's life? Who was the "troublemaker" in this family? Why? How might this have been prevented?

- Summarize the reasons for Amasa's disloyalty when he chose to affiliate himself with a rebellious cause and did things his own way in his own time. Ask the family, "How do we do these very same things in our lives?"

- Go to prayer, asking each one to pray for such things as increased loyalty to other family members, more thorough acceptance of one another, grace to maintain a clear conscience, and wisdom to help each other to avoid problems such as these.

SECOND SESSION—

- Put the character quality and definition up before the family to review it.

- Use question #4 on page 22 to introduce the topic. "What bird nests in the winter to provide for its young in the spring?" Here,  it might be appropriate to show the three birds on the page and have the children guess which it

is—the black-headed gull, the yellow-shafted flicker, or the great horned owl.

- Read the introductory paragraph on page 29. Show the picture of the owl on page 31. Describe the boundaries of its habitat using the maps on page 29.

- Read the story on page 30 or tell it, whichever is most comfortable for you. Be sure to include all the interesting facts about the owl.

- Emphasize that animals do not have character in the same way that people do. Animals do what is right by instinct; people must listen to their consciences and to the voice of the Holy Spirit speaking through God's Word. "If we copy what the owl does by instinct, we will be loyal."

- Explain the major features that God designed for the owl on pages 33–36. Show your family the pictures as you present the material. Prepare insightful questions to help your family make applications to their lives as a result of studying these features.

- Prepare a chart to fill in for your family as you discuss applications. Use a chalkboard or poster board.

Physical Characteristics	Application
1. Builds nest in the cold: Gets snowed on.	All will experience difficult times. Hebrews 12:4–6
2. Large mouth: From ear to ear. Why?	Open your mouth wide. Psalm 81:10
3. Food: Swallows it whole. No teeth.	Need the Holy Spirit to help us digest spiritual food. Natural man cannot receive the things of God. I Corinthians 2:14
4. Eyes: Many rods— adjusts to all light. Binocular— tell distance.	Be alert in season and out—at all times. II Timothy 4:2

5. Hearing: Pinpoint. Which way do ears point?	Still small voice. Hebrews 5:14 Revelation 3:22 Sheep know voice. John 10:27
6. Feet: Good grip. In what ways are his feet like tennis shoes?	As we follow the ways of the Lord, we will not fall down. I John 2:6
7. Wings: Frayed edge. Silent flight.	*"Be still, and know that I am God. . . ."* *Psalm 46:10*

- Close with a prayer time, asking God to continue to develop the quality of loyalty in the life of each family member.

HOW A FATHER USED WISDOM SEARCHES TO ACHIEVE MAJOR BREAKTHROUGHS IN THE LIVES OF HIS SONS

"We began studying the principle of ownership in hopes of cutting down some of the squabbling between our two sons.

"While studying Matthew 5:22 one night, I asked my older son why he would get so upset and angry with his brother. I cited an incident. He responded, 'Because he is better than I am.'

"I, too, had grown up with similar feelings and had not resolved them until attending the Basic Seminar as an adult. So I knew it was important to help my son overcome them.

"In exploring further, we discovered that the older son was in competition with the younger to prove himself. The older felt he was not as smart, so he attempted to prove his expertise in other ways. This would result in teasing, arguing, fighting, bragging, and other negative expressions.

"Our *Wisdom Search* took us through a study of Cain and Abel; Jacob and Esau; Joseph and his brothers, James and John; and Peter and Andrew. In each relationship we noted how God had made the brother different, and yet how each had a potential for serving Him.

"One night the older son blurted out, 'But Daddy, if I'm not smart, I won't be able to be a preacher. My brother will make a good preacher, but I won't.'

"This opened the door to a sharing time of my own background. I was the youngest of three boys. The oldest was a 'straight A' student all through his schooling. Today he is an excellent pastor of a large church.

"The second-born had struggles all through school. He barely passed from year to year. Today he is in the top ten percent among the aeronautic mechanics in our country. I was average in school and today pastor a small church.

"But all three of us love the Lord. We are doing what God created us to do and are content in it. Each of us can say that we are in the center of God's will and are experiencing God's joy and happiness.

"Through this conversation, the older son was able to see that whether God chose him to be a pastor, a mechanic, a builder, or whatever, the important matter is to accept the way God made him and do what God made him to do.

"We then went on to explore exactly how God made each son, emphasizing the positive qualities of each and their potential opportunities for service to God.

"This was a breakthrough! The older son is improving in his studies. Since being 'smart' is no longer an issue, he is free to be his own person. The comparison has stopped; whereas studying was an area that once crushed his spirit, it is now an area that is building his spirit. The two brothers are becoming quite the friends!"

A father in Connecticut

THE KEY TO MAKING THE WISDOM SEARCH TIME "LIVE" IS PREPARATION.

1. Make supplication to God. Ask God to help you prepare a meaningful sharing time for your family. Ask Him to change your own life through the preparation process. Ask Him to free you from preconceived ideas so that He may be your Teacher.

2. Preview the material. Underline or take notes on key ideas. Highlight the sections your family needs right now. Make yourself thoroughly familiar with the things you desire to present.

3. Seek God's face for creativity, special direction, discernment, and perspective as you design questions to raise curiosity and teach principles. Be alert to daily experiences which provide illustrations for the concepts you are teaching.

4. Provide opportunities to exercise newly discovered truths in special projects. Encourage your family to record the results of these experiences.

CAN YOU TRACE SURFACE PROBLEMS TO ROOT CAUSES AND SOLUTIONS?

The most effective way to share the life-changing principles taught at the Seminar is to relate people's problems to the lasting solutions of God's Word.

Match each problem with the two Seminar Topics which best relate to it.

	DEFINING CAUSE	STEPS OF SOLUTION
1. *"I've never loved my wife."*	☐	☐
2. *"I wish I could break this habit."*	☐	☐
3. *"I have thought of suicide."*	☐	☐
4. *"My husband left me."*	☐	☐
5. *"My son ran away."*	☐	☐
6. *"I'm deeply in debt."*	☐	☐
7. *"I don't believe the Bible."*	☐	☐
8. *"I can't control my child."*	☐	☐
9. *"I can't stand my boss."*	☐	☐
10. *"I hate my father."*	☐	☐

Seminar Topics

A. Tracing Surface Problems to Root Causes
B. Principles of Self-Acceptance
C. Four Types of Suicide
D. Abnormal Social Developments
E. Four Essential Attitudes in Marriage Harmony
F. Seven Steps of Responding to Authority
G. Characteristics of First-, Second-, and Third-born
H. Gaining a Clear Conscience
I. Turning Bitterness to Forgiveness
J. Removing the Cause of Anger
K. Transforming Sources of Irritation
L. The Development of Reprobation
M. Seven Steps to Conquer Habits
N. Principles of Music Evaluation
O. Cleansing the Home
P. Praying a Hedge of Protection
Q. Removing Doubts about Salvation
R. Principles of Meditation
S. Three Aspects of the Ways of God
T. Finding Life Purpose through Eight Callings
U. Developing Genuine Friendships
V. Principles for Successful Dating
W. Steps to Financial Freedom
X. Seven Goals for Rebuilding Marriages
Y. Developing Genuine Love
Z. Principles of Discipline

ANSWERS:

1. B,Y 2. O,M 3. C,H 4. E,X 5. D,P 6. A,W
7. L,Q 8. J,Z 9. G,F 10. H,I

1 DESIGN

Self-acceptance is the key to the principle of Design.

JEPHTHAH

HOW ARE FOOLISH VOWS AND SELF-REJECTION RELATED?

Jephthah's life was shaped by his reaction to the unchangeable factors which were given to him. Had he accepted God's design, he probably would have avoided the unwise responses which caused him to make the foolish vow.

JEPHTHAH'S "UNCHANGEABLES"
IMMORAL PARENTS

"Now Jephthah the Gileadite was a mighty man of valour, and he was the son of an harlot . . ." (Judges 11:1).

Jephthah could not choose the parents that would bring him into the world. This unchangeable gave him the stigma of being "illegitimate."

UNLOVING BROTHERS

"And Gilead's wife bare him sons; and his wife's sons grew up, and they thrust out Jephthah . . ." (Judges 11:2).

Jephthah's family would not tolerate any defect to their reputation since they themselves were striving for the admiration of their countrymen. (See Judges 12:4.)

FIRST-BORN RESPONSIBILITIES

". . . And [they] said unto him, Thou shalt not inherit in
250

our father's house; for thou art the son of a strange woman" (Judges 11:2).

As the first son of Gilead, Jephthah had the potential of receiving a double inheritance but with it extra family responsibilities.

INHERITED WEAKNESSES

"Then Jephthah fled from his brethren, and dwelt in the land of Tob: and there were gathered vain men to Jephthah, and went out with him" (Judges 11:3).

Jephthah's father became involved with an immoral woman. God compensated for this weakness by giving him more grace and making him "a mighty man of valour." Jephthah resisted God's grace, became bitter, and fell in with worthless companions.

TROUBLED TIMES

"And it was so, that when the children of Ammon made war against Israel, the elders of Gilead went to fetch Jephthah out of the land of Tob: And they said unto Jephthah, Come, and be our captain . . ." (Judges 11:5–6).

The unchangeables in Jephthah's life now take an exciting new meaning as the larger purposes of God's judgment are brought upon his nation and family.

JEPHTHAH'S WRONG RESPONSES TO GOD'S DESIGN FOR HIS LIFE
DEMANDING HONOR

"And Jephthah said unto the elders of Gilead, Did not ye hate me, and expel me out of my father's house? . . . If ye bring me home again to fight against the children of Ammon, and the Lord deliver them before me, shall I be your head?" (Judges 11:7, 9).

Jephthah was not content with acceptance and equality. He seized upon the plight of his brothers to demand their servitude if he succeeded.

BARGAINING WITH GOD

"And the elders of Gilead said unto Jephthah, The Lord be witness between us, if we do not so according to thy words" (Judges 11:10).

Jephthah did not go out to fight for God's reputation. He went out to fight for his own position and reputation, and he paid dearly for it.

"And Jephthah vowed a vow unto the Lord, and said, If thou shalt without fail deliver the children of Ammon into mine hands . . . whatsoever cometh forth of the doors of my house to meet me, when I return in peace, . . . I will offer it up for a burnt offering. . . . And, behold, his daughter came out to meet him . . . and it came to pass, when he saw her, that he rent his clothes . . ." (Judges 11:30–31, 34–35).

DESIGN (Accepting Ourselves As God's Workmanship)

SELF-ACCEPTANCE COMES BY SEEING THE PRINCIPLE OF DESIGN FROM:

☐ GOD'S PERSPECTIVE

- God has given each of us at least ten unchangeables.
  1. Our parents
  2. Our time in history
  3. Our racial backgrounds
  4. Our national heritages
  5. Our genders
  6. Our birth orders
  7. Our brothers and sisters
  8. Our physical features
  9. Our mental abilities
  10. Our aging and death
- These unchangeables are designed by God to produce Christ's character in us by conforming us to His image.

- God allows "defects" in our unchangeable make-ups in order to humble us. We can then receive the enabling grace of God which gives us the desire and power to do His will. (See James 4:6.)
- If we resent our unchangeables, we resist the grace of God, develop roots of bitterness, and miss God's potential for our lives.
- Realize that only God can change our unchangeables when they have fulfilled His purpose of character development.

☐ A PARTNER'S PERSPECTIVE

- Marriage requires us to identify and accept our partners' unchangeable make-ups just as we accept our own.
- The only way to truly accomplish this is to delight in inward holiness more than outward perfection.
- This requires learning how to praise our partners without vain flattery.

- Realize that God is using your partner's unchangeable "defect" to develop such qualities as humility, gratefulness, sensitivity, patience, gentleness, meekness, and self-control.
- As you see value in his or her "defect," he or she will be motivated to thank God for it. Even the spots and wrinkles of past failures can become cleansed and sanctified by the washing of God's Word. (See Ephesians 5:27.)

☐ A CHILD'S PERSPECTIVE

- As a son or daughter becomes aware of unchangeable "defects," parents must teach him or her to view these as God's marks of ownership, which daily remind each of us that our bodies belong to God.
- Parents must not show favoritism to any child.
- Parents must never mock or ridicule a child's "defect."
- Children must learn to reverence their bodies and realize that Satan hates their bodies.

Satan hates our bodies because they are:
  1. Made in the image of God
     (See Genesis 1:27.)
  2. The temple of the Holy Spirit
     (See I Corinthians 6:19.)
  3. Members of the Body of Christ
     (See I Corinthians 6:15.)
  4. God's instruments of righteousness
     (See Romans 6:13.)

☐ OTHER PEOPLE'S PERSPECTIVES

- Based on this principle, it would never be appropriate to mock the unchangeable make-ups of other people.
- In order to help others respond to this principle, we should be alert to the symptoms of self-rejection, such as:
  ☐ Self-criticism
  ☐ Excessive shyness
  ☐ Overattention on clothes

  ☐ Extravagant status symbols
  ☐ Attempts to change hair color
  ☐ Attitudes of superiority
  ☐ Awkward attempts to hide defects
- Explain how God used unchangeables in your life to build character.
- Realize that almost everyone has a hidden or obvious "defect" that they wish they could change.

251

2 AUTHORITY

Scriptural submission and appeal are the keys to the principle of Authority.

ABSALOM

HOW DO THE SEEDS OF A WOUNDED SPIRIT PRODUCE A CROP OF REBELLION?

From all outward appearances Absalom was destined for success. He was the son of the king, and "... *from the sole of his foot even to the crown of his head there was no blemish in him*" (II Samuel 14:25).

Yet within Absalom's heart were the following seeds that eventually lead to his destruction.

SEQUENCE OF REBELLION

SINS OF THE FATHERS

"... *When king David heard [that his son Amnon had forced Tamar to do an immoral act] ... he was very wroth*" (II Samuel 13:21).

God warns that the iniquities of the fathers are visited upon their children. (See Exodus 20:5.) David had Bathsheba commit an immoral act with him. Now his oldest son forced his own half sister into an immoral act. David's response of anger and apathy in discipline were both out of place.

TAKING UP AN OFFENSE

"... *Absalom hated Amnon, because he had forced his sister Tamar*" (II Samuel 13:22).

Absalom took up his sister's offense against his older brother's immorality. In so doing he

resisted God's grace to him, and a root of bitterness sprang up and defiled him. (See Hebrews 12:15.)

TAKING MATTERS INTO HIS OWN HANDS

"*And it came to pass after two full years, that Absalom ... commanded his servants, saying, Mark ye now when Amnon's heart is merry with wine, and when I say unto you, Smite Amnon; then kill him ...*" (II Samuel 13:23, 28).

"*And the servants of Absalom did unto Amnon as Absalom had commanded. ... Then the king arose, and tare his garments. ... So Absalom fled, and went to Geshur, and was there three years*" (II Samuel 13:29, 31, 38).

Because David failed to bring God's discipline to his erring son, Absalom lost confidence in his father's leadership and took matters into his own hands. Not incidently, this act removed a rival to his father's throne.

LACK OF GENUINE REPENTANCE

"*So Joab arose and went to Geshur, and brought Absalom to Jerusalem. And the king said, Let him turn to his own house, and let him not see my face. ... So Absalom dwelt two full years in Jerusalem, and saw not the king's face*" (II Samuel 14:23–24, 28).

Although David sinned, he fully repented. (See Psalm 51.) He was waiting to see that same repentance in Absalom. It never came.

PRIDE AND SELF-EXALTATION

"*And it came to pass after this, that Absalom prepared him chariots and horses, and fifty men to run before him*" (II Samuel 15:1).

The king rode a mule. Absalom proclaimed his own presence with horses, chariots, and fifty men! The rejection that he felt from his father would be replaced by the admiration and acclaim of other people.

MAGNIFYING DISCONTENT

"*Absalom said moreover, Oh that I were made judge in the land, that every man which hath any suit or cause might come unto me, and I would do him justice!*" (II Samuel 15:4).

Absalom sought out those who had grievances. He listened to their complaints and pointed out that his father's administration did not provide for their needs.

"... *So Absalom stole the hearts of the men of Israel. ... And the conspiracy was strong; for the people increased continually with Absalom*" (II Samuel 15:4, 6, 12).

"*And David said ... Arise, and let us flee; for we shall not else escape from Absalom ...*" (II Samuel 15:14).

AUTHORITY (Getting Under God-ordained Protection)

OBEDIENCE REQUIRES SEEING THE PRINCIPLE OF AUTHORITY FROM:

☐ GOD'S PERSPECTIVE

- *"Let every soul be subject unto the higher powers. For there is no power but of God: the powers that be are ordained of God. Whosoever therefore resisteth the power, resisteth the ordinance of God: and they that resist shall receive to themselves damnation"* (Romans 13:1–2).
- God has established four basic authority structures to provide for our protection and direction.
  1. Parents—Husband
  2. Church leaders
  3. Employers
  4. Government officials

- All authorities are subject to the principles of God's Word. Thus, no person or angelic being can force us to violate Scripture.
- Those under authority must learn how to appeal when a command is given that conflicts with God's Word.
- The effectiveness of our appeals will depend on our attitudes of loyalty, gratefulness, humility, and diligence.
- For this reason Scripture always speaks to those under authority first.

☐ A PARTNER'S PERSPECTIVE

- Wives are to be *"... obedient to their own husbands, that the word of God be not blasphemed"* (Titus 2:5).
- Every wife's ultimate obedience is to God and His Word. Therefore a wife is never to do evil commanded by a husband. *"Even as Sara obeyed Abraham ... whose daughters ye are, as long as ye do well ..."* (I Peter 3:6).
- A wife who has Godly attitudes and uses them in wise appeals, actually has more power than her husband, since the power of influence is greater than the power of position.

- God ordained marriage as a human object lesson of divine relationships.
- The husband is to lay down his life for his wife as Christ sacrificed Himself for the Church. (See Ephesians 5:25.)
- As a husband desires submission from his wife, he must be obedient to the authority of God's Word and open to wise counsel.

☐ A CHILD'S PERSPECTIVE

- God's principles are opposite to our natural inclinations. Thus, the law of the Lord must convert the child's soul (mind, will, and emotions). (See Psalm 19:7.)
- As long as a child has an obedient spirit, he or she is under God's "umbrella of protection." A rebellious spirit exposes a child to the power of Satan. (See I Samuel 15:23.)

- Every child must be committed to the final authority of God's Word and purpose to stand alone whenever he or she is asked to do evil.
- Parents must define discipline roles. The father is like a lamp to give a command of direction. The mother is like the light to illuminate and apply the command. (See Proverbs 6:20–24.)

☐ OTHER PEOPLE'S PERSPECTIVES

- By learning how to respond to difficult authorities, we develop vital character qualities that are needed for successful relationships with others.
- The most important factor for job success is not "job know-how" but the ability to get along with others, especially those in management.
- The primary function of government is to punish those who do evil and to praise those who do well.

When government fails in either of these, we must appeal to them with Godly attitudes and Scriptural truth.

- Each one of us should voluntarily put ourselves under the authority of a local church which honors and obeys God's Word. Church leaders must give an account to God for us. (See Hebrews 13:7, 17.)

3 RESPONSIBILITY

A clear conscience is the key to the principle of Responsibility.

THE PRODIGAL SON

HOW ARE LIMITATIONS AND FREEDOMS BOTH PART OF A CLEAR CONSCIENCE?

The message contained in the story of the prodigal son involves a young man who went astray, repented, and returned to his father and restored fellowship. A closer examination of the parable reveals important steps and results of gaining a clear conscience.

THE STEPS AND RESULTS OF GAINING A CLEAR CONSCIENCE

RECOGNITION OF FAILURE

"And when he came to himself, he said, How many hired servants of my father's have bread enough and to spare, and I perish with hunger!" (Luke 15:17).

The prodigal son demanded his inheritance so that he could be a success on his own. When his resources and contacts ran out, he measured what he had by what he had given up.

ACKNOWLEDGEMENT OF RESPONSIBILITY

"I will arise and go to my father, and will say unto him, Father, I have sinned against heaven, and before thee" (Luke 15:18).

Those who fail usually blame others or circumstances for their misfortunes. True repentance is saying with clear understanding, "I have sinned."

254

HUMILITY

"And am no more worthy to be called thy son" (Luke 15:19).

When the prodigal son recognized his unworthiness before God and his family, he put himself in line to receive the enabling power which God gives to overcome a sinful way of life. He also worked out the wording of his confession ahead of time.

ACCEPTANCE OF LIMITATIONS

". . . Make me as one of thy hired servants" (Luke 15:19).

The prodigal son realized that by repenting of his sin and returning to his father he would not automatically regain everything that he lost. The limitations of discipline which he threw off when he got out from under his father's umbrella of protection he was now willing to accept in the position of a servant.

A NEGLECTED CONFESSION

"But the father said to his servants, Bring forth the best robe, and put it on him; and put a ring on his hand, and shoes on his feet: And bring hither the fatted calf, and kill it; and let us eat, and be merry" (Luke 15:22–23).

"Now his elder son was in the field. . . . And he was angry, and would not go in: therefore came his father out, and entreated him" (Luke 15:25, 28).

"And he answering said to his father, Lo, these many years do I serve thee, neither transgressed I at any time thy commandment: and yet thou never gavest me a kid. . . . But as soon as this thy son was come, which hath devoured thy living with harlots, thou hast killed for him the fatted calf" (Luke 15:29–30).

The prodigal son did not sin only against God and his father—every other family member was also affected. A confession to his older brother might have mellowed or removed the older brother's anger.

A PERIOD OF PROBATION

"And he said unto him, Son, thou art ever with me, and all that I have is thine. It was meet that we should make merry, and be glad: for this thy brother was dead, and is alive again; and was lost, and is found" (Luke 15:31–32).

The father restored his son to full fellowship. However, he did not restore his inheritance. With its loss, the prodigal son would one day be under direction and accountability to his older brother. We can be certain that he would be treated skeptically until he proved himself.

RESPONSIBILITY (Clearing Our Consciences)

A CLEAR CONSCIENCE INVOLVES SEEING THE PRINCIPLE OF RESPONSIBILITY FROM:

☐ GOD'S PERSPECTIVE

- A clear conscience means that we can look people in the eye and know that none of them can say, "You offended me and never tried to make it right."
- In order to have a conscience void of offense toward God and man, we must assume personal responsibility in the following five areas.
  1. Every thought (See II Corinthians 10:5.)
  2. Every word (See Matthew 12:36.)
  3. Every action (See II Corinthians 5:10.)
  4. Every attitude (See Philippians 2:5.)
  5. Every motive (See Jeremiah 17:10.)

- Guilt is a powerful motivation to bring us to repentance. If neglected, it will be a destructive force within our lives.
- Genuine repentance comes by comparing our actions to God's holy law and by reliving our offenses through the eyes of those who were offended.
- Clearing our conscience should be done in person or by phone, and the circle of confession should only be as large as the circle of offense.
- Paul compares a clear conscience for a Christian to weapons for a soldier. (See I Timothy 1:19.)

☐ A PARTNER'S PERSPECTIVE

- Before marriage past moral failures should be discretely shared. This will avoid fear of rejection in the marriage and provide a basis for protecting one another.
- The first year is often most critical to the success of a marriage. Offenses committed during this time must be quickly confessed and cleared up. For this reason God instructed men to give special concentration to their marriage during the first year. (See Deuteronomy 24:5.)

- Marriages are often destroyed by little offenses that are never cleared up rather than by one big offense.
- The number one priority for both partners is to guard the spirit of their marriage. (See I Corinthians 7:33–34.)
- A husband needs to understand the four levels from which a wife communicates: her mind, her emotions, her will, and her spirit.
- A wife needs to know that she is special because she is meeting needs that no other woman can meet.

☐ A CHILD'S PERSPECTIVE

- For a child to avoid evil, he or she must learn to fear the Lord.
- The fear of the Lord is the continual awareness that God is watching and will reward and judge every thought, word, action, attitude, and motive.
- A first step to learn the fear of the Lord is engrafting in the heart of the child such verses as Genesis 16:13: ". . . Thou God seest me. . . ." Also Psalm

139:2, 4, 12; Proverbs 5:21; 15:3; and Jeremiah 16:17.
- Children need to learn from the parents' corrected failures. Do not say, "I stole and got caught," but say, "I stole and was so convicted that I had to make restitution."
- Parents can pray "a hedge" around a rebellious son or daughter.

☐ OTHER PEOPLE'S PERSPECTIVES

- If we do not allow God to correct us through the conviction of the Holy Spirit or the chastening of parents or the reproofs of friends, we are then to be disciplined by the church. (See I Corinthians 5:5.)
- If discipline by the church is neglected or rejected, God will then use the government as His instrument of chastening. Three times in the first six verses of Romans 13 law officers are called "the ministers of God."

- If a person fails to confess and forsake sin, especially immorality, the guilt will begin to dictate his or her philosophy and theology.
- Once major failures are properly confessed and forsaken, they can become a part of our life message as we explain how God used them to teach us obedience, Godly character, and daily dependence upon Him.

4 SUFFERING

A forgiving spirit is the key to the principle of Suffering.

ESAU

HOW DOES BITTERNESS DESTROY THE PROCESS OF FORGIVENESS?

God uses the story of Esau to warn us of the serious danger of having a root of bitterness. (See Hebrews 12:15–16.) A careful look at Esau's life reveals the hidden causes of such a spirit.

THE ROOT CAUSES OF BITTERNESS

LACKING A SERVANT'S SPIRIT

"And the Lord said unto her [Rebekah], Two nations are in thy womb ... and the elder shall serve the younger" (Genesis 25:23).

Jesus taught, *"But he that is greatest among you shall be your servant" (Matthew 23:11).* This principle was so vital for the success of both Esau and Jacob that God gave it as a special revelation to their mother. Both brothers ended up serving their own interests, as did their descendants. Esau was the elder brother and probably the stronger.

COMPETING FOR RECOGNITION

"And the boys grew. . . . And Isaac loved Esau, because he did eat of his venison . . ." (Genesis 25:28).

Rather than serving his brother, Esau used his energy and skill to win his father's affection. His competition caused both parents to show favoritism and brought division between the brothers.

DESPISING SPIRITUAL THINGS

"Then Jacob gave Esau bread and pottage of lentiles [in exchange for Esau's birthright] ... thus Esau despised his birthright" (Genesis 25:34).

As the older son, Esau had special spiritual responsibilities in the family. These came with his birthright, but he despised his birthright and traded it for the momentary satisfaction of his physical desires.

COMMITTING FORNICATION

"And Esau was forty years old when he took [wives] ... Which were a grief of mind unto Isaac and to Rebekah" (Genesis 26:34–35).

The reason that Esau despised his birthright is given to us by God: *"Lest there be any fornicator, or profane person, as Esau . . ." (Hebrews 12:16).* His immoral acts eventually resulted in marriages which brought grief to his parents.

LOSING THE BLESSING

"And it came to pass, that when Isaac was old, and his eyes were dim, so that he could not see, he called Esau his eldest son, and said unto him, My son ... make me savoury meat, such as I love, and bring it to me, that I may eat; that my soul may bless thee before I die. . . .

"And Rebekah took goodly raiment of her eldest son Esau . . . And she gave the savoury meat and the bread, which she had prepared, into the hand of her son Jacob. . . .

"And Jacob said unto his father, I am Esau thy firstborn . . . sit and eat of my venison, that thy soul may bless me. . . .

"And it came to pass, as soon as Isaac had made an end of blessing Jacob . . . that Esau his brother came in from his hunting. . . .

"And when Esau heard the words of his father, he cried with a great and exceeding bitter cry. . . .

"And Esau hated Jacob because of the blessing . . ." (Genesis 27:1, 4, 15, 17, 19, 30, 34, 41).

The first-born was in line to receive his father's blessing. Esau wanted this, but Jacob stole it by deception.

BLAMING HIS BROTHER

". . . And Esau said in his heart . . . I [will] slay my brother Jacob" (Genesis 27:41).

Esau blamed Jacob for taking away his father's blessing. It did not occur to him that his own immoral life kept him from God's blessing, which was more important than his father's blessing. *". . . When he would have inherited the blessing, he was rejected: for he found no place of repentance . . ." (Hebrews 12:17).*

SUFFERING (Turning Bitterness to Forgiveness)

A FORGIVING ATTITUDE REQUIRES SEEING THE PRINCIPLE OF SUFFERING FROM:

☐ GOD'S PERSPECTIVE

- Every Christian is called to suffer for Christ's sake. *"For even hereunto were ye called: because Christ also suffered for us, leaving us an example, that ye should follow his steps" (I Peter 2:21).*

- When we suffer, especially at the hands of others, it is a humbling experience. Our pride is damaged. If we respond with a Christ-like spirit, God rewards us with more grace. His grace gives us the desire and power to do his will. *". . . God resisteth the proud, but giveth grace unto the humble"(James 4:6).*

- When we suffer, we can resist the grace of God by rejecting our suffering and refusing to forgive our offenders. The result will be bitterness. (See Hebrews 12:15.)

- We may also suffer open shame for our own sins. This open shame is what Christ suffered for our sins. It is the result of God's judgment on sin. It is designed to help us to break sinful habits. *"Forasmuch then as Christ hath suffered for us in the flesh, arm yourselves likewise with the same mind: for he that hath suffered in the flesh hath ceased from sin" (I Peter 4:1).*

☐ A PARTNER'S PERSPECTIVE

- Wives and husbands are warned not to let bitterness spoil their marriage.

- A symptom of bitterness is a damaged prayer life together. (See I Peter 3:7.)

- A rule for harmony is never to go to bed angry. *". . . Let not the sun go down upon your wrath" (Ephesians 4:26).*

- A deeper rule is to respond to your partner's offenses the same way that Christ responded to His offenders. *"Not rendering evil for evil, or railing for railing: but contrariwise blessing; knowing that ye are thereunto*

called, that ye should inherit a blessing" (I Peter 3:9).

- When a husband or wife falsely accuses the other, it is like the trial of bitter water in Numbers 5:12–31. The one accused will be closely watched. If he or she becomes bitter, the other will assume that the accusation is true. If there is a forgiving spirit, the one accused will be given more grace by God. This grace will enable the falsely accused to see new insights in Scripture, develop more of God's character, and accomplish more for eternal rewards.

☐ A CHILD'S PERSPECTIVE

- Every child must learn that God did not design life according to human fairness.

- Fairness requires equal treatment and rewards now. God's justice involves unseen compensations and a longer time frame than ours. He gives the rich extra sorrow and the poor extra faith. (See I Timothy 6:9; James 2:5.) With faith, a poor person is able to ask and receive from God all that he or she needs.

- A child can learn the fifteen aspects of genuine love by engrafting I Corinthians 13:4–8 into his or her mind, will, and emotions.

- Special training should be given to every child on how to cry out to God if ever morally attacked.

- When offenses come, respond with the insight of Joseph: *". . . Ye thought evil against me; but God meant it unto good . . ." (Genesis 50:20).*

☐ OTHER PEOPLE'S PERSPECTIVES

- If we are dedicated to God, we can conclude that anyone whom He allows to offend us is actually God's agent to accomplish His higher purposes in our lives, such as in Job's life. After others robbed him, he was able to say, *". . . The Lord gave, and the Lord hath taken away; blessed be the name of the Lord" (Job 1:21).*

- If a son or daughter is killed, we can avoid bitterness by focusing on the number of years that God gave us with the child rather than the number of years we think God should have given us with the child.

- A spirit of forgiveness comes as we realize the magnitude of our offenses toward a holy God compared to the minuteness of others' offenses toward us. (See Matthew 18:21–35.)

5 OWNERSHIP

Yielding our rights is the key to the principle of Ownership.

RICH YOUNG RULER

HOW DO ANGER AND WORRY RELATE TO THE PRINCIPLE OF OWNERSHIP?

God's ways are opposite to our ways. We think that we gain by collecting money and possessions. God knows that we gain by making the right exchanges.

Life itself is one continuous series of exchanges. We exchange our time and talents for money. Then we exchange our money for food and clothing.

However, there is an exchange that must precede all other exchanges. This is what Jesus explained to the rich young ruler.

THINGS THAT ROBBED THE RICH YOUNG RULER

HUMAN EFFORT

". . . There came one running, and kneeled to him [Jesus], and asked him, Good Master, what shall I do that I may inherit eternal life?" (Mark 10:17).

The root cause of all contention is pride: *"Only by pride cometh contention . . ."* (Proverbs 13:10).

One of the chief producers of pride is human achievement. Nebuchadnezzar said, *". . . Is not this great Babylon, that I have built . . . by the might of my power . . ."* (Daniel 4:30). The rich young ruler's life was also built around what he could do.

258

Like Naaman the leper, he was willing to do great exploits for God but he was unwilling to humble himself in the way that God chose.

EARTHLY RICHES

"And Jesus said unto him, Why callest thou me good? there is none good but one, that is, God" (Mark 10:18).

". . . But if thou wilt enter into life, keep the commandments. He saith unto him, Which? Jesus said, Thou shalt do no murder, Thou shalt not commit adultery, Thou shalt not steal, Thou shalt not bear false witness, Honour thy father and thy mother: and, Thou shalt love thy neighbour as thyself.

"The young man saith unto him, All these things have I kept from my youth up: what lack I yet?" (Matthew 19:17–20).

The diligence and moral character of the rich young ruler had already brought to him great achievements. He had riches, honor, power, and a lifetime to enjoy them. Yet he was already discovering that earthly achievements do not produce genuine fulfillment.

NARROW VISION

"Then Jesus beholding him loved him, and said unto him, One thing thou lackest: go thy way, sell whatsoever thou hast, and give to the poor, and thou shalt have treasure in heaven: and come, take up the cross, and follow me" (Mark 10:21).

"And when he heard this, he was very sorrowful: for he was very rich" (Luke 18:23).

It would not have been a major struggle for the rich young ruler to sell all his goods and give them to himself. And he had just stated that he loved his neighbor in the same way that he loved himself. Thus, Jesus' instructions revealed that he did not keep the commandments the way he claimed.

ETERNAL POVERTY

"And when Jesus saw that he was very sorrowful, he said, How hardly shall they that have riches enter into the kingdom of God!" (Luke 18:24).

By exchanging earthly riches at Christ's command, we turn them into eternal riches! By hoarding them for ourselves, we are not rich toward God. (See Luke 12:16–21.)

BONDAGE TO POSSESSIONS

"For it is easier for a camel to go through a needle's eye, than for a rich man to enter into the kingdom of God" (Luke 18:25).

What we own soon owns us. It dictates what we can do, where we can go, and whom we can serve.

OWNERSHIP (Yielding Our Rights)

YIELDING OUR RIGHTS REQUIRES SEEING THE PRINCIPLE OF OWNERSHIP FROM:

☐ GOD'S PERSPECTIVE

- God has a double claim of ownership on all that we are and have. He created us, and He redeemed us with the blood of His Son. (See I Peter 1:18–19.)
- We have the choice of acknowledging His ownership by dedicating ourselves and our possessions to Him, or of claiming what we are and have as our own. *"For whosoever will save his life shall lose it: and whosoever will lose his life for my sake shall find it"* (Matthew 16:25).

- Temporal things get in the way of eternal achievement. Thus God wants us to trade our ownership of things for more of Him. This was the secret of Paul's success: *"Yea doubtless, and I count all things but loss for the excellency of the knowledge of Christ Jesus my Lord: for whom I have suffered the loss of all things . . . that I may win Christ"* (Philippians 3:8).
- Meekness is yielding our rights to God. The opposite of meekness is anger. God gives special guidance to the meek. (See Psalm 25:9.)

☐ A PARTNER'S PERSPECTIVE

- Before entering into marriage, each partner must know how to yield personal rights to God and to each other.
- All anger can be traced to personal rights which others violated. By giving rights to God, we remove the root cause of anger.
- Each person who gets married usually has expectations of the partner. These expectations can cause the partner to feel imprisoned.
- Expectations also tend to cause the one having them

to be ungrateful for whatever is done, since it was expected.
- The key to having a grateful spirit is to transfer all expectations to God. *"My soul, wait thou only upon God; for my expectation is from him"* (Psalm 62:5).
- We know that we have given God our rights and expectations when we have purposed ahead of time to thank God whatever happens.
- Rights are to be distinguished from our God-given responsibilities.

☐ A CHILD'S PERSPECTIVE

- Each child must be taught how to identify personal rights and to transfer them to God.
- A child should be taught to concentrate on responsibilities rather than on rights. Focusing on rights leads to rebellion. Focusing on responsibilities leads to revival.
- Every child must learn to distinguish between personal needs and personal wants. Parents should provide for the child's needs and encourage the child to pray and work for wants.

- Parents must demonstrate and teach contentment with basics such as food and clothing. *"But godliness with contentment is great gain"* (I Timothy 6:6).
- Insecurity for a child is the result of building life around people or objects which can be taken away.
- Security is the by-product of building our lives and affections around the Lord Jesus Christ and His eternal Word.

☐ OTHER PEOPLE'S PERSPECTIVES

- Since most people have built their lives and affections around temporal things, they experience worry, fear, anxiety, and anger if those things are threatened or taken away.
- When others see us experience loss of things, they watch to see if our responses are the same as theirs would be. Paul commended the early Christians for the great reward they would receive because they exchanged their possessions to advance the cause

of Christ. *"For ye had compassion of me in my bonds, and took joyfully the spoiling of your goods, knowing in yourselves that ye have in heaven a better and an enduring substance"* (Hebrews 10:34).
- When others see that our possessions truly belong to God, that He has given them, and that we do not become angry when He takes them, they have a new respect for God and what He has given to us.

6 FREEDOM

Conquering moral impurity is the key to the principle of Freedom.

SAMSON

HOW IS FREEDOM RELATED TO THE DISCIPLINE OF OUR EYES?

Samson was the strongest man who ever lived. Solomon was the wisest man who ever lived. Each of these and other great men were defeated by unscriptural relationships with women.

Their tragic testimonies reinforce Paul's warning to Timothy, *"Flee also youthful lusts . . ."* (II Timothy 2:22).

STEPS THAT LED TO MORAL BONDAGE

MINGLING WITH GOD'S ENEMIES

"And Samson went down to Timnath . . ." (Judges 14:1).

We are to be in the world but not of the world. (See John 17:15–16.) We are not to look for marriage partners among those who reject the Lord. Samson put himself in danger by going into the territory of God's enemies.

WALKING IN THE LUST OF HIS EYES

". . . And saw a woman in Timnath of the daughters of the Philistines" (Judges 14:1).

Next to salvation, marriage is life's most important decision. Only with God's help can the right choice be made. (See Proverbs 19:14.) Samson depended on nothing more than what pleased his eye.

GETTING OUT FROM UNDER AUTHORITY

"Then his father and his mother said unto him, Is there never a woman among the daughters of thy brethren, or among all my people, that thou goest to take a wife of the uncircumcised Philistines? And Samson said unto his father, Get her for me; for she pleaseth me well" (Judges 14:3).

God puts each of us under parents whom He has personally prepared for our protection. By Samson's getting out from under his parents' authority, he exposed himself to the destructive power of Satan.

DEMANDING HIS OWN WAY

"And he came up, and told his father and his mother, and said, I have seen a woman in Timnath of the daughters of the Philistines: now therefore get her for me to wife" (Judges 14:2).

God gave Samson the desire of his heart but sent leanness to his soul. (See Psalm 106:15.)

GETTING ANGRY

". . . And his anger was kindled, and he went up to his father's house. But Samson's wife was given to his companion, whom he had used as his friend" (Judges 14:19–20).

God warns that if we do not honor our father and mother, things will not go well for us. (See Ephesians 6:2–3.) When things did not go Samson's way, he became angry rather than repenting from his selfish lifestyle.

TURNING TO FORNICATION

"Then went Samson to Gaza, and saw there an harlot, and went in unto her. . . . And it came to pass afterward, that he loved a woman in the valley of Sorek, whose name was Delilah" (Judges 16:1, 4).

Rebellion and bitterness will usually lead to immorality. The pride of being his own boss cut off Samson's ability to overcome temptation.

RECEIVING GOD'S JUDGMENT

"And it came to pass, when she pressed him daily with her words . . . That he told her all his heart . . ." (Judges 16:16–17).

". . . And he wist not that the Lord was departed from him. But the Philistines took him, and put out his eyes . . . and bound him with fetters of brass; and he did grind in the prison house" (Judges 16:20–21).

Jesus' teaching on plucking out the eye is clearly illustrated in the life of Samson. The eyes that he refused to bring under God's control were given to God's enemies.

FREEDOM (Conquering Moral Impurity)

CONQUERING MORAL IMPURITY REQUIRES SEEING THE PRINCIPLE OF FREEDOM FROM:

☐ GOD'S PERSPECTIVE

- We do not have victory because we are:
  1. Depending on human energy instead of God's Spirit
  2. Being double-minded
  3. Not understanding our victory in Christ
  4. Making provision for sinful pleasures
  5. Attempting to hide secret sins
- Victory over habits begins by victory over thoughts. (See II Corinthians 10:4–5.)
- Sinful habits of the mind, will, or emotions can be overcome by engrafting Scripture into our souls. (See James 1:21.)

- To meditate on Scripture requires us to put it in the first person and use it as a personal prayer as we go to sleep, as we wake up, and whenever we are tempted.
- Quoting Scripture in the face of temptation is like a falling eagle stretching out its wings. The law of lift immediately overcomes the law of gravity. Similarly, God's Word overcomes the law of sin in our members. (See Romans 8:1–4.)
- The key to victory is not praying for it but recognizing (reckoning) that we already have it in Christ. As Christians we died and rose again with Him.
- To insure victory there is need for daily accountability.

☐ A PARTNER'S PERSPECTIVE

- God did not design marriage to fulfill perverted sex drives. Perversion is taking that which God designed for one function and misusing it for another function.
- God states that marriage is honorable for all; therefore, do not defile the marriage bed, for he will destroy all whoremongers. (See Hebrews 13:4.)
- It is essential for the husband to have moral victory so that he can be a protector to his wife and children.
- The husband is instructed to cleanse his wife by the Word. (See Ephesians 5:25–28.)

- Before marriage a couple should dedicate themselves to God's purposes in marriage and the means God designed to achieve them.
  1. Companionship—Wise understanding
  2. Enjoyment—Self-control
  3. Completeness—Oneness of spirit
  4. Fruitfulness—Multiply life
  5. Protection—Rear a Godly seed
  6. Illustrate Church/Christ relationship
- Every husband must make the covenant with his eyes that Job did. (See Job 31:1.)

☐ A CHILD'S PERSPECTIVE

- Unborn children are capable of comprehending Scripture because Scripture is spiritually discerned. Therefore, parents who read Scripture to their children before birth are giving them greater alertness to spiritual truth. (See II Timothy 3:15.)
- Even before obedience, a child must be taught to be attentive to the parents, the words of Scripture, and the "voice" of his or her conscience.
- Engrafting Scripture in the mind of a child is the best way to guard him or her from evil.

- Allowing children to live with secret sin or unconfessed offenses, allows Satan to gain great advantage. Only truth and proper discipline bring freedom. (See Proverbs 28:13.)
- Establish daily accountability questions.
  1. What did you get from the Bible today?
  2. What Scripture did you meditate on last night?
  3. Did you effectively quote Scripture when you were last tempted?
  4. Do you have a clear conscience?

☐ OTHER PEOPLE'S PERSPECTIVES

- We must realize that a man's morality will dictate his theology and philosophy. (See Romans 1:21; and II Thessalonians 2:10–11.)
- When people reject God's moral law, they become fools. Scripture identifies five types of fools and how we should respond to each one.
  1. Simple fool—Warn him
  2. Reactionary fool—Discipline him
  3. Silly fool—Sternly reprove him

  4. Scorning fool—Avoid him
  5. Committed fool—Have no association with him
- A wise Christian will not argue religion or philosophy but will patiently teach others how to conquer destructive habits. (See II Timothy 2:24–26.)
- We are to exhort one another daily lest any of us be hardened through the deceitfulness of sin. (See Hebrews 3:13.)

7 SUCCESS

Accepting God's priorities is the key to Success in life.

THE RICH MAN

HOW DO WRONG PRIORITIES RELATE TO SUCCESS IN LIFE?

True success is identifying God's will for our lives and fulfilling it. Boredom is the result of failing to develop our God-given interests, aptitudes, and capacities.

Achieving God's purposes for our lives depends on our focusing in on things of eternal importance instead of things of temporal value.

God identifies several symptoms in the life of the rich man which explain why he missed God's purpose for his life.

SYMPTOMS OF FAILURE

NO PERSONAL RELATIONSHIP WITH GOD

"There was a certain rich man..." (Luke 16:19).

If we look on outward appearance, we will be tempted to show partiality to the rich. God warns that in so doing we are judges of evil thoughts. (See James 2:4.) In contrast, God looks on the heart. Accordingly, the rich man did not even warrant being named because of his unbelief, while the beggar is named because of his faith.

TEMPORAL FOCUS

"...Which...fared sumptuously every day: And there was a certain beggar named Lazarus...desiring to

be fed with the crumbs which fell from the rich man's table: moreover the dogs came and licked his sores"* (Luke 16:19–21).

Important principles about life are discovered as we learn how to abound and to suffer need. The rich man should have shared his plenty with the beggar, and in so doing the beggar would have had opportunity to share his faith with the rich man.

DISREGARD FOR DEATH

"And it came to pass, that the beggar died, and was carried by the angels into Abraham's bosom: the rich man also died, and was buried" (Luke 16:22).

God's final judgment is more certain than the death which precedes it. Every time someone around us dies, it should be a call to evaluate our preparation for eternity.

DEMAND TO BE SERVED

"And in hell he lift up his eyes, being in torments.... And he cried and said, Father Abraham, have mercy on me, and send Lazarus, that he may dip the tip of his finger in water, and cool my tongue; for I am tormented in this flame" (Luke 16:23–24).

We discover purpose in life and greatness by serving others. The rich man expected continuous service. Even in hell he wanted Lazarus to serve him.

DISREGARD FOR SCRIPTURES

"But Abraham said, Son, remember that thou in thy lifetime receivedst thy good things, and likewise Lazarus evil things: but now he is comforted, and thou art tormented.

"... Then he said, I pray thee therefore, father, that thou wouldest send him to my father's house: For I have five brethren; that he may testify unto them, lest they also come into this place of torment.

"Abraham saith unto him, They have Moses and the prophets; let them hear them.

"And he said, Nay, father Abraham: but if one went unto them from the dead, they will repent.

"And he said unto him, If they hear not Moses and the prophets, neither will they be persuaded, though one rose from the dead" (Luke 16:25–31).

We may think that unless we have a spectacular testimony we will be ineffective in winning others to Christ. However, God reveals here that to faithfully give out the message of His written Word is as convincing as having someone rise from the dead. The rich man's response reveals his own rejection of Scripture while he was alive.

SUCCESS (Fulfilling God's Priorities)

FULFILLING LIFE'S CALLING REQUIRES SEEING THE PRINCIPLE OF SUCCESS FROM:

☐ GOD'S PERSPECTIVE

- God wants to give every Christian a "vision" of how he or she can advance the cause of Christ. Moses had a vision to free God's people. Nehemiah's vision was to rebuild the wall. Paul's vision was to bring the Gospel to the Gentiles.
- We should expect to experience a "death of our visions"—unexpected circumstances which hinder us from carrying them out.
- During the death of a vision God wants us to concentrate on building such character qualities as faith, hope, patience, meekness, and self-control.
- During the death of a vision Satan will often tempt us to fulfill it with fleshly efforts. For example, Abraham and Sarah used human means to fulfill God's promise of a son.
- Human effort to fulfill God's vision will produce continuing conflicts, as with Sarah and Hagar and their decendants.
- In God's time He will fulfill our vision with supernatural power.
- Each time God demonstrates His principles and power in our lives, we have new "chapters" of our "life messages" which we can share with others.
- Our real fulfillment in life will come as we see God reproducing Christ's character in the lives of others through our lives and witnesses.

☐ A PARTNER'S PERSPECTIVE

- The decision for marriage should be made when each partner sees how he or she can be more effective married than he or she can be single.
- Once a couple gets married, they must purpose not to violate the Scriptural teachings which their relationship illustrates. For example, Christ will not divorce the Church. Neither should a married person divorce his or her partner.
- Young wives should seek out mature women and ask them for special instructions on how to be serious-minded, how to love their husbands, how to rear their children, how to manage the home, and how to be discreet.
- As teaching is applied, records should be kept so that the results can be taught to the next generation. (See Titus 2:3–5.)
- Husbands are to sacrifice for their wives and children in order to raise up the foundations of many Godly generations.
- Financial freedom should be maintained in order not to hinder the potential that God would have for their marriage and family.

☐ A CHILD'S PERSPECTIVE

- Instill life goals in your children by emphasizing the spiritual values and concerns which you have.
- Expose your children to the lives of great Christians through biographies and by inviting Godly Christians into your home.
- Use mealtimes to discuss the importance of world events in the light of prophecy and to read from God's Word.
- Assist your children in beginning Life Notebooks. Show them how to record what God teaches them from the Bible, how they are applying Scriptural principles, opportunities they have to stand alone, and answers to prayer. This will become an invaluable basis for their "life messages."
- Expose each child to successful Christian work such as witnessing, counseling, and visiting.

☐ OTHER PEOPLE'S PERSPECTIVES

- Learn how to use questions which will help others identify precise spiritual needs. Then use the insights and principles from Scripture to guide them toward a right decision.
  QUESTIONS:
  1. What were the events leading up to your salvation? Do you have doubts about your salvation?
  2. Since you became a Christian, have you ever totally dedicated your life to Christ?
  3. If you had the power to change anything about the way you look, what would you change?
  4. Would your parents say that you were obedient to their authority?
  5. Do you have a clear conscience?
  6. Has anyone deeply hurt you in the past?
  7. Do you have a problem with anger?
  8. Is there some habit you wish you could break? (Have you engrafted Romans 6?)
  9. When you get to the end of your life, what do you want to say that God accomplished through you?

263

APPLYING BASIC PRINCIPLES

1. Seeing life from God's perspective enables each of

DESIGN	AUTHORITY	RESPONSIBILITY
• Accept our unchangeables • Purpose of "defects" • Thank God for the way that He made us	• Become a Christian • Submit will to God • Accept God's four authority structures • Learn to appeal • Learn to stand alone	• Be responsible to thoughts, words, actions, attitudes, and motives • Acknowledge offenses • Gain clear conscience

2. Seeing life from our partner's perspective enables

• Accept partner's unchangeables • Praise Godly character • Confirm value in partner's "defects" • Avoid comparisons and flattery • Identify and develop spiritual gifts	• Each submits to God • Wife: Honor and submit • Have Godly attitudes • Learn how to appeal • Husband: Love, lead, and appeal • Meet basic needs • Illustrate Christ's relationship to Church	• Be transparent with discretion • Clear offenses daily • Learn four levels of communication • Guard spirit of marriage • Make wife "special"

3. Seeing life from our child's perspective enables each

• Accept each child • Give meaning of name • Teach how "scars" are marks of ownership • Four reasons Satan hates our bodies • Develop and reward Godly character • Understand needs of birth order • Detect and develop spiritual gifts	• Bring to salvation • Convert soul from natural inclinations • Get under authority– "umbrella of protection" • Father: Give "commands" • Mother: Make "laws" • Teach to stand alone • Teach how to appeal • Acknowledge sins of forefathers	• Teach the fear of God • Engraft verses of fear of God • Teach lessons from corrected failure • Explain how God disciplines you • Pray "hedge of thorns" around rebellious child • Bring hidden sins to light by questions • Punish evil–Praise good

4. Seeing life from other people's perspectives enables

• Never mock "defects" or "unchangeables" • Detect symptoms of self-rejection • Help to accept God's design • Praise character	• Develop character by responding to difficult employers • Submit to authority of church leaders • Obey all laws • Appeal when needed	• A person's theology and philosophy will be dictated by his morality • Church discipline • Civil discipline • Law officers are ministers of God

A SUCCESSFUL PERSON

SUFFERING	OWNERSHIP	FREEDOM	SUCCESS
• Accept suffering as part of our calling • Forgive offenders • Invest value in their lives	• Dedicate self to God • Yield rights • Trade things for more of Christ • Balance expectations • Gain financial freedom	• Engraft Romans 6–8 • Enter into Christ's victory on cross • Remove provision for fleshly desires • Be accountable	• Ask God for "vision" of Godly achievement • Seek God • Welcome trials • Expect death of vision

A SUCCESSFUL PARTNER

• Quickly forgive offenses • Respond to sources of irritation • Engraft I Corinthians 13 • Accept false accusations as "trial of bitter water" • Honor marriage vows	• Use anger to signal unyielded rights • Use worry to reveal ownership • Give expectations to God • Build gratefulness by "expecting nothing" • Distinguish rights from responsibilities	• Make covenant with eyes • Allow no secret sin • Husband's victory is effective "umbrella" • Husband must cleanse wife by Word • Be accountable to each other	• Rearrange priorities • Serve each other • Illustrate Christ's relationship to Church • Fulfill six purposes of marriage • Purpose to raise up many Godly generations • Financial freedom

A SUCCESSFUL PARENT

• Define justice and mercy versus fairness • Respond to mocking and rejection by love • Do not take up offenses • Cry out to God if morally attacked • Bitterness proves partial guilt • Judging others pinpoints our "blind spots" • Daily reading vow (Five Psalms per day)	• Identify and transfer personal rights to God • Focus on responsibilities versus rights • Separate needs from wants • Learn to be content with basics • Build life around Christ and Bible • Teach prayer and fasting	• Read Bible to unborn child • Teach attentiveness to parents, conscience, and Holy Spirit • Engraft Word • Expose secret sin • Have daily accountability questions • Build self-control: Instant obedience to the initial prompting of the Holy Spirit	• Explain how our ways are opposite of God's ways • Instill God's goals • Read biographies of great Christians • Entertain Godly Christians • Make mealtimes meaningful • Begin life notebook • Build life message • Start Christian service

A SUCCESSFUL PROCLAIMER

• Offenders are "God's agents" • Compare God's forgiveness of us to our need to forgive • Complete Christ's suffering for lost	• Discern insecurity in others • Be example when losses occur • Illustrate purposes of money	• Discern five types of fools • Do not argue theology– Lead to moral freedom • Exhort each other daily	• Use questions to reveal basic spiritual needs • Lead others to salvation • Train faithful men and women

NOTES

DIAGRAMS

HOW TO TEACH SONS AND DAUGHTERS TO "STAND ALONE"

Dover, Leslie's, Vol. 21

"Wherefore take unto you the whole armour of God, that ye may be able to withstand in the evil day, and having done all, to stand.

"Stand therefore, having your loins girt about with truth, and having on the breastplate of righteousness;

"And your feet shod with the preparation of the gospel of peace;

"Above all, taking the shield of faith, wherewith ye shall be able to quench all the fiery darts of the wicked.

"And take the helmet of salvation, and the sword of the Spirit, which is the word of God:

"Praying always with all prayer and supplication in the Spirit, and watching thereunto with all perseverance and supplication for all saints" (Ephesians 6:13–18).

NOTES

DIAGRAMS

HOW TO TEACH SONS AND DAUGHTERS TO "STAND ALONE"

THE IMPORTANCE OF SONS AND DAUGHTERS "STANDING ALONE" FOR TRUTH

• Parents give their sons and daughters purpose in life when the family has Scriptural convictions which are worth living for and worth dying for.

• The desire to "stand alone" is the heritage of those who know by experience that following Scriptural principles constitutes a superior way of life.

• "Standing alone" for God's truth begins with an inward attitude and expresses itself in outward words and actions.

• The motivation to "stand alone" is a wholesome fear of the Lord and a confident assurance of His presence and supernatural power.

• The ability to "stand alone" comes by the desire and power of God's grace as we walk in harmony with the Holy Spirit.

What begins to occur when we make the decision to "stand alone"?

• _____

_____

"Whereby are given unto us exceeding great and precious promises: that by these ye might be partakers of the divine nature, having escaped the corruption that is in the world through lust" (II Peter 1:4).

What is the first important step in teaching your sons and daughters to "stand alone"?

1 _____

_____

_____

What if my children react to rules?

• _____

_____

"More to be desired are they than gold, yea, than much fine gold: sweeter also than honey and the honeycomb. Moreover by them is thy servant warned: and in keeping of them there is great reward" (Psalm 19:10–11).

When sons and daughters understand the basic concepts behind "standing alone," rules no longer appear as "fence posts" limiting their freedom, but as "sign posts" warning them of danger.

Scriptural principles are like laws of nature; they are universal and nonoptional. They apply to the non-Christian as well as to the Christian. If any principle is broken, a predictable consequence will follow. Because of this cause-and-effect sequence, it is wise to work out rules based on principles.

Based on the law of gravity, for example, rules are needed to protect a person from stepping over a high ledge. This practical rule is contained in God's Law by the instruction that home builders are to construct a railing around the roof. Failure to do so made the builder liable for anyone who would fall from the roof. (See Deuteronomy 22:8.)

Bausch & Lomb

Sir Isaac Newton shed new light on gravity and color by explaining the principles behind them.

Our Christian forefathers understood Biblical principles and the rules which logically flowed from them. However, many forefathers passed on to their children only the rules. Their children did not understand the principles from which the rules came and began to reject some of them.

When these children grew up and tried to pass on inconsistent rules to their children, there was further reaction and rejection. A further problem also developed based on the tendency to make rigid and stereotyped application of rules when the principle is forgotten.

The style of the "railing" may change from generation to generation; however, the principle of gravity and the rule to have a protection does not change.

The great need today is for parents to explain basic life principles to their sons and daughters and then work with their children to identify Biblical "guidelines" to ensure that these principles will not be violated.

How do parents prepare children to "stand alone"?

2_____

_____

Can a child "stand alone" without saying a word?

• _____

_____

_____

"But sanctify the Lord God in your hearts: and be ready always to give an answer to every man that asketh you a reason of the hope that is in you with meekness and fear:

"Having a good conscience; that, whereas they speak evil of you, as of evildoers, they may be ashamed that falsely accuse your good conversation in Christ.

"For it is better, if the will of God be so, that ye suffer for well-doing, than for evil-doing" (I Peter 3:15–17).

God's work is accomplished through words. He created the world by the Word of His power. He designed Christians to be witnesses of His truth. Silence is too often understood by the world as approval or rejection of them, and the basic issues are never properly addressed.

What is the best phrase to use in "standing alone"?

• _____

_____

_____

"Whosoever therefore shall confess me before men, him will I confess also before my Father which is in heaven. But whosoever shall deny me before men, him will I also deny before my Father which is in heaven" (Matthew 10:32–33).

This phrase can be very effective with those who are non-Christians. However, some of the most difficult "standing alone" situations are required with other Christians. Rather than using this phrase with them, explain the concept if the person is not a scorner.

DISCERNING WISE RESPONSES BY IDENTIFYING FIVE TYPES OF FOOLS

"Standing alone" requires a clear understanding of the types of people with whom we speak. To those who would understand, we should explain more. To those who would not understand, we should say far less.

Often people who ask us to do evil are those whom Scripture identifies as foolish people. Scripture goes on to define five types of fools and gives clear instruction for responding to each one:

1. THE "SIMPLE FOOL"
He is without knowledge and easily seduced. He needs to be instructed, and we should try to do this with Scriptural principles.

2. THE "REACTIONARY FOOL"
He simply wants his own way. He needs to be disciplined. We should direct him back to his God-given authorities.

3. THE "SILLY FOOL"
He is only interested in a good time. He needs major reproofs. If appropriate, we should try to explain to him how he is violating Scriptural principles, and we should avoid him until he corrects his ways.

4. THE "SCORNING FOOL"
He has rejected truth and delights in mocking Christians and their standards. He will hate a reprover and blot his name. Remove yourself from him.

5. THE "COMMITTED FOOL"

He is the victim of his own passions. He is committed to teaching you. We should reject his teachings and have no association with him.

For further information, see *Men's Manual*, Volume I, pages 95–96.

What is the normal response to a Christian who "stands alone"?

● _____

_____

"But foolish and unlearned questions avoid, knowing that they do gender strifes. And the servant of the Lord must not strive; but be gentle unto all men, apt to teach, patient, In meekness instructing those that oppose themselves; if God peradventure will give them repentance to the acknowledging of the truth; And that they may recover themselves out of the snare of the devil, who are taken captive by him at his will" (II Timothy 2:23–26).

HOW A TEENAGER DEEPENED A FRIENDSHIP BY "STANDING ALONE"

"A friend invited me to her birthday party. Those who attended were going to see a movie. I knew the movie was something God did not want me to see. I remembered what I had learned about "standing alone" and realized that this was now something that I needed to do.

"I talked to my dad because I was a little scared, and he told me that if I stood alone, my friend would respect me. So I called her and told her that I had given my life to Jesus Christ and He was my personal Lord and Savior. I explained that I wasn't able to go to the movie with her.

"The next day I went to give her the birthday gift I had bought. On her front door was a note addressed to me. I have to admit I was a little shaky as I opened it. I read the note and was filled with joy.

"She told me, 'I understand the way you feel, and I respect you for your faith in the Lord.' She said she respected me—the very same thing my father said would happen. I was excited.

"God really strengthened my life through this situation. He allowed me to experience a closer relationship with my friend. God showed me that He desires to demonstrate His power through my life when I obey Him. This experience gave me confidence to stand alone again.

"It also deeply encouraged me, and it proved that my parents were good counselors.

"I want to thank you for making it possible for young and old alike to hear Godly principles. It means so much to me."

A teenager from Nebraska

How can you prepare wise responses for different situations?

● _____

_____

"And your feet shod with the preparation of the gospel of peace" (Ephesians 6:15).

Having a "prepared answer" produces confidence in the one who has it. When another person senses this confidence, he is more hesitant to ask this person to do something which he himself knows is not right.

This confidence, however, must be balanced by meekness, and our answers must be based upon a clear application of Scripture. To gain a solid footing in Scripture, *"Study to shew thyself approved unto God, a workman that needeth not to be ashamed, rightly dividing the word of truth"(II Timothy 2:15).*

How can parents help sons and daughters in overcoming the fear of standing alone for truth?

3 _____

_____

Just as God stands ready to assist the Christian who calls upon Him, so parents should assure their children that whenever they face a special "standing alone" situation or need, they as parents will drop whatever they are doing and give the proper assistance.

If they are unable to reach you, the children should have an alternate phone number of a Godly friend who can be called in a time of need.

Certain occasions may require one or both parents to reinforce the stand that a son or daughter has taken against evil. This reinforcement

271

may be given by their physical presence or by a physical contact from the parents. When parents do reinforce a child's "stand against evil", it is important for the parents to have the goal of clarifying the truth upon which the son or daughter is standing and in all cases to show a genuine spirit of meekness and sincerity.

What assurance does a son or daughter need in order to "stand alone"?

● _____

"…lo, I am with you alway, even unto the end of the world. Amen" (Matthew 28:20).

Mordecai was honored for "standing alone."

The success of Esther's "standing alone" before the king came because of her uncle who was watching, praying, and available outside the gate. She remained under the protection of his counsel, and therefore knew that he was with her in spirit while she was away from him.

Mordecai was able to give wise and strong counsel to Esther because he was also "standing alone" by not bowing in worship to wicked Haman. God rewarded Mordecai when the king commanded his enemy to lead him through the city in honor.

An additional message of Mordecai's life is demonstrated in his Godly respect for the king and support of the king during a time when others reacted to him.

What response should a father expect when he presents the material on "standing alone" to his sons and daughters?

4 _____

_____

● _____

_____

Making a decision to "stand alone" should follow the same procedure as any other decision made to the Lord. First, the child should understand as fully as possible the meaning and significance of his decision. Second, the decision must be based clearly on Scriptural authority. The decision should be made to the Lord, not just to the parents.

"O give thanks unto the Lord; for he is good: for his mercy endureth for ever" (Psalm 136:1).

"Then they that feared the Lord spake often one to another: and the Lord hearkened, and heard it, and a book of remembrance was written before him for them that feared the Lord, and that thought upon his name" (Malachi 3:16).

How can a child's decision to "stand alone" be reinforced?

5 _____

_____

● _____

_____

"All scripture is given by inspiration of God, and is profitable for doctrine, for reproof, for correction, for instruction in righteousness: That the man of God may be perfect, throughly furnished unto all good works" (II Timothy 3:16–17).

Daniel was protected while "standing alone."

It would be important to point out to sons and daughters that there was often an immediate price to pay when a Godly man or woman in Scripture "stood alone"; however, that "price" turned out to be the very means through which God exalted them to higher positions and opportunities.

Daniel "stood alone" and was sent to the lion's den. Then he was given a new position of authority in the kingdom. Joseph "stood alone," and because he did, he was sentenced to prison. But from there he was exalted to the position of second highest ruler in Egypt. Esther "stood alone", and by so doing put her life in jeopardy. However, through her stand God's enemies were destroyed, and she and her people were not only spared from death but also highly honored throughout the empire.

What accountability is necessary for "standing alone"?

6 _____

_____

• _____

_____

"Now the end of the commandment is charity out of a pure heart, and of a good conscience, and of faith unfeigned: From which some having swerved have turned aside unto vain jangling" (I Timothy 1:5-6).

When a Christian "stands alone" against compromise or evil doing, it usually causes immediate conviction and reaction from those who are involved in or give approval to the action being questioned. These individuals will usually not reevaluate the activity if they can find some justification to condemn or discredit the Christian who opposes it.

Therefore, God warns us to have the attitude of meekness whenever we must "stand alone" or instruct those who oppose God's righteous standards. (See II Timothy 2:24-26.)

Meekness involves an attitude of humility before God and others, combined with a loving firmness to carry out God's will whatever the cost. Meekness is yielding our rights in deference to the clear commands of Scripture.

How will "standing alone" enrich the fellowship and communication within a family?

• _____

_____

FAMILY SESSION TO EXPLAIN STANDING ALONE

What is the correct motivation to "stand alone"?

• _____

_____

_____

"O how I love thy law! it is my meditation all the day. Thou through thy commandments hast made me wiser than mine enemies: for they are ever with me.

I have more understanding than all my teachers: for thy testimonies are my meditation. I understand more than the ancients, because I keep thy precepts. I have refrained my feet from every evil way, that I might keep thy word. I have not departed from thy judgments: for thou hast taught me.

How sweet are thy words unto my taste! yea, sweeter than honey to my mouth! Through thy precepts I get understanding: therefore I hate every false way" (Psalm 119:97-104).

WHAT ARE GOD'S PREREQUISITES TO "STANDING ALONE"?

☐ Receiving Jesus Christ as our personal Savior and becoming a child of God (See Romans 10:9.)

☐ Renewing our mind with the truths of God's Word and beginning to see life from God's point of view (See Romans 12:2.)

☐ Becoming obedient to the promptings of the Holy Spirit and applying God's truth to daily living (See Romans 8:13.)

☐ Identifying with Christ's death, burial, and resurrection and drawing upon His power to do what is right (See Romans 6-8.)

☐ Loving the Lord to the point where we are more concerned about protecting His reputation than about pleasing ourselves (See John 14:21.)

NOTES

DIAGRAMS

☐ Realizing that we are not really alone because God will never forsake us (See Matthew 28:20.)

☐ Realizing that rejection and persecution immediately bring more of God's grace and that it is God's grace that gives us the desire and power to do His will (See James 4:6.)

☐ Learning Scriptural concepts and applying them to daily situations (See Proverbs 3:6; Psalm 119:105.)

☐ Having an attitude of humility before God and man without any trace of pride or rebellion

"The fear of the Lord is to hate evil: pride, and arrogancy, and the evil way . . ." (Proverbs 8:13).

☐ Having a true hatred of evil and not secretly wanting to do what we condemn as evil in others (See Romans 2:1.)

"Standing alone" is actually motivated by having a proper fear of the Lord and by understanding the cause-and-effect relationships which come from violating God's principles.

How does independence grow by "standing alone"?

● _____

_____

_____

"That our sons may be as plants grown up in their youth; that our daughters may be as corner stones, polished after the similitude of a palace" (Psalm 144:12).

When parents are confident that a son or daughter will make wise and Godly decisions, they are able to give that son or daughter increased responsibility with its accompanying freedoms.

1 CONCEPT: A "one-woman man" or "one-man woman"

"Therefore shall a man leave his father and his mother, and shall cleave unto his wife: and they shall be one flesh" (Genesis 2:24).

"A bishop then must be . . . the husband of one wife . . ." (I Timothy 3:2).

"Honour widows . . . having been the wife of one man" (I Timothy 5:3, 9).

Accepting God's design in marriage is building on a solid foundation.

God designed a man to have only one wife and a woman to have only one husband. If it would have been otherwise, God would have made several wives for Adam or several husbands for Eve.

When sons or daughters come to the decision early in life that they will keep themselves pure for that special one according to God's design, the son becomes a "one-woman man" and the daughter becomes a "one-man woman." There are tremendous rewards for every son or daughter who will make this decision and "stand alone" whatever the cost.

Being committed to this concept allows the son or daughter to have clear direction for many other decisions, including friendships, activities, appearance, and thoughts. It also gives an inward peace that God will provide the one of His choosing at the right time.

What is God's definition of a "strange woman"?

● _____
_____
_____

"Say unto wisdom, Thou art my sister; and call understanding thy kinswoman: That they may keep thee from the strange woman, from the stranger which flattereth with her words" (Proverbs 7:4–5).

"The way of man is froward and strange: but as for the pure, his work is right" (Proverbs 21:8).

"For of this sort are they which creep into houses, and lead captive silly women laden with sins, led away with divers lusts" (II Timothy 3:6).

How will this concept affect dress?

☐ _____
_____

"In like manner also, that women adorn themselves in modest apparel, with shamefacedness and sobriety; not with broided hair, or gold, or pearls, or costly array; But (which becometh women professing godliness) with good works" (I Timothy 2:9–10).

"And they were both naked, the man and his wife, and were not ashamed" (Genesis 2:25).

"And the eyes of them both were opened, and they knew that they were naked; and they sewed fig leaves together, and made themselves aprons" (Genesis 3:7).

"Unto Adam also and to his wife did the Lord God make coats of skins, and clothed them" (Genesis 3:21).

● _____
_____
● _____
● _____

By studying the following material, this step should be unnecessary.

● _____
_____

LEARN TEN WAYS TO DIRECT THE EYES OF OTHERS TO YOUR COUNTENANCE

1 WEAR A SMILE.

Your face reveals your inner attitudes, your needs, your joys, your struggles, and your victories. A cheerful countenance provides a ministry of encouragement for others. Apart from your actual words, your countenance can be the most effective means you have to express the love of the Lord Jesus Christ to others around you. In fact, your face can actually cancel the effect of your words, so powerful are its expressions.

A smile brightens the countenance, giving it a healthy glow. It causes the eyes to sparkle and the facial muscles to be relaxed. A smile reveals a cheerful spirit, and thus draws others to you.

A sad countenance demonstrates a selfish spirit because it forces the sympathies of others to determine what trouble is at the root of the frown.

Observers tend to look away from a frown because it makes them feel awkward.

A smile draws observers because it says, "I care," "I have noticed you," "I am experiencing the joy of the Lord inside." Observers tend to answer a smile with a smile of their own.

2 CHOOSE COLORS WHICH ENHANCE YOUR SKIN TONES. [1]

When God created the world, He made the seasons each with their special characteristics and special coloring. He designed tremendous variety in hue, intensity, and shading. All of nature harmonizes with the Creator's color plan.

During the time of the Bauhaus school of art in Germany, Johannes Itten noticed that his students consistently chose colors for their paintings that were complementary to their own skin tone, hair, and eyes in both tone and intensity.

Itten concluded that everyone has a personal palette of colors, the ones to which you are drawn naturally, and that those are the very ones that look best on you.

Itten's theory has been adapted to the four seasonal palettes as guides for clothing, makeup, and wardrobe planning. Your natural coloring is either cool (blue undertones) or warm (yellow undertones).

- *THE WINTER PALETTE* has either blue-based colors or true colors—colors with a balance between blue and yellow, black and white.

- *THE SUMMER PALETTE* has either blue, rose, or gray undertones. Because of these undertones, winter and summer are the cool palettes.

- *THE AUTUMN PALETTE* is based on golden tones.

- *THE SPRING PALETTE* is based on clear, yellow undertones. Autumn and spring are the warm palettes.

When you wear the right colors next to your face, your complexion is smoothed and clarified. Lines, shadows, and circles are minimized. A healthy color is drawn out, pushing the clothing color into the background.

When you wear the wrong colors, your complexion will look pale, sallow, or "muddy." Lines or shadows around the mouth and nose and dark circles around the eyes will be accentuated. Blotches on the face and the effects of aging will be emphasized.

Wrong colors tend to draw attention to themselves, pushing your face into the background.

WHICH GROUP IS BEST FOR YOU?

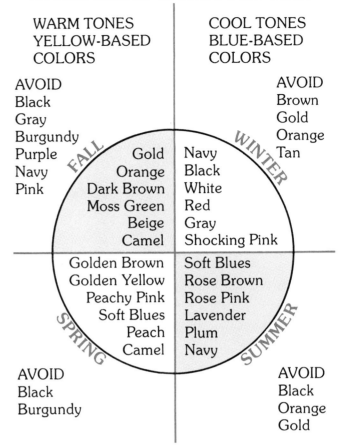

WARM TONES YELLOW-BASED COLORS

COOL TONES BLUE-BASED COLORS

AVOID
Black
Gray
Burgundy
Purple
Navy
Pink

FALL

Gold
Orange
Dark Brown
Moss Green
Beige
Camel

WINTER

Navy
Black
White
Red
Gray
Shocking Pink

AVOID
Brown
Gold
Orange
Tan

SPRING

Golden Brown
Golden Yellow
Peachy Pink
Soft Blues
Peach
Camel

SUMMER

Soft Blues
Rose Brown
Rose Pink
Lavender
Plum
Navy

AVOID
Black
Burgundy

AVOID
Black
Orange
Gold

3 CHOOSE A HAIRSTYLE WHICH COMPLEMENTS THE SHAPE OF YOUR FACE. [2]

Your hair provides a frame for your face. Basically, there are six facial shapes: oval, round, square, rectangle, triangle, long oval. The goal in choosing the proper frame for the face is to "ovalize" that shape as much as possible.

Consider the following examples.

Round   Square

Better   Better

Triangle   Long

Better   Better

Fine hair   Curly hair   Thin hair

Fine hair should be cut short and in layers to add thickness and volume. Curly hair is best controlled when kept close to the sides of the head. If it is left too long on the sides, the shape of the head will appear too round, and the excess volume of hair will detract from the face. Thinning hair and a receding hairline are made less noticeable by a shorter hairstyle.

Your hairstyle should also be proportionate to your overall appearance and should communicate a message of obedience to the authorities in your life. (See I Corinthians 11:14–15.)

4 WEAR SPECIAL ACCENTS NEAR YOUR FACE.

Special accents near your face draw the attention of the observer to your countenance.

Women can wear scarves, bows, lace trim on collars, ruffles at the neckline, a flower on the shoulder or in the hair (if appropriate for the occasion), or appropriate jewelry—earrings, short necklace, brooch or stickpin.

Men can accent their faces by wearing a tie, a collared shirt when wearing a sweater, and by contrasting shirt colors with their suits. Men should note that facial hair tends to obscure the countenance.

5 WEAR CLOTHING THAT FITS PROPERLY.

Clothing that is too snug draws the attention of the observer away from your face in addition to declaring to the world that you are not conscientious about how you look.

Clothing that is too baggy does the same thing. People notice that your clothes do not fit well and wonder if you have been ill or have lost a great deal of weight.

Suit jacket too loose   Suit jacket too tight   Sleeve of jacket too short   Sleeve of jacket too long

Conscientious attention to details when preparing your wardrobe will prevent the eyes of others from being drawn to flaws in your presentation of yourself.

Trousers too short   Trousers too long   Trousers too tight

Many times people do strange things with clothing that does fit well, such as pulling a belt too tight or constantly tugging at a skirt when seated, pulling the hem out of proportion.

Anything unusual will draw an observer's attention. If the attention is on the garment, it is not on your face.

6 AVOID EYE TRAPS.

• *EYES ARE ATTRACTED TO SKIN.*

Low or plunging necklines, shirts or blouses with several buttons open, bare shoulder designs (sundresses, off the shoulder sleeves, strapless or halter tops), slits in skirts, low cut backs, and bare midriff styles—all draw the eye of the observer to see just how far the opening goes.

Bare leg designs such as short skirts or pants (shorts) draw the observer's attention to the legs.

• *EYES ARE ATTRACTED TO TEASING.*

Sheer fabrics and clinging fabrics reveal by suggestion rather than by fact. The effect of this suggestiveness is a greater allurement than bold nakedness would be.

Bright spots of color strategically placed on a garment or lacy designs on sheer hose for women draw the eyes of observers away from the face.

• *EYES ARE ATTRACTED TO WRITTEN MESSAGES.*

Many of the messages on tee-shirts draw the

eyes of the observer simply to read what is written. This distraction is magnified when the message is one of a double or suggestive meaning.

The wearer of the garment must realize that the observer's eyes are drawn away from the face to that portion of the anatomy where the message appears.

- *EYES ARE ATTRACTED TO FADS.*

Unusual details on garments such as jagged hemlines, garrish color contrasts (e.g., clashing colors or loud colors of hose), details placed in unexpected places on a garment, strange lines in the garment design, and jangling jewelry all draw the observer's curiosity and attention.

- *EYES FOLLOW THE LINES OF ACCESSORIES.*

A string of beads knotted low and hanging to the waist, for example, will draw the observer's eyes down the length of the string. Long scarves, fringes, chain belts around the hips, sweatshirts or sweaters knotted around the hips all have this effect.

Long, dangling earrings draw attention away from the face to the shoulders. Sandals which lace up to the knee draw attention the entire length of the cords. Shoes (especially with high heels) that have open, slipper-type backs draw attention to ankles.

- *EYES ARE ATTRACTED TO EXCESSES.*

Cosmetics should be used to enhance your facial appearance by minimizing flaws in skin. Excessive use of these products (e.g., unnatural colors, heavy eye makeup, false eyelashes, or makeup improperly applied) draws attention away from the spirit of your countenance. Excessively long nails and dark bright shades of nail polish will draw attention to hands and feet.

7 PRACTICE PERSONAL DISCIPLINES OF NEATNESS, CLEANLINESS, EXERCISE, AND WEIGHT CONTROL.

A grateful spirit and good stewardship demand that clothes be kept clean, orderly, and well-pressed. The most expensive garment can look shoddy if not properly maintained.

Personal hygiene and fitness are necessary as well, if flaws are not to distract the observer's eye.

Proper rest and carefully exercised discipline in scheduling obligations all contribute to the total impression of a Spirit-controlled personality.

The outer man cannot present a positive message unless the inner man is properly nurtured day by day.

8 STAND TALL—SIT GRACEFULLY.[2]

Sagging posture draws attention to itself; slouching in a chair communicates a lack of alertness and often disrespect. Flaws in posture draw the observer's attention away from your face to the problem.

HEAD—chin parallel to the floor; ears directly over shoulders.

NECK—upright, straight column rising from the shoulders.

STOMACH—pulled in and up; keep these muscles in tone.

KNEES—slightly flexed; never locked.

SHOULDERS—rolled back and down, relaxed rather than stiff.

BACK—straight and tall, having only a slight curve at the waistline.

DERRIERE—the pelvis should be tipped somewhat down and under.

FEET—weight evenly distributed over balls and heels. Feet should be parallel to each other—neither pointed out nor in.

Knees must always be kept together when sitting. For the best impression and good health, legs should be crossed at the ankles. Your body should not look as though it were "draped" over the chair.

9 MATCH YOUR CHOICE OF CLOTHING TO THE OCCASION OR ACTIVITY.

Discretion or deference means wearing the right thing at the right time to the right place.

Wearing the wrong thing to an activity calls attention to its inappropriateness; therefore, the eye of the observer is distracted from your countenance.

When preparing to attend an event, decide what is the goal of the activity and what are its requirements in terms of modesty and propriety. Do not simply evaluate what everyone else in the situation is going to do or what is the least that is expected. Set a good example for others.

Casual   Business or Church   Formal

Wise stewardship would require that the garments you choose be more classical in style so that they can be worn out rather than phased out of style.

Scripture also teaches that your moderation should be known unto all men. To be deliberately years behind in style when there is no problem with convictions is to make a mockery of the separation God requires and to place unnecessary barriers between you and the people you desire to reach with the message of the Gospel.

The casual look can be "dressed up" to fit the occasion.

Where no matter of conviction is involved, it is generally good advice to not be the first to adopt a new style, nor to be the last to discard an old one.

10 SAY THE RIGHT THINGS WITH YOUR EYES.

It has been said that "the eyes are the window of the soul." Your eyes reveal your thoughts and attitudes.

Your eyes can communicate a spirit of boldness versus a spirit of discretion. Staring at another person, looking too long or with implied intimacy, winking with a flirtatious eye, and challenging someone's authority are all done with eyes that have not been brought into proper discipline.

WHAT ARE THESE EYES SAYING?

Eyes reveal a person's character. Insincerity, dishonesty, or treachery are often conveyed with eyes that avoid contact with the observer.

Expressive eyes will draw the observer's attention to your countenance. "Keep your heart with all diligence" so that your expression is an edifying one.

PROJECT:

A. Study the following words in Scripture by using your concordance: countenance, eyes, modest, apparel, attire, adorning, and hair. Summarize in your own words God's instructions to His children concerning their appearance.

B. Take the following quiz to demonstrate your understanding of problems in appearance which Christians should avoid.

Can you identify the eyetraps in these pictures?

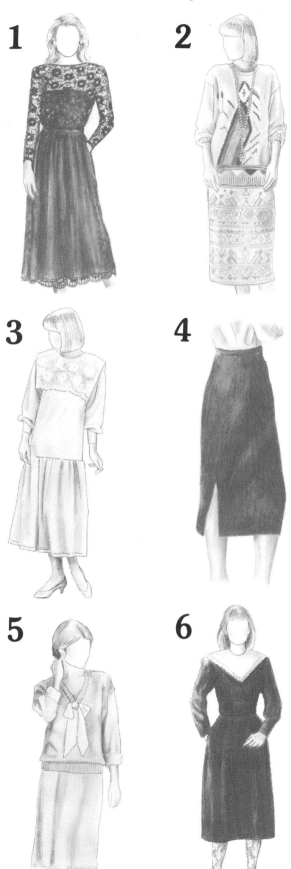

1

2

3

4

5

6

C. Your choice of clothing gives a message. In the light of what you have learned, go through your closet and evaluate each outfit. Where would the observer's eyes be drawn when that outfit is worn? What is the overall message given by your wardrobe? Do any items need to be discarded because they give a confusing or negative message?

D. Review a clothing catalog or magazine, and evaluate where the observer's eyes would be drawn for each outfit you see pictured. What is the message conveyed by the clothing and the posture of the model?

E. Visit a public place such as a shopping mall or airport. Observe how people passing by are dressed. Evaluate not only clothing, but also posture and movement of the people you observe. What messages are conveyed by the various outfits, responses, and movements?

Can you identify five things this lady has done to make it easy for you to focus on her countenance?

FOR FURTHER DETAIL AND STUDY:

[1]*Color Me Beautiful* by Carole Jackson, Ballantine Books, New York.

[2]*Beauty and the Best* by Beneth Peter Jones, Bob Jones University Press, Greenville, South Carolina.

Your Clothes Say It For You by Elizabeth Rice Handford, Sword Publications, Murfreesboro, Tennessee.

NOTES

DIAGRAMS

● *Wording:*_____

_____

_____

_____

"The woman shall not wear that which pertaineth unto a man, neither shall a man put on a woman's garment: for all that do so are abomination unto the Lord thy God" (Deuteronomy 22:5).

HOW A TEENAGER "STOOD ALONE" IN THE AREA OF DRESS.

Every girl in a west coast high school wore jeans or pants except the three daughters of a pastor. In a student body of 2,100, they were quite conspicuous.

One day the teacher in a psychology class singled out one of these teenage daughters and said, "Why do you wear dresses every day to school?"

At first the girl was shocked and did not answer him, but simply put her head down. The teacher persisted, "Tell me, I really want to know. Does your father make you do it?"

The class grew totally silent as the teenager politely said, "No he doesn't."

"Is it because of your religion?" retorted the professor.

"No," replied the teenager.

"Why do you wear dresses then?"

She replied in a gentle but determined voice, "God made me a woman, I'm proud to be a woman, and I want to look like one."

Then the teacher surprised the entire class by complimenting the girl for wearing a dress and offering extra credit for the rest of the week to any other girl who would also wear a dress!

No other girl wore a dress the rest of the week, but the Christian teenager benefited by the extra credit and was the only one in the class to get a final grade of an A+.

How will the commitment to be a one-woman man or a one-man woman affect our moral standards?

☐ _____

"For this is the will of God, even your sanctification, that ye should abstain from fornication: That every one of you should know how to possess his vessel in sanctification and honour" (I Thessalonians 4:3-4).

● _____

". . . It is good for a man not to touch a woman" (I Corinthians 7:1).

● _____

"Therefore shall a man leave his father and his mother, and shall cleave unto his wife: and they shall be one flesh" (Genesis 2:24).

HOW DOES A COVENANT DIFFER FROM A CONTRACT?

- A covenant is based on trust between parties. A contract is based on distrust.

- A covenant is based on unlimited responsibility. A contract is based on limited liability.

- A covenant cannot be broken in new circumstances. A contract can be voided by mutual consent.

Based on the covenant of marriage, the following balance is required to achieve true fulfillment.

Spiritual Emphasis—	60%
Psychological Emphasis—	30%
Physical Emphasis—	10%

● _____

_____

● _____

_____

"For I am jealous over you with godly jealousy: for I have espoused you to one husband, that I may present you as a chaste virgin to Christ" (II Corinthians 11:2).

Years ago the fear of contracting syphilis or gonorrhea from promiscuous relationships was a deterrent to immorality. When penicillin was discovered to "cure" these diseases, a new sexual freedom was encouraged.

However, God will not be mocked. If man finds a remedy for the immediate physical consequences of one sin, God will bring judgment in greater and more devastating ways. Medical researchers now admit defeat in their war against venereal diseases, because for *every* "cure" that is discovered, new and more lethal strains of drug-resistant infections develop.[1]

For example, present estimates are that twenty million Americans are afflicted by herpes II. This disease does not respond to penicillin treatment, and it has devastating physical and psychological consequences.

1 James C. Hill, National Institute of Allergy and Infectious Diseases, *U.S. News & World Report*, February 28, 1983, pp. 35-36.

"For the lips of a strange woman drop as an honeycomb, and her mouth is smoother than oil: But her end is bitter as wormwood, sharp as a two-edged sword. Her feet go down to death; her steps take hold on hell.

". . . Remove thy way far from her, and come not nigh the door of her house[3] . . . Lest strangers be filled with thy wealth; and thy labours be in the house of a stranger; And thou mourn at the last, when thy flesh and thy body are consumed, And say, How have I hated instruction, and my heart despised reproof" (Proverbs 5:3–5, 8, 10–13).

• *Wording:* _____

_____

What is true maturity?

• _____

_____

_____

How will a commitment to God's design in marriage provide the basis for victory in our thought life?

☐ _____

_____

"Finally, brethren, whatsoever things are true, whatsoever things are honest, whatsoever things are just, whatsoever things are pure, whatsoever things are lovely, whatsoever things are of good report; if there be any virtue, and if there be any praise, think on these things" (Philippians 4:8).

In order to save our delight for the marriage partner whom God brings into our life, we must not look lustfully at others. This is such a serious violation of God's concept of a one-woman man or a one-man woman that He equates it with the sin of adultery.

"But I say unto you, That whosoever looketh on a woman to lust after her hath committed adultery with her already in his heart" (Matthew 5:28).

This means that if somebody invites us to look at sensual pictures, pornographic magazines, lewd movies, or immodestly dressed people, we must say, "I've given my life to Jesus, and I'm not able to do that."

Whatever response we receive, we can be confident that we have pleased the Lord, we have been a valuable example, and we have avoided the destruction of mental or physical fornication.

"For the ways of man are before the eyes of the Lord, and he pondereth all his goings. His own iniquities shall take the wicked himself, and he shall be holden with the cords of his sins. He shall die without instruction; and in the greatness of his folly he shall go astray" (Proverbs 5:21–23).

Conquering lustful thoughts is one of the most important battles that any Christian will ever face, because the thoughts of our heart determine secret motives, outward actions, and life direction.

For this reason, God wants us to be *". . . bringing into captivity every thought to the obedience of Christ"* (II Corinthians 10:5).

Job took an important step by making the following commitment:

• _____

"I made a covenant with mine eyes; why then should I think upon a maid?" (Job 31:1).

• _____

_____

Lustful thoughts or actions will destroy our mind, will, and emotions and will distort our view of marriage.

If we are being defeated by lustful thoughts or actions, we can experience consistent victory over them by learning and applying the seven steps of action explained in the book, *The Eagle Story.*

"Mortify therefore your members which are upon the earth; fornication, uncleanness, inordinate affection, evil concupiscence, and covetousness, which is idolatry: For which things' sake the wrath of God cometh on the children of disobedience" (Colossians 3:5-6).

☐ _____

"Flee also youthful lusts . . ." (II Timothy 2:22).

IS MASTURBATION SINFUL?

Scripture gives us a clear and definite "yes."

The seed of man belongs to the Lord in an even greater way than man's body since it is through the seed that God gives the heritage of children. The swift judgment that God brought upon Onan for "spilling his seed on the ground"

(Genesis 38:9) should be a clear warning to all men that it is not to be misused whether in a marriage situation as in Onan's case or in personal gratification.

The willful act of self-gratification is certainly "sinful uncleanness" since God identifies the accidental discharge of seed as uncleanness.

"And if any man's seed of copulation go out from him, then he shall wash all his flesh in water, and be unclean until the even" (Leviticus 15:16).

"Now the works of the flesh are manifest, which are these; Adultery, fornication, uncleanness, lasciviousness" (Galatians 5:19).

Additional New Testament references to uncleanness are Ephesians 4:19, Ephesians 5:3, Colossians 3:5, and I Thessalonians 4:7.

Those who engage in self-gratification whether male or female, must yield the members of their bodies as instruments to uncleanness. This violates the instructions in Romans 6:13-14, *"Neither yield ye your members as instruments of unrighteousness unto sin: but yield yourselves unto God, as those that are alive from the dead, and your members as instruments of righteousness unto God. For sin shall not have dominion over you. . . ."*

Once a person fulfills the lusts of the flesh in a way that God did not intend, it often becomes a binding habit which brings further guilt. This sin will not separate a Christian from eternal life, but it will certainly damage his fellowship with the Lord as further explained in Romans 6:15-16:

"What then? shall we sin, because we are not under the law, but under grace? God forbid. Know ye not, that to whom ye yield yourselves servants to obey, his servants ye are to whom ye obey; whether of sin unto death, or of obedience unto righteousness?"

Many have been caught in the destructive habit of self-gratification, but God wants to assure us that this sin can be conquered by entering into our victory in Christ.

"But God be thanked, that ye were the servants of sin, but ye have obeyed from the heart that form of doctrine which was delivered you. Being then made free from sin, ye became the servants of righteousness" (Romans 6:17-18).

". . . For as ye have yielded your members servants to uncleanness and to iniquity unto iniquity; even so now yield your members servants to righteousness unto holiness" (Romans 6:19).

NOTES

DIAGRAMS

HOW A YOUNG MAN CONQUERED LUSTFUL HABITS BY FULLY FOLLOWING SCRIPTURAL GUIDELINES.

"For five years I had struggled with the sin of masturbation. I tried to overcome it in my own strength, but each attempt just brought failure and discouragement.

"Then I attended my first Basic Seminar in 1981. I learned why I had been unsuccessful in overcoming this habit and began to apply the steps that were given on overcoming it. There was one step, however, which I purposely omitted. That was the step of being accountable to a God-given authority. I would not humble myself and go to my parents. Because of this, I never had lasting success.

"I attended two more Basic Seminars and in each one the Lord showed me that I had to apply that sixth step if I was going to have lasting success in overcoming this habit. But in each case I refused to humble myself and to be accountable to my parents.

"Finally, at this year's Seminar, the Lord seemed to be saying to me, 'If you don't become accountable to your parents and conquer this habit, you will not go any further in your spiritual growth.'

After the Seminar I did become accountable to my parents, and I'm very happy to report that I have now been able to overcome this habit by applying *all* seven steps.

"As a result of conquering this habit and controlling my thought life, the Lord has made me much more sensitive to people whom I have offended in the past. One was a former employer. I went back and asked him to forgive me. He did so.

"There is no way you could ever know how my life has been blessed by the victory that I am now experiencing in this area."

A young man from Mississippi

HOW CLEANSING THE HOME BECAME THE KEY TO VICTORY OVER LUST

"This letter has been in the making for a long time. I want to express my gratitude. Over many years I could not get victory over temporary bouts of masturbation. While attending a Seminar you explained seven steps for conquering this sin.

"You also spoke of removing 'leaven' from the house. You identified leaven as anything which gives Satan operating room. I came home and destroyed all of the textbooks in my office which were used basically for sensual stimulation. From that day the victory was won."

A father from Missouri

What steps can a Christian take to begin conquering masturbation?

● _____
_____

● *Wording:* _____
_____
_____
_____

How will commitment to God's design in marriage rule out "homosexuality"?

☐ _____

● _____

HOW DID "A CRIME AGAINST NATURE" DESTROY THE "LIGHT" AND LIFE OF A BEAUTIFUL CITY?

The city of Sodom was a tourist attraction

A wealthy and attractive family arrived at the city of their dreams. Its setting and surroundings were the most beautiful in the entire region, rivaling the lushness and prosperity of the famed entrance to Egypt.

The family received an enthusiastic welcome. The father was soon appointed as an official of the

287

city, and his daughters caught the eyes of eligible young men in the community.

Everything seemed to be ideal except for one shocking condition. This beautiful city had become tolerant toward deviant forms of immorality. The citizens assumed that those who practiced this abhorrent "lifestyle" had a right to their own preference in the matter and deserved the privacy to carry it out.

The righteous father, who was now a city elder, grieved over the "rights" that were demanded by and given to these men. He concluded that his influence was not enough to change the mind of the city; thus, all he could do was to live his own life and try to protect his own family.

Neither he nor the citizens of that city realized the full extent of what was actually taking place until the turmoil of one night. The events of that night have been recorded and documented so that they could serve as a warning and reminder to the citizens and officials of every other city in the world.

As you read this account, ponder the following questions: How widespread did the perversion in this city actually turn out to be? Why would such perversion spread so rapidly? What prompts this perversion to become violent? Does a physical affliction hinder the pursuit of this perversion?

THE ACTUAL ACCOUNT

"And there came two angels to Sodom at even; and Lot sat in the gate of Sodom: and Lot seeing them rose up to meet them; and he bowed himself with his face toward the ground;

"And he said, Behold now, my lords, turn in, I pray you, into your servant's house, and tarry all night, and wash your feet, and ye shall rise up early, and go on your ways. And they said, Nay; but we will abide in the street all night.

"And he pressed upon them greatly; and they turned in unto him, and entered into his house; and he made them a feast, and did bake unleavened bread, and they did eat.

"But before they lay down, the men of the city, even the men of Sodom, compassed the house round, both old and young, all the people from every quarter:

"And they called unto Lot, and said unto him, Where are the men which came in to thee this night? bring them out unto us, that we may know them.

"And Lot went out at the door unto them, and shut the door after him,

"And said, I pray you, brethren, do not so wickedly.

"Behold now, I have two daughters which have not known man; let me, I pray you, bring them out unto you, and do ye to them as is good in your eyes: only unto these men do nothing; for therefore came they under the shadow of my roof.

THE VIOLENT NATURE OF THE PROBLEM

"And they said, Stand back. And they said again, This one fellow came in to sojourn, and he will needs be a judge: now will we deal worse with thee, than with them. And they pressed sore upon the man, even Lot, and came near to break the door.

"But the men put forth their hand, and pulled Lot into the house to them, and shut to the door.

"And they smote the men that were at the door of the house with blindness, both small and great: so that they wearied themselves to find the door. . . .

"And when the morning arose, then the angels hastened Lot, saying, Arise, take thy wife, and thy two daughters, which are here; lest thou be consumed in the iniquity of the city. . . .

Salt formations reminiscent of the pillar of salt that Lot's wife became when she disobeyed the Lord and looked back at the burning city of Sodom are still present in the Dead Sea.

"Remember Lot's wife."

"Then the Lord rained upon Sodom and upon Gomorrah brimstone and fire from the Lord out of heaven; . . . But his wife looked back from behind him, and she became a pillar of salt" (Genesis 19:1–11, 15, 24, 26).

David Alexander

Salt rocks, parched earth, and an acrid smell near the site of Sodom are all that remain of the once beautiful city.

WHY ARE LAWS AGAINST SODOMY VITAL AND BENEFICIAL FOR ALL CITIZENS, INCLUDING SODOMITES?

The first purpose of a law is to give instruction to those who violate universal standards of conduct which bring destruction to themselves and to those around them.

"Knowing this, that the law is not made for a righteous man, but for the lawless and disobedient, for the ungodly and for sinners, for unholy and profane, for murderers of fathers and murderers of mothers, for manslayers, For whoremongers, for them that defile themselves with mankind, for menstealers, for liars, for perjured persons, and if there be any other thing that is contrary to sound doctrine" (I Timothy 1:9–10).

Sodomy is a self-consuming passion which will not satisfy those who engage in it. Instead it will produce enslavement to ever-increasing cravings for fulfillment. If no law exists to prohibit sodomy or, worse yet, if laws are made to protect it, thousands of unsuspecting citizens will be drawn into it without knowing of its dangers.

WHY IS IT IMPOSSIBLE TO CONTAIN SODOMY ONCE IT IS LEGALIZED?

The true nature of sodomy was explained in the testimony of expert witnesses in the 1983 lawsuit of Gay Rights vs. Texas A & M University. The following is an excerpt from the record of that trial.

"Dr. Charles Webb testified at the trial of this case that homosexual men commonly 'have twenty to thirty [sexual] contacts in a single night' (TR. 75). Dr. Webb further testified that the anonymous nature of these homosexual contacts makes disease control extremely difficult among homosexuals: 'The anonymous contact, of course, makes it almost impossible for a venereal disease control worker to find a person identified as a contact' (TR. 71).

"Other sources certainly corroborate Dr. Webb's testimony [of the promiscuity of homosexuals]. For example, the Kinsey Institute studies indicate that approximately fifty percent of homosexual males have between one hundred and one thousand different (usually anonymous) sexual partners, while almost thirty percent of such homosexuals have had more than one thousand such sexual contacts" (A. Bell and M. Weinberg, *supra* at 308).

(Quoted from *Brief Amicus Curiae* of Dallas Doctors against A.I.D.S., Inc. in Support of Defendants-Appellees, No. 82-2366, "Gay Rights, et al., Plaintiffs-Appellants vs. Texas A & M University, et al.," page 15.)

HOW HAS SODOMY BEEN DEFINED IN CRIMINAL LAW?

Sodomy is the crime of unnatural copulation. From early times, sodomy has been referred to in statutes and court cases as "the crime against nature" by a man with a man, by a man with an animal (beastiality), or in an unnatural manner by a man with a woman. (Definition is taken from the *Family Legal Guide*.)

HOW HAS SODOMY BEEN DEFINED IN GOD'S LAW?

"Thou shalt not lie with mankind, as with womankind: it is abomination.

"Neither shalt thou lie with any beast to defile thyself therewith: neither shall any woman stand before a beast to lie down thereto: it is confusion.

"Defile not ye yourselves in any of these things: for in all these the nations are defiled which I cast out before you:

"And the land is defiled: therefore I do visit the iniquity thereof upon it, and the land itself vomiteth out her inhabitants.

"Ye shall therefore keep my statutes and my judgments, and shall not commit any of these abominations; neither any of your own nation, nor any stranger that sojourneth among you:

"(For all these abominations have the men of the land done, which were before you, and the land is defiled;)

"That the land spue not you out also, when ye defile it, as it spued out the nations that were before you.

"For whosoever shall commit any of these abominations, even the souls that commit them shall be cut off from among their people.

"Therefore shall ye keep mine ordinance, that ye commit not any one of these abominable customs, which were committed before you, and that ye defile not yourselves therein: I am the Lord your God" (Leviticus 18:22–30).

Doré Bible Illustrations

The Amorites were an immoral people in Canaan upon whom *". . . the Lord cast down great stones from heaven . . ."* to destroy them. (See Joshua 10:11.)

WHY IS IT IMPORTANT TO ACCURATELY DEFINE THE BIBLICAL TERMS RELATED TO SODOMY?

One of the deceptive characteristics of those who practice perversion is their tendency to avoid understanding its true nature by redefining it. As a result, we are now barraged by the media with such misleading terms as "homosexuality," "gays," "gay rights," "toleration," "liberation," "discrimination," "right to privacy," and "consenting adults."

By accepting and using these terms rather than God's terms, we lose an honest perspective in any discussion of the subject. Man's terms remove the moral implications of a sinful perversion and treat it as an activity outside God's realm of control.

It is for this reason that God warns us not to try to explain spiritual concepts with human expressions. (See I Corinthians 2:13.)

Although some modern translations of the Bible use the word *homosexuality*, the following are more precise Biblical terms used by God to describe and condemn this perversion.

Notice that the terms, while precise, do not describe the actual details of sodomy. This discretion is in harmony with the warning of Scripture, *"For it is a shame even to speak of those things which are done of them in secret" (Ephesians 5:12)*. Discussing the details of sodomy will produce a toleration of it as described in the following lines:

Lust [sodomy] is a monster of such awful mien,
That to be hated needs but to be seen,
But seen too oft, familiar with face,
We first endure, then pity, then embrace.
Alexander Pope

Doré Bible Illustrations

Canaan, the grandson of Noah, was cursed by Noah for "uncovering Noah's nakedness." Canaan's descendants corrupted the land with sodomy.

SCRIPTURAL TERMS OF "HOMOSEXUALITY"

1 SODOMY qâdêsh

The Hebrew term for *sodomite* literally means "devoted to evil." It refers to male prostitutes devoted to the worship of pagan fertility gods.

*"There shall be no whore of the daughters of Israel, nor a **sodomite** of the sons of Israel"* (Deuteronomy 23:17).

The word *sodomy* is a proper reminder of the abominable practices of the men of Sodom and of the judgment that God brought upon them.

God commended King Asa for moving against the sodomites during his reign, *"And Asa did that which was right in the eyes of the Lord, as did David his father. And he took away the **sodomites** out of the land . . ."* (I Kings 15:11-12).

King Josiah also exercised his authority when *". . . he brake down the houses of the **sodomites**, that were by the house of the Lord . . ."* (II Kings 23:7).

There are several important points that must be understood about sodomites from the Genesis 19 account.

- Sodomites love darkness to carry on their "works of darkness." *"But before they lay down . . ."* (v. 4).
- Sodomy is not confined to adults: *". . . Both old and young . . ."* (v. 4).
- The craving of perverted gratification requires continual recruiting and assaulting, which soon affects everyone in the city: *". . . All the people from every quarter"* (v. 4).
- Sodomites despise authority: *". . . This one fellow came in to sojourn, and he will needs be a judge . . ."* (v. 9).
- Sodomites become violent with any who stand in their way: *". . . Now will we deal worse with thee . . ."* (v. 9).
- Sodomites do not allow a physical handicap to deter them: *". . . With blindness . . . they wearied themselves to find the door"* (v. 11).
- Sodomites tend to associate with religious form. *". . . The houses of the sodomites . . . were by the house of the Lord . . ."* (II Kings 23:7).

2 ABOMINATION tô'êbâh

The Hebrew word denotes something extremely disgusting, the practice of which provokes aversion; that which is abhorrent and to be regarded with horror. God's Law defines sodomy as abomination.

*"Thou shalt not lie with mankind, as with womankind: it is **abomination**"* (Leviticus 18:22).

The related activity of sodomite men wearing women's clothing is also condemned as an abomination. *". . . Neither shall a man put on a woman's garment: for all that do so are **abomination** unto the Lord thy God"* (Deuteronomy 22:5).

The spread of infectious diseases by sodomites adds new understanding to why the Israelites were to destroy all the inhabitants of Canaan.

*"And there were also sodomites in the land: and they did according to all the **abominations** of the nations which the Lord cast out before the children of Israel"* (I Kings 14:24).

3 VILE AFFECTIONS atimia pathŏs

The Greek word for *vile* means "that which brings infamy, disgrace, dishonor, reproach, and shame." The word *affections* identifies "passions, sexual lust, evil emotions, concupiscence."

The term *vile affections* is precisely chosen by God to identify the perversion of sodomy. *"For this cause God gave them up unto **vile affections**: for even their women did change the natural use into that which is against nature: And likewise also the men, leaving the natural use of the woman, burned in their lust one toward another; men with men working that which is unseemly, and receiving in themselves that recompence of their error which was meet"* (Romans 1:26-27).

4 BURNING WITH LUST ŏrĕxis ĕkkaiō

The word *burning* in the Greek means "to inflame deeply, to set on fire, to consume, to burn vehemently, to be intense, fierce, to act impetuously with great force." The word *lust* relates to the excitement of the mind and the emotions with sensual pleasure.

As a raging forest fire destroys whatever is in its path, so the burning lusts of perversion devour more and more of that which belongs to others. *". . . The men, leaving the natural use of the women, **burned in their lust** one toward another . . ."* (Romans 1:27).

5 DISHONORING THE BODY atimazō sōma

The Greek word for *dishonor* means "to treat with contempt as something vile or worthless, to abuse, to treat roughly, to mistreat, to render infamous."

*"Wherefore God also gave them up to uncleanness through the lusts of their own hearts, to **dishonor their own bodies** between themselves"* (Romans 1:24).

It is important to note that the vile affections of sodomy are a by-product of rejecting God-given moral restraints which He has written in every person's heart and conscience. (See Romans 2:14–15.)

6 LUSTING FOR STRANGE FLESH
hĕtĕrŏs sarx

The Greek word for *strange* means "foreign, alien, inappropriate, improper." The word *flesh* relates to the body and the carnal human nature.

*"Even as Sodom and Gomorrha, and the cities about them in like manner, giving themselves over to fornication, and **going after strange flesh**, are set forth for an example, suffering the vengeance of eternal fire"* (Jude 7).

Notice that the perversion of sodomy follows a man's decision to reject God's moral Law and surrender to the demands of sensual gratification.

Doré Bible Illustrations

God's judgment of Sodom and Gomorrah was to be a continuing warning to the entire world.

7 FILTHY DREAMERS ĕnupniazŏmai

The Greek word *filthy* relates to licentiousness, lasciviousness, and wantonness (lewdness or negligence of restraint) coupled with *dreamer*, "one who conceives vile and impure thoughts, mental pictures, and imaginations."

This term is used to depict the evil men of Sodom and Gomorrah. *"Likewise also these **filthy dreamers** defile the flesh, despise dominion, and speak evil of dignities"* (Jude 8).

Notice the correlation of perversion and rebellion against moral disciplines and legal authorities.

8 ABUSERS OF THEMSELVES
arsĕnŏkŏites

This Greek word is another term for sodomite or one who has carnal copulation in any unnatural way.

*"Know ye not that the unrighteous shall not inherit the kingdom of God? Be not deceived: neither fornicators . . . nor **abusers of themselves with mankind**"* (I Corinthians 6:9).

In this verse both fornication and sodomy are listed as sins of the body. God warns against the self-destruction of fornication: *"Flee fornication. Every sin that a man doeth is without the body; but he that committeth fornication sinneth against his own body"* (I Corinthians 6:18).

Those who commit the perversion of sodomy experience a unique judgment of God in their physical bodies. *". . . Men with men working that which is unseemly, and receiving in themselves that recompence of their error which was meet"* (Romans 1:27).

9 DEFILERS OF THEMSELVES
arsĕnŏkŏites

Notice that the Greek word that was used for *abusers of themselves* is translated as *defilers of themselves* in the following verse.

*"Knowing this, that the law is not made for a righteous man, but for the lawless and disobedient, for the ungodly and for sinners, for unholy and profane, . . . For whoremongers, for them that **defile themselves** with mankind . . ."* (I Timothy 1:9–10).

10 VIOLATING NATURE
para phusis

The Greek word for *against* means "to be contrary to" or "to go beyond that which God designed." The word for *nature* refers to "growth by reproduction" or to "that which God designed as normal, wholesome, and healthy."

*". . . Their women did **change the natural use into that which is against nature**: And likewise also the men, **leaving the natural use** of the woman . . ."* (Romans 1:26–27).

11 UNSEEMLY (SHAMEFUL) LUSTS aschēmŏsunē

The phrase *shameful lusts* is translated in the following verse as *unseemly*. Its Greek origin means "indecent, morally offensive, unfit to be seen or heard."

"*. . . Men with men working that which is **unseemly**, and receiving in themselves that recompence of their error which was meet*" (Romans 1:27).

12 EFFEMINATE malakŏs

The Greek word translated *effeminate* refers to a man who takes on the qualities, characteristics, or appearance of a woman; one who is not manly or masculine.

"*Know ye not that the unrighteous shall not inherit the kingdom of God? . . . Neither fornicators, . . . nor **effeminate**, . . . shall inherit the kingdom of God*" (I Corinthians 6:9–10).

13 WICKEDNESS rah

The Hebrew word for *wicked* means "evil, harmful, hurtful; causing misery, sorrow, trouble, and wretchedness." The word *wickedly* means "spoiling, making good for nothing, afflicting, harmfully."

God identifies sodomites as wicked people and condemns their actions as wickedness. "*But the men of Sodom were **wicked** and sinners before the Lord exceedingly*" (Genesis 13:13).

Lot said to the men of Sodom, "*. . . I pray you, brethren, do not so **wickedly***" (Genesis 19:7).

The wicked perversions of the men of Sodom were repeated years later by the tribe of Benjamin. A Levite went to Bethlehem to appeal to his concubine. She had become a harlot, but decided to return with him. As they traveled, they came to the city of Gibeah, but no one would give them lodging for the night.

Finally, an elderly man came in from the field and invited them into his home. However, that night sodomites surrounded his house and beat on the door. They shouted, "*. . . Bring forth the man that came into thine house, that we may know him*" (Judges 19:22).

Notice the similarity of the actions and attitudes of the men in this city to the men of Sodom (Genesis 19).

Doré Bible Illustrations

The Levite finds his concubine dead.

"*. . . The master . . . went out unto them, and said unto them, Nay, my brethren, nay, I pray you, do not so wickedly; seeing that this man is come into mine house, do not this folly. Behold, here is my daughter a maiden, and his concubine; them I will bring out now, and humble ye them, and do with them what seemeth good unto you: but unto this man do not so vile a thing.*

"*But the men would not hearken to him: so the man took his concubine, and brought her forth unto them; and they knew her, and abused her all the night until the morning: and when the day began to spring, they let her go. Then came the woman in the dawning of the day, and fell down at the door of the man's house where her lord was, till it was light.*

"*And her lord rose up in the morning, and opened the doors of the house, and went out to go his way: and, behold, the woman his concubine was fallen down at the door of the house . . .*" (Judges 19:23-27).

When the Levite reported what had happened, the entire nation of Israel was horrified and demanded that the men of Gibeah be brought out for punishment. However, the extent of the evil influence which the sodomites of Gibeah had over the Benjamites was revealed when the whole tribe gathered together to defend the sodomites.

As a result, civil war broke out and the tribe of Benjamin was destroyed except for seven hundred men who fled to the mountains.

14 REPROBATE adŏkimŏs nŏus

The Greek word for *reprobation* identifies a mind that is void of moral judgment. It refers to those who have received strong delusions because of their own moral impurity and now believe the lie that man is the dictator of his own destiny.

*"And even as they [sodomites] did not like to retain God in their knowledge, God gave them over to a **reprobate mind**, to do those things which are not convenient"* (Romans 1:28).

God made us so that all aspects of life would be related to the spiritual drives in each person. When the mental, emotional, and volitional drives (psychological functions) are integrated with the spiritual, and when the physical drives are disciplined by spiritual standards, inner **balance** and **freedom** result, which make it possible to live in harmony with God's standards.

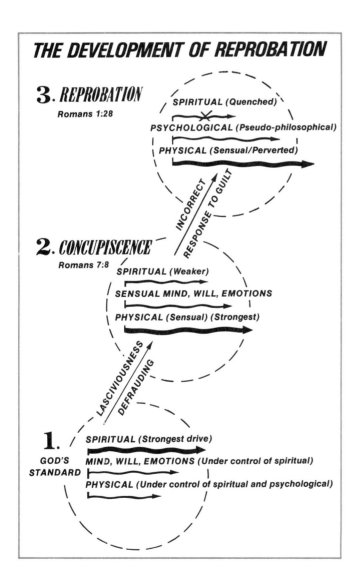

THE DEVELOPMENT OF REPROBATION

3. REPROBATION
Romans 1:28

SPIRITUAL (Quenched)
PSYCHOLOGICAL (Pseudo-philosophical)
PHYSICAL (Sensual/Perverted)

INCORRECT RESPONSE TO GUILT

2. CONCUPISCENCE
Romans 7:8

SPIRITUAL (Weaker)
SENSUAL MIND, WILL, EMOTIONS
PHYSICAL (Sensual) (Strongest)

LASCIVIOUSNESS DEFRAUDING

1.
GOD'S STANDARD

SPIRITUAL (Strongest drive)
MIND, WILL, EMOTIONS (Under control of spiritual)
PHYSICAL (Under control of spiritual and psychological)

When the sensual drives are allowed to become stronger than the spiritual drives, an inner tension builds in the mind, will, and emotions. One part of us wants to be spiritual; the other part wants to be sensual.

These two opposing forces will result in double-mindedness. (See James 1:8.) At this point many will try to combine these opposing forces in sensual forms of religious worship.

WHY IS IT TRUE THAT SODOMY DOES NOT DESCRIBE A "CLASS OF PEOPLE" BUT A TYPE OF SIN?

The statement, "Some people are born homosexuals" is not true. It is true that every person is born with a sin nature. That sin nature is capable of all kinds of vile affections. In order to practice them, however, a person must first reject the moral laws of God which are written in his heart (See Romans 2:15) and then surrender himself to sensuality. (See Romans 1:24.)

The false notion that sodomites are "born that way" leads to the political chaos described in the following quotes:

"It is no longer a matter of whether homosexuals will achieve political power, so much as what they will try to do with it. Will they demand absolute sexual freedom as in San Francisco? Will this challenge to traditional values stir still more hostility and controversy?" (Commentator Harry Reasoner after research on San Francisco).

"Our message to city hall politicians everywhere is that if they think it's difficult to deal with homosexual influences now, they'll be dealing with a total political monster if they pass these bills. They'll face pressures and agonies they've never before dreamed of" (Dr. David Innes, minister in downtown San Francisco).

What if a boy or girl does not have a natural attraction toward the opposite sex? Does this mean that he or she is a "homosexual"?

WHY IS IT UNTRUE THAT ANYONE UNINTERESTED IN THE OPPOSITE SEX IS A "HOMOSEXUAL"?

Some people are born without the ability or the interest to have a physical relationship with one of the opposite sex. These people are called "eunuchs" in Scripture.

Jesus discussed three types of eunuchs in Matthew 19. He explained that some are born eunuchs, some are made eunuchs by men (such as Daniel), and some make themselves eunuchs in a practical sense for the kingdom of heaven's sake (see verse 12). God promises special blessings to eunuchs in this third class. (See Isaiah 56:3–6.)

Not to have a desire or ability for a physical relationship with the opposite sex is one matter; however, to burn with lust toward the same sex is an entirely different matter.

HOW DOES THE SNARE OF UNCONTROLLED LUSTS LEAD TO THE PRISON OF PERVERTED AFFECTIONS?

God designed the physical relationship between a married man and woman to be a strong bonding force. When sexual desires are fulfilled in a perverted way, a similar bonding occurs.

There will be an immediate and lasting association between physical desires and that perversion. Whenever the desires which God intended for marriage return, the lust of the mind will call for the fulfillment of previous perversions. As these burn out, new passions and perversions will be sought after.

When there is mutual respect and proper times of abstinence are practiced in marriage, the joy of the physical relationship is both fulfilling and rewarding.

When perversion occurs either in or out of the marriage relationship, guilt and lust do not allow fulfillment to take place. Perverted lusts can be tremendously powerful; therefore, God warns us to flee them in the same way we would a dreadful plague. (See II Timothy 2:22.)

HOW CAN A "HOMOSEXUAL" OVERCOME VILE AFFECTIONS?

The first vital step for a sodomite to achieve victory is for him to personally accept the Lord Jesus Christ as his Savior from all sin. This step is explained in Romans 10:9–13.

The second step is for him to realize that God has provided victory over every sin, including sodomy. God affirms that the basic temptations which result in sodomy are common to all people.

"There hath no temptation taken you [including vile affections] but such as is common to man: but God is faithful, who will not suffer you to be tempted above that ye are able; but will with the temptation also make a way to escape, that ye may be able to bear it" (I Corinthians 10:13).

Human remedies cannot cure sodomy. Only the power of God's truth and God's grace can bring freedom. Paul affirmed the fact that sin shall not have dominion over us. (See Romans 6:14.) God said, *"Behold, I am the Lord, the God of all flesh: is there any thing too hard for me?"* (Jeremiah 32:27).

Romans six through eight explains how a Christian can enter into victory in Christ and experience freedom from the desire and power of all sin. Many former sodomites have followed these steps and found lasting freedom.

● WORDING:_____

_____

_____

HOW A MAN CONQUERED "HOMOSEXUALITY" BY ENTERING INTO CHRIST'S VICTORY

"I became a Christian many years ago and was exposed to a lot of good Bible teaching as I was growing up. I became active in Christian work and quickly found myself in a leadership position.

"Soon, however, I began to experience major moral defeat. When I came to the Basic Seminar I was looking for answers; they came when I heard the seven steps of conquering moral impurity.

"Although I had known Romans 6–8 for years and had even taught it to others, I lived all my life in moral defeat. I got involved in homosexuality, and no one was aware of my plight. Then I heard of the principles of Christ's death, burial, and resurrection, and the Lord opened my eyes to the way of victory. Now I have complete freedom from the chains of sin."

NOTES

DIAGRAMS

2 CONCEPT:

"Umbrella of protection"

"For rebellion is as the sin of witchcraft, and stubbornness is as iniquity and idolatry" (I Samuel 15:23).

What are the Scriptural terms for "umbrella of protection"?

* _____

_____

"But I would have know, that the head of every man is Christ; and the head of the woman is the man; and the head of Christ is God" (I Corinthians 11:3).

"He shall cover thee with his feathers, and under his wings shalt thou trust: his truth shall be thy shield and buckler" (Psalm 91:4).

Explain the benefit of God-given protection.

* _____

_____

_____

_____

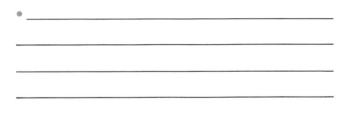

SATAN

PROTECTION

Explain the consequences of rejecting protection.

* _____

_____

_____

_____

How will accepting the concept of authority influence our attitude toward it?

☐ _____

_____

"He, that being often reproved hardeneth his neck, shall suddenly be destroyed, and that without remedy" (Proverbs 29:1).

Should a Christian take part in a demonstration?

* _____

_____

"Thou shalt not follow a multitude to do evil; neither shalt thou speak in a cause to decline after many to wrest judgment" (Exodus 23:2).

How does God want us to view police officers?

* _____

_____

"For he is the minister of God to thee for good. But if thou do that which is evil, be afraid; for he beareth not the sword in vain: for he is the minister of God, a revenger to execute wrath upon him that doeth evil" (Romans 13:4, see Romans 13:1-7).

How does driving reflect our attitude toward authority?

* _____

_____

The more that we become mighty in spirit the more alert we will be to little violations of the law and the more we will take seriously the warning of Scripture, *"Therefore to him that knoweth to do good, and doeth it not, to him it is sin"* (James 4:17).

"But strong meat belongeth to them that are of full age, even those who by reason of use have their senses exercised to discern both good and evil" (Hebrews 5:14).

• *Wording:* _____

_____

_____

_____

How will respect for authority influence our respect for property?

☐ _____

"Thou shalt not steal" (Exodus 20:15).

The concept of private property was instituted by God. Money and possessions are, therefore, entrusted to individuals who must look upon themselves as stewards of that which belongs to God.

• _____
_____
_____
_____
_____

Why are practical jokes not very practical?

• _____
_____

"As a mad man who casteth firebrands, arrows, and death, So is the man that deceiveth his neighbour, and saith, Am not I in sport?" (Proverbs 26:18–19).

How can we rob God of His glory?

_____
_____

Review the "Demonology Chart" on page 103.

"For all have sinned, and come short of the glory of God" (Romans 3:23).

• *Wording:* _____
_____
_____

If we are given incorrect commands, how can we make effective appeals?

☐ _____
_____

"Rebuke not an elder, but entreat him as a father; and the younger men as brethren; The elder women as mothers; the younger as sisters, with all purity" (I Timothy 5:1).

"Let every soul be subject unto the higher powers. For there is no power but of God. . . . Whosoever therefore resisteth the power, resisteth the ordinance of God: and they that resist shall receive to themselves damnation" (Romans 13:1–2).

APPEALING TO AUTHORITY

Every human authority is under the ultimate authority of God's word. Because of this, we are never required by God to do those things which violate clear Scriptural principles, no matter who tells us to do them.

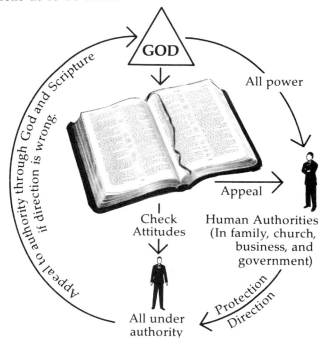

If we are ever asked to disobey Scripture and do something that is wrong, we must first appeal. If we appeal with a proper attitude and with Scriptural grounds and our appeal is rejected, then we must be willing to suffer the consequences for not doing evil.

HOW PARENTS CAN REINFORCE THIS CONCEPT:

• By verbally affirming to our parents, in the presence of our children, how grateful we are for them and for what they have done for us.

• By recalling instances in which we honored or dishonored our authorities and received God's corresponding blessings or reproofs.

• By referring to law officers as ministers of God.

What are the prerequisites in appealing to an authority?

● _____

_____

What are the balancing concepts to authority?

● _____

_____

Just as there are three types of power in government (executive, legislative, and judicial), so there are three concepts that make up the principle of authority (chain of command, balance of power, and appeal to authority).

A thorough understanding of each one of these aspects is essential in order to properly respond to authority.

HOW TO MAKE AN *Appeal*

The seven basic requirements for making an effective appeal are contained in the booklet, *How to Make an Appeal.* They can be taught directly from the booklet to sons and daughters. The booklet can also be used as a checklist to make sure that an appeal is properly made.

3 CONCEPT:

The temple of God's Spirit

"What? know ye not that your body is the temple of the Holy Ghost which is in you, which ye have of God, and ye are not your own?" (I Corinthians 6:19).

How will viewing our body as God's temple affect our use of drugs?

☐ _____

"Wine is a mocker, strong drink is raging: and whosoever is deceived thereby is not wise" (Proverbs 20:1)

Does the Scripture directly condemn drugs?

● _____

_____

". . . For by thy sorceries [pharmakeia] were all nations deceived" (Revelation 18:23).

Is social drinking acceptable?

● _____

_____

See information on alcohol on page 26.

How should I respond to someone who offers me a drink?

● _____

It is all too easy to reject sin and compromise with an arrogant and prideful attitude. Those who see these wrong responses will react to us and the principles for which we stand. If a person's motive in offering you a drink is simply to quench your thirst, be sure to thank him for his thoughtfulness with a gracious and grateful spirit.

● _____

"The fear of the Lord is to hate evil: pride, and arrogancy, and the evil way, and the froward mouth, do I hate" (Proverbs 8:13).

● *Wording:* _____

_____

_____

_____

NOTES

DIAGRAMS

Why must we stand alone?

The ability to "stand alone" for that which is right is one of the clearest evidences of maturity. This ability is the heritage of a dedicated Christian who has discovered and **verbally identified** with a superior way of life.

When a Christian "stands alone" in doing what is right or refusing to do what is wrong, he is saying to the Lord, "I revere You and Your Word," and he is saying to the world, "I have something worth standing for." This type of commitment attracts people who are looking for something worth living for, and it builds mature qualities of leadership in the one who takes a stand.

Ewing Galloway

He looked for people who "stood alone."

The leadership qualities which are developed through "standing alone" are being recognized in the business world. The president of a growing corporation gave the following explanation as to why his personnel director was so successful in selecting qualified staff for executive positions.

"When the personnel director interviews a person for leadership, he will ask him about his family, his education, and his hobbies, but he is really looking for only one thing: "Has this person ever had an experience when it cost him something for standing up for doing right?"

This personnel director has discovered over the years that if an individual has never had an experience in which he "stood alone" for doing right, he would not make a good leader of men. When he selects an executive, he rarely misses selecting the best man.

When must we stand alone?

An important aspect of maturity is being able to see farther down the road than those around us. With this in mind, let us think through some of the situations in which we must "stand alone." By picturing them in our minds and visualizing our response to them, we will be "ready always to give an answer." We will also demonstrate the kind of wisdom described in Proverbs 22:3: *"A prudent man forseeth the evil, and hideth himself: but the simple pass on, and are punished."*

There are three questions we must ask about situations before "standing alone" in them:

1 IS THIS A SITUATION THAT I SHOULD NOT BE IN?

There is no glory in "standing alone" in a situation in which God never intended us to be involved.

It is not wise, for example, for a Christian to accompany a friend to a bar and then feel that he is "standing alone" because he refuses a drink. In such a situation he would be violating the overriding principle of avoiding all appearance of evil. (See I Thessalonians 5:22.)

The same would be true for one who attends a dance and tries to "stand alone" by saying "no" to some aspect of the evening's activities. God's prior command is to "flee youthful lusts." (See II Timothy 2:22.)

Baalam stood for truth when the king asked him to curse Israel, but he was cooperating with God's enemies, and God judged him for it. David found himself in a difficult situation when he went to a Philistine city for refuge and he felt he had to be deceptive in order to escape danger.

2 IS A CLEAR BIBLICAL PRINCIPLE INVOLVED?

When people know that you are willing to "stand alone," they will try to get you involved in their causes. All too often causes which sound right and look reasonable actually violate a clear Biblical principle.

For example, you might be asked to join a group which refuses to pay taxes because the government uses the funds for wrong purposes. This movement violates both precept and testimony of Scripture.

Few governments excelled ancient Rome for corruption. Yet God used their taxation program to bring Mary and Joseph to Bethlehem for the fulfillment of Scripture in the birth of

Christ. It is not inconceivable that the tax money paid by Joseph could have been used to slaughter innocent children by the command of Herod.

Jesus paid taxes after establishing the principle with Peter that because Jesus was King, He did not technically need to pay them. He said, however, to Peter, "... *Lest we should offend them, go thou ... and give unto them for me and thee" (Matthew 17:27).* It is also possible that the temple tax which Jesus paid was used to put Him on the cross.

Taxes paid by Joseph supported a corrupt empire.

Added to the testimony of Christ, Scripture gives the following commands: *"Let every soul be subject unto the higher powers. For there is no power but of God: the powers that be are ordained of God. Whosoever therefore resisteth the power, resisteth the ordinance of God: and they that resist shall receive to themselves damnation. . . .*

"For this cause pay ye tribute also: for they are God's ministers, attending continually upon this very thing. Render therefore to all their dues: tribute to whom tribute is due; custom to whom custom; fear to whom fear; honour to whom honour" (Romans 13;1-2,6-7).

The importance of supporting government is emphasized in I Peter 2:13-15: *"Submit yourselves to every ordinance of man for the Lord's sake: whether it be to the king, as supreme; Or unto governors, as unto them that are sent by him for the punishment of evildoers, and for the praise of them that do well. For so is the will of God, that with well-doing ye may put to silence the ignorance of foolish men."*

Remember that the government Peter referred to had already wrongly jailed him, beaten him, and killed many fellow Christians!

Part of our well-doing is to appeal to government when they are not punishing evildoers or praising those who do well; however, they will never listen to our appeal if we refuse to pay taxes. Refusing to pay taxes is a "power play" which violates the order of Scripture. Power must come from above; appeal must come from those beneath.

If someone convinces you that the government does not have a constitutional right to collect income tax from you, "stand alone for truth" by saying, "As a Christian I am governed by a higher law than the Constitution and that Law commands me to pay taxes."

3 SHOULD "STANDING ALONE" ALSO INVOLVE AN APPEAL?

When you are required to do something that you know is contrary to Scripture, it may be wiser to "stand alone" by making an effective appeal. Ask yourself, "Is the one giving me this instruction acting on his own or by the authority of another?"

An appeal should be made to the one in authority whenever possible. If a fellow student asks you to sell a product for a fund-raiser that you in good conscience cannot sell, don't "stand alone" to the student, but rather go to the one in charge of the program. Present your reasons for not being able to sell the product, and offer a creative alternative.

When Daniel was offered the king's meat, he didn't speak with the waiter but went to the prince of the eunuchs and made his appeal. In the appeal he suggested a creative alternative.

SITUATIONS IN WHICH WE MUST "STAND ALONE."

☐ When asked to participate in deals or activities which would cause personal loss to any other individual (See Proverbs 1:10-19.)

- [ ] When asked by a family member, a Christian friend, or an unbeliever to do anything that would violate your moral conscience (See Daniel 1:8; I Thessalonians 4:1–8.)

- [ ] When asked to look at sensual pictures, magazines, books, movies, or TV programs (See Matthew 5:28; I John 2:15–16.)

- [ ] When pressured to wear clothes or follow fads which violate modesty (See Romans 12:2.)

- [ ] When invited by a non-Christian to go out on a date (See II Corinthians 6:14.)

- [ ] When encouraged to participate in a "practical joke" (See Proverbs 26:18–19.)

- [ ] When urged to defy authority to gain approval from peers who think the authority is unfair (See Romans 13:1–7.)

- [ ] When asked to disregard parents' curfew or other restrictions which others tell you don't apply (See Ephesians 6:1.)

- [ ] When challenged to take a dare in order to prove your courage (See Matthew 4:6.)

- [ ] When offered liquor, tobacco, or any other harmful drugs (See Proverbs 20:1.)

- [ ] When asked to participate in carnal or worldly music (See Ephesians 5:19.)

STANDING ALONE IN FRIENDSHIPS

The most difficult situations in which to "stand alone" do not come from unbelievers or strangers but from fellow Christians who have compromised in an important area of their lives and who refuse any counsel or help you try to give them. The Scriptural instructions for dealing with such a person are given in I Corinthians 5:11:

> "But now I have written unto you not to keep company, if any man that is called a brother be a fornicator, or covetous, or an idolater, or a railer, or a drunkard, or an extortioner; with such an one no not to eat" (I Corinthians 5:11).

The Consequences of Not Standing Alone

DEDICATED CHRISTIAN   CARNAL CHRISTIAN

If a close or intimate friendship exists between these two, the following responses will be prompted in those who watch them from the outside:

His friend has a bad reputation. If I associate with him, mine will be damaged too.

He is not a very good influence because his friend wronged me and never tried to make it right.

His friend dislikes me. He probably does, too.

He spends so much time with his friend, I'm sure he wouldn't have time for me.

His friend is very immoral, I wonder if he is too?

"Be not deceived: evil communications corrupt good manners [morals]" (I Corinthians 15:33).

The Benefits of Standing Alone

DEDICATED CHRISTIAN → CARNAL CHRISTIAN

If the Christian uses the freedom of a close friendship and gives wise and loving counsel but the friend rejects it and walks away, the following types of responses will occur in those who watch.

He has something I wish I had!

He's done what I should do with some of my friends.

He's really grown in his Christian life.

Maybe he'll have time to help me with some personal problems.

I sure admire him for the stand he's taken!

The Basis of Verbal Identification

When we verbally identify with the Lord Jesus Christ, those who love Him or who are seeking Him will desire to have fellowship with us; however, those who reject Christ will also reject us.

"I have given thy word; and the world hath hated them, because they are not of the world, even as I am not of the world" (John 17:14).

When we verbally identify with the Lord Jesus Christ, those who reject Him and His standards will usually also separate themselves from us. This situation means that we do not reject them; they reject us.

"Blessed are ye, when men shall hate you, and when they shall separate you from their company, and shall reproach you, and cast out your name as evil, for the Son of man's sake. Rejoice ye in that day, and leap for joy: for, behold, your reward is great in heaven . . ." (Luke 6:22–23).

HOW TO VERBALLY IDENTIFY WITH THE LORD JESUS CHRIST.

Whenever we are personally confronted with an invitation to violate Scriptural principles, we must not be vague or reactionary, but we must verbally explain why we cannot comply in a clear and gracious manner.

The following illustration provides specific insights on how an effective verbal identification was made.

HOW AN EMPLOYEE TURNED A WRONG INVITATION INTO A RIGHT DECISION BY VERBALLY IDENTIFYING WITH CHRIST

A freshman in college secured a job helping a truck driver deliver newspapers. On one of the routes, the driver suggested that they stop at a certain tavern and have drink.

(Note: The basic intention of the driver was to have company and approval for something he wanted to do.)

The student became embarrassed as he tried to explain that he didn't do this type of thing. Finally, however, he agreed to accompany the driver but not to have a drink.

Going into the bar with the driver troubled the conscience of the Christian young man, and later that week he asked his church youth director if he had done the right thing. The youth director had been working on material that explained how to verbally identify with Jesus Christ. He showed the young man how he could have responded to the driver and explained why it would have been more effective.

A week later another truck driver was assigned to the same route. When the new driver stopped at the tavern, he made the same suggestion. This time, however, the student had a ready answer and very cheerfully and respectfully said, "Would it be all right with you if I just waited for you out here?"

(Note: A cheerful, friendly attitude is essential in verbally identifying with Christ. A warm smile communicates the message, "I accept *you* even though I am not able to accept your invitation.")

The driver didn't accept the young man's request and urged him more strongly to come in and have a drink. At this point the young man sincerely stated with a smile, "Recently I committed my life to Jesus Christ, and I am not able to do this. But don't let me interfere with what you wanted to do. I'll just wait for you here in the truck.

(Note: Right wording involves stating personal conviction without projecting a judgmental attitude toward the other person.)

The driver got out of the truck and walked into the bar. However, a few minutes later he returned. As he started up the engine, he apologetically blurted out, "Boy, I'm sorry kid. I didn't realize you had that kind of dedication. I wouldn't have asked you if I had known."

(Note: The driver began to reveal personal conviction about his lack of a meaningful relationship with God.)

As they drove down the road the driver continued to explain, "I go to church, but I should be more dedicated. How did you commit your life to Jesus Christ?"

The student repllied that if he had a few minutes he could show him. The truck driver pulled off the road and eagerly listened as the student showed him, step by step, how to become a Christian. The driver prayed and invited Jesus Christ into his life to become his Savior.

(Note: The student had learned how to effectively share the Gospel.)

Later that week the student enthusiastically reported to his youth director: "I was able to identify with Christ seven times this week. Four of the seven times I was asked how I dedicated my life to Christ. This gave me the opportunity to share the plan of salvation with each one."

A student from Michigan

HOW TO MAKE A COMMITMENT TO VERBALLY IDENTIFY WITH CHRIST.

In your own words express the following points to the Lord in a sincere and genuine prayer.

☐ I hereby commit myself to the Lord Jesus Christ and to the principles and concepts of His Word.

☐ I am purposing right now to stand alone whenever I am asked to violate Scriptural convictions.

☐ Whenever I am asked to do what I know is wrong, I will verbally identify with the Lord Jesus Christ.

☐ Based on this commitment, I am willing to have those who reject Christ reject me.

☐ In areas of questionable activities, I purpose to take the position, "Others may, but I may not." I base this position on the Scriptural command not to offend a weaker brother or cause him to stumble. (See Romans 14.)

Date prayed _____

SITUATIONS IN WHICH I WILL PROBABLY BE CALLED UPON TO STAND ALONE:

_____

_____

_____

OPPORTUNITIES I HAVE HAD TO STAND ALONE AND TO VERBALLY IDENTIFY WITH CHRIST

_____

_____

For additional information and illustrations on "standing alone," study the booklet entitled *How to Stand Alone.*

NOTES　　　　　　　　　　　　　　　　　**DIAGRAMS**

HOW TO APPLY
PRINCIPLES OF DISCIPLINE

INSTRUCTION

"My son, hear the instruction of thy father, and forsake not the law of thy mother" (Proverbs 1:8).

WARNING

"He, that being often reproved hardeneth his neck, shall suddenly be destroyed, and that without remedy" (Proverbs 29:1).

CORRECTION

"My son, despise not the chastening of the Lord; neither be weary of his correction: For whom the Lord loveth he correcteth; even as a father the son in whom he delighteth" (Proverbs 3:11–12).

NOTES

DIAGRAMS

PREPARATIONS FOR DISCIPLINE

The potential for training sons and daughters to be mighty in spirit is far greater than most parents imagine. God promises that parents who have a proper reverence for Him and instruct their children out of a great delight in His commandments will have descendants who are mighty upon the earth. (See Psalm 112:1–2.)

When does the instruction of a child begin?

1 _____

_____

The ability of a child to respond to communication while still in the womb is now well-documented. A researcher at the University of North Carolina made the following statement after a series of studies: "It is clear that the child's perceptual preferences are profoundly affected by auditory experience before birth." (Dr. Anthony J. DeCasper)

Another researcher, who has authored the book *The Secret Life of the Unborn Child* (Dell Publishers), draws the following conclusions:

"We now know the unborn child is an aware, reacting human being who from the sixth month on—perhaps even earlier—leads an active emotional life. He can sense and react to not only his mother's large, undifferentiated emotions such as love and hate, but to more shaded, complex feeling states like ambivalence and ambiguity."

This researcher further clarifies his findings this way:

"By the sixth month, the unborn child can see, hear, experience, taste and . . . even learn while in the womb.

"What he feels and perceives in the womb begins shaping his attitudes and expectations about himself. Whether he sees himself as happy or sad, aggressive or meek, secure or anxiety-ridden later in life depends, in part, on the messages he gets about himself in the womb.

"The chief source of these 'shaping messages' in the womb is the mother. This does not mean that every fleeting worry, doubt, or anxiety a woman has rebounds on her child. . . . What matters are deep, persistent, patterns of feeling. Chronic anxiety or a wrenching ambivalence about motherhood can leave a deep scar on an unborn child's personality. On the other hand, such life-enhancing emotions as joy, elation, and anticipation can contribute significantly to the emotional development of a healthy child.

"Father also counts. How a man feels about his wife and unborn child is one of the most important factors in the success of a pregnancy." (Dr. Thomas Verny)

HOW A FATHER TALKED HIS BABY THROUGH A DIFFICULT DELIVERY

The factor of the father's importance in communicating with the unborn child was employed by an assistant professor of nursing at UCLA during the birth of a baby. The baby had a depressed heart-variability rate. The attending physician feared that the infant was under too much stress and considered performing a cesarean section.

The assistant professor, who was also a midwife, instructed the father to begin talking to his child in the womb. As soon as he started talking, the baby recognized his voice because the father had been talking to him during the previous months. The fetal monitor took an immediate leap and remained in the normal range for the next two hours as the father continued talking the child through a natural delivery. (Dr. Susan M. Ludington)

HOW COMMUNICATION IN THE WOMB INCREASES CAPACITY FOR LEARNING OUTSIDE THE WOMB

"As a young man," says Boris Brott, conductor of the Hamilton Philharmonic in Ontario, "I was mystified by an unusual ability I had to 'play,' as it were, certain pieces sight unseen. I'd be conducting a score for the first time, and suddenly the cello line would jump out at me; I'd know the flow of the piece even before I turned the page of the score.

"One day I mentioned this to my mother, who is a professional cellist. I thought she would be intrigued because it was always the cello line that was so distinctive in my head. She was; but when she heard what the pieces were, the mystery quickly resolved itself. All of the scores I knew sight unseen were ones she had prepared for a program while she was pregnant with me, but never had occasion to play after that." (*The Christian Reader*, September-October, 1985)

HOW A FATHER ESTABLISHED A "SPIRIT TO SPIRIT" COMMUNICATION WITH HIS UNBORN CHILD

"My wife and I recently experienced what was termed a 'crisis pregnancy'—our son was diagnosed as having a blocked urethra while still in the womb. As we went from doctor to doctor, we were surprised to have them ask us whether or not we were talking to the baby to prepare him for birth.

"We told them that we were and we were praying for him. We also indicated that my wife was reading Scripture to him. These unsaved doctors told us that we were doing the best thing possible to make him ready for delivery.

"After delivery, with several tubes, probes, etc. connected to him in the Intensive Care Unit, I saw my son for the first time—screaming and terrified. When I spoke to him, he immediately stopped crying. I told him that he was going to be all right. Then I prayed with him. Since his birth, I know he understands, spirit to spirit, what is being communicated to him."

A pastor in New York

Why is it important to read the Scriptures to an unborn child?

● _____

The Scriptures are understood by spiritual perception. Therefore, even though the intellectual ability of an unborn child is not developed, the spiritual perception of that child is developed. Furthermore, research and personal experiences document the fact that a child develops a greater capacity to respond to whatever material was spoken to him in the womb.

Why should the father as well as the mother instruct the child in the womb?

● _____

Why should an unborn child hear only good music?

● _____

The benefits of proper pre-birth training cannot be over-estimated when you consider that the child will be calmer, more attentive, more responsive to the parents' voices, and will possess a greater capacity to learn spiritual truth.

One couple who had read the Bible to their child every night during the nine months prior to birth reported that their baby was the happiest, calmest child they had ever seen and that the baby rarely cried.

How can discipline begin the day a child is born?

● _____

2 _____

How does a regular schedule benefit a child?

● _____

The daily schedule of the parents, especially the mother, plays a tremendous part in the formation of disciplines within the child. A Swiss study shows that early-to-bed mothers give birth to early-to-bed babies. The same is true for late-to-bed mothers giving birth to late-to-bed children.

How does a child learn contentment?

● _____

One of the most important factors in the schedule which parents develop for a child is consistency. If a routine is established, it must be maintained except for unusual circumstances.

Is it good to feed a child on demand?

● _____

What is the most important factor to develop in the education of a child?

3 _____

How does a parent communicate with the spirit of a child before the child learns to speak?

● _____

There are five possible levels of communication which a parent can build with a child: physical, emotional, volitional, intellectual, and spiritual. Although each is interwoven with the other, there are also distinct aspects of each level which can take place independently of the others.

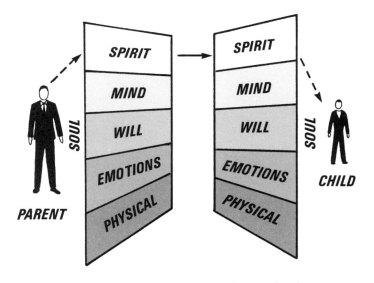

The key to a deepening relationship between a child and his parents depends upon the depth of communication that the parents develop between their spirit and the spirit of the child.

The ability of an infant to recognize and respond to the sprit of a parent is an observable fact. The infant can "read" the facial expressions of the parent and know whether the parent is happy or sad, pleased or displeased.

The spirit of the parent is also communicated by tone of voice, actions, and attitudes.

One of the first tasks of a parent in communicating to the spirit of the child is to teach him the meaning of the word *no*. When a baby does that

which is unacceptable, the parent should reflect a serious facial expression and accompany it with the word, "No."

Facial expressions of delight and approval should accompany the word *yes*.

Why must a parent check his spirit while communicating with a child?

● _____

Because the child reads the spirit of a parent before he understands the words of the parent, he may receive many messages which the parent did not intend to communicate. It is at this level that parents often instill their own attitudes into the lives of their children. Thus, it is important that parents be very careful to make sure that their spirit is consistent with their words.

Why is it essential that parents develop communication with the spirit of their child?

● _____

As the child matures, he will develop "independence" in meeting his own physical needs; he will also develop much independence in meeting his emotional, intellectual, volitional, and spiritual needs.

However, his spiritual maturity will unite him with his parents in a continuing and deepening fellowship. Unless this line of spiritual communication is developed, there is often little reason in the child's mind to continue communicating with his parents after he grows to adulthood.

What is the continuing reward to the child of "spirit to spirit" instruction?

● _____

"My son, keep thy father's commandment, and forsake not the law of thy mother: Bind them continually upon thine heart, and tie them about thy neck.

"When thou goest, it shall lead thee; when thou sleepest, it shall keep thee; and when thou awakest, it shall talk with thee" (Proverbs 6:20–22).

The continuing effectiveness of early instruction answers the question, "How can I get counsel if my parents are not around or if they have died?" Their counsel, communicated to the spirit of the child, and confirmed as true by the conscience and the spirit of God, will continue "to talk [to the son or daughter] in the way."

What can destroy the spirit of communication between parent and child?

● _____

_____

_____

How can parents provide consistent instruction and discipline to their children?

4 _____

_____

Inconsistent instruction and "rule setting" usually result when parents have not analyzed their individual responsibilities of child training in the light of Scriptural teaching.

Which parent should give the general direction?

● _____

_____

When God wanted to give direction to Mary and Joseph, He communicated that direction through Joseph:

Doré Bible Illustrations

". . . *The angel of the Lord appeareth to **Joseph** in a dream, saying, Arise, and take the young child and his mother, and flee into Egypt, and be thou there until I bring **thee** word. . . .*

"*But when Herod was dead, behold, an angel of the Lord appeareth in a dream to **Joseph** in Egypt, Saying, Arise . . .*" (Matthew 2:13, 19–20).

God has ordained His laws or order, and He works within them to accomplish His will. This fact demonstrates how important His principles are to Him since He could just as easily work outside of them.

Which parent should work out the details when basic direction has been given?

● _____

_____

God designed the mother to be with her children throughout the day so that she will discern how to relate instructions to the needs and abilities of each child:

● _____

_____

● _____

_____

Light

"*My son, keep thy father's commandment,*   *and forsake not the law of thy mother . . .*

For the commandment is a lamp;   *and the law is light . . .*" (Proverbs 6:20, 23)

If the children rebel against the initial command, the father gives the correction.

If the children disobey the rules which grow out of the commands, the mother should give the correction, supported by the father.

For additional information about this important concept of discipline, study pages 24–27.

What can parents do to produce the best possible behavior in the lives of their children?

APPLY THREE ASPECTS OF **DISCIPLINE**

Correcting a child for misbehavior is not simply administering appropriate punishment. It is first of all a relationship between parents and child in which continuous instruction takes place.

What must take place in the mind of the child before he will understand God's principles?

1 _____

_____

True instruction enables the child to see life situations from God's point of view. The degree to which he is able to do this will determine his ability to develop mature attitudes, meaningful goals, and successful relationships.

The necessity for effective discipline is amplified by the fact that the child's natural inclinations are **directly contrary** to God's principles of life.

"Foolishness is bound in the heart of a child; but the rod of correction shall drive it far from him" (Proverbs 22:15).

"There is a way which seemeth right unto a man, but the end thereof are the ways of death" (Proverbs 14:12).

The following points illustrate this principle:

HOW NATURAL INCLINATIONS OPPOSE BASIC PRINCIPLES

A. We think we can gain approval by looking and acting like somebody else who is accepted.

ACCEPTANCE OF SELF

God states that we gain approval by becoming the unique individuals which He has intended us to be. *". . . We are [present, continuous action] his workmanship"* (Ephesians 2:10).

B. We think we gain *independence* by getting out from under the authority over us.

AUTHORITY

God states that we gain independence by inward harmony and obedience to the authority He has placed over us. *"Children, obey your parents in all things . . ."* (Colossians 3:20).

"Let every soul be subject unto the higher powers. For there is no power but of God: the powers that be are ordained of God. Whosoever therefore resisteth the power, resisteth the ordinance of God: and they that resist shall receive to themselves damnation" (Romans 13:1–2).

C. We think we gain *admiration* by covering up our mistakes and failures.

CLEAR CONSCIENCE

God states that we gain admiration by acknowledging our failures and asking for forgiveness from those we have offended. *"Confess your faults one to another, and pray one for another . . ."* (James 5:16). *". . . before honour is humility"* (Proverbs 18:12).

D. We think we *get even* with those who offend us by hurting and avoiding them.

SUFFERING

God states that we "get even" with those who offend us by doing all the good we can for them. *"Recompense to no man evil for evil. Provide things honest in the sight of all men. Be not overcome of evil, but overcome evil with good"* (Romans 12:17, 21).

E. We think we will be *exalted* by pointing out the faults of others as well as letting people know what we have accomplished.

SUFFERING

God states that we will be exalted by humbling ourselves and exalting others. *"Humble yourselves in the sight of the Lord, and He shall lift you up"* (James 4:10). *". . . In lowliness of mind let each esteem other better than themselves"* (Philippians 2:3).

F. We think we gain *respect* from others by demanding our personal rights.

YIELDING RIGHTS

God states that we gain respect by yielding our personal rights to Him and then to others. *"But seek ye first the kingdom of God, and his righteousness; and all these things shall be added unto you"* (Matthew 6:33).

G. We think the way to *greatness* is being above everyone else.

YIELDING RIGHTS

God states that the way to greatness is to be the servant of everyone else. *"But it shall not be so among you: but whosoever will be great among you, let him be your minister; And whosoever will be chief among you, let him be your servant"* (Matthew 20:26–27).

H. We think we gain *prosperity* by holding on to what we have.

YIELDING RIGHTS

God states that the way to prosperity is by giving all we have to Him and then to others as He directs. *"Give, and it shall be given unto you . . ."* (Luke 6:38). *". . . He which soweth sparingly shall reap also sparingly; and he which soweth bountifully shall reap also bountifully"* (II Corinthians 9:6).

I. We think we will gain *joy* by avoiding irritations and trials.

SOURCES OF IRRITATION

God states that we will gain joy by welcoming and responding correctly to irritations and trials over which we have no control. "My brethren, count it all joy when ye fall into divers temptations; knowing this, that the trying of your faith worketh patience" (James 1:2–3).

J. We think that the way to *enjoy life* is to satisfy all of our desires.

MORAL FREEDOM

God states that the way to enjoy life is to die to our desires so that He can give us His desires. *"Delight thyself also in the Lord; and he shall give thee the desires of thine heart"* (Psalm 37:4).

K. We think that *health* is primarily achieved by eating the right food and having sufficient exercise.

SUCCESSFUL LIVING (MEDITATION)

God states that health is primarily achieved by knowing and obeying the principles of His Word. *". . . Man shall not live by bread alone, but by every word that proceedeth out of the mouth of God"* (Matthew 4:4).

L. We think that we will discover a *meaningful life* by accomplishing the goals which we have planned.

PURPOSE IN LIFE

God states that we will discover a meaningful life by giving our life to Him in order to achieve His purposes. *"For whosoever will save his life shall lose it: and whosoever will lose his life for my sake shall find it"* (Matthew 16:25).

HOW CAN PARENTS TRANSFORM THE NATURAL INCLINATIONS OF THEIR CHILDREN?

The only way to change the natural inclinations of sons and daughters is to "convert the soul." This expression does not refer to eternal salvation of the spirit. It refers to eternal salvation of the spirit. It refers to the necessity of transforming the mind, will, and emotions which is described in Romans 12:2:

"And be not conformed to this world: but be ye transformed by the renewing of your mind, that ye may prove what is that good, and acceptable, and perfect, will of God."

When the soul is converted, natural inclinations are recognized for what they are—direct opposites of God's perfect will. With this understanding, the heart of a son or daughter will rejoice when it hears right statutes.

BASIC SEQUENCE FOR INSTRUCTION
TO TRANSFORM NATURAL INCLINATIONS (PSALM 19:7-9)

GOD'S ORDER	DEFINITION	PURPOSE TO BE ACHIEVED
1. LAW OF THE LORD (Torah) Basic Principles	PERFECT (complete)	CONVERTING THE SOUL (mind, will, and emotions) • Replacing natural inclinations • Transforming mind - Rom. 12:2
2. TESTIMONY (witness) Supporting illustrations (biographies)	SURE (firm and established)	MAKING THE SIMPLE WISE • Applying principles to daily living - II Tim. 3:16-17 • Seeing God's ways
3. STATUTES (mandates) Case law (standards)	RIGHT (equitable and trustworthy)	REJOICING THE HEART • Giving practical direction in difficult situations - I Cor. 9:9
4. COMMANDMENT (directive) Revealed way (concepts)	PURE (clear and precise)	ENLIGHTENING THE EYES • Providing fresh insight for living - John 14:21
5. FEAR (awesome respect) Continual awareness (convictions)	CLEAN (morally pure)	ENDURING FOREVER • Extending life, gaining eternal life - Eph. 6:1-3
6. JUDGMENTS (verdict) Consequences (reproofs)	TRUE AND RIGHTEOUS (just and sure)	BEING DESIRED MORE THAN GOLD • Warning God's servants • Leading to great rewards

EVALUATING YOUR CHILD'S FAITH

Name of Child _____

Each principle below has seven behavioral descriptions by which its understanding can be measured in your child's life. Check "yes" if the statement is descriptive of your child; check "no" if the statement does not describe your child.

DESIGN

Our child knows God as the Creator of his/her own person, heritage, and physical being. He/She understands and accepts himself/herself as a unique creation and responds to God by specifically thanking Him for how he/she has been made.

Yes No Our son/daughter:

☐ ☐ 1. Would like to change how he/she looks and complains about his/her physical appearance
☐ ☐ 2. Is usually sensitive to or aware of the needs of others
☐ ☐ 3. Says negative things about himself/herself, people, or situations
☐ ☐ 4. Maintains good eye contact with those who speak with him/her
☐ ☐ 5. Usually compares himself/herself to others or frequently makes comments like: "I can run faster than _____;" or "I wish I were like _____."
☐ ☐ 6. Participates with ease in groups and makes friends easily
☐ ☐ 7. Feels it is important to have many possessions (or the best or the most)

AUTHORITY

Our child understands the importance and role of authority in his/her life. He/She is able to discern God's purposes in using authorities and demonstrates right responses to the authorities in his/her life.

Yes No Our son/daughter:

☐ ☐ 1. Often says, "Why do I have to do it?"
☐ ☐ 2. Cheerfully obeys instructions without delay
☐ ☐ 3. Admires those who mock authority and encourage rebellion
☐ ☐ 4. Makes wise appeals to those in authority when needful
☐ ☐ 5. Responds correctly to only some authorities in his/her life, but not all
☐ ☐ 6. Is continually aware that God is watching his/her words, thoughts, actions, motives, and attitudes
☐ ☐ 7. Frequently complains about the decisions of those in authority

RESPONSIBILITY

Our child has learned how to take responsibility for his/her thoughts, words, and actions. He/She has learned the importance of seeking and maintaining a clear conscience.

Yes No Our son/daughter:

☐ ☐ 1. Finds it difficult to admit when he/she is wrong and seldom asks for forgiveness on his/her own
☐ ☐ 2. Usually resists peer pressure and often stands alone on the side of right
☐ ☐ 3. Has difficulty following through on assigned tasks
☐ ☐ 4. Reflects a disciplined mind in the way that he/she speaks
☐ ☐ 5. Usually responds to conflict in our family with, "It wasn't my fault!"
☐ ☐ 6. Delivers what he/she promises even when it hurts to do so
☐ ☐ 7. Often takes on the responsibilities of others, leaving his/her own responsibilities unattended

OWNERSHIP

Our child is able to overcome anger by giving his/her personal rights to God.

Yes No Our son/daughter:

☐ ☐ 1. Is easily angered
☐ ☐ 2. Finds it easy to share or give to others
☐ ☐ 3. Frequently uses expressions like, "It's mine! You can't have it!"

Yes	No	
☐	☐	4. Uses anger as a signal to stop, pray, and give his/her right to God
☐	☐	5. Frequently demonstrates a stubborn and unteachable spirit
☐	☐	6. Has made a deliberate, known dedication of his/her person and rights to God
☐	☐	7. Frequently needs to be prompted to thank others for the ways in which they have benefited his/her life

SUFFERING

Our child knows that the ultimate purpose of his/her life is to become more and more like Jesus Christ. He/She has learned to let disappointments and offences build this character in him/her. He/She is able to forgive and invest in the lives of his/her offenders.

Yes	No	Our son/daughter:
☐	☐	1. Frequently makes statements like, "I hate him."
☐	☐	2. Prays for those who have hurt or ridiculed him/her
☐	☐	3. Usually carries a grudge after having been hurt
☐	☐	4. Finds it easy to express forgiveness through actions
☐	☐	5. Often manifests a revengeful spirit
☐	☐	6. Gives evidence of the ability to discern God's ways of working in the circumstances of his/her life
☐	☐	7. Has difficulty accepting times of suffering in response to doing right

FREEDOM

Our child knows that true freedom is not the right to do what he/she wants to do, but the power to do what he/she should do. Our child has a hatred for evil.

Yes	No	Our son/daughter:
☐	☐	1. Desires to get involved in ungodly trends, insisting that "Everybody's doing it!"
☐	☐	2. Uses engrafted Scripture to combat temptation
☐	☐	3. Is attracted to magazines, books, movies, and/or music which promote moral impurity
☐	☐	4. Stands alone on the side of right even when it means unpopular treatment
☐	☐	5. Argues about specific rules (do's and don'ts) rather than concentrating on understanding and applying God's principles in his/her life
☐	☐	6. Shows the ability to discern good/better/best and voluntarily chooses that which is spirit-strengthening
☐	☐	7. Seeks to be sophisticated in regard to worldly activities

SUCCESS

Our child is motivated to depend on the Scriptures. He/She is learning to meditate on and delight in God's Word. Wisdom and understanding are evident in his/her life.

Yes	No	Our son/daughter:
☐	☐	1. Shows a lack of consistent interest in the Bible and frequently makes comments like, "I don't like to read the Bible."
☐	☐	2. Has a consistent personal time of prayer and Bible study each day
☐	☐	3. Frequently does not participate wholeheartedly in singing, reading Scripture, or listening attentively when in church services
☐	☐	4. Is eager to enter new insights from Scripture or the teaching of God's principles into his/her *Life Notebook*
☐	☐	5. Does not readily see applications to his/her own life from the Scriptures
☐	☐	6. Has large sections of God's Word implanted in his/her mind
☐	☐	7. Has worldly heroes

A need to strengthen your child's growth in any area is indicated when odd-numbered characteristics are answered "yes" and even-numbered characteristics are answered "no."

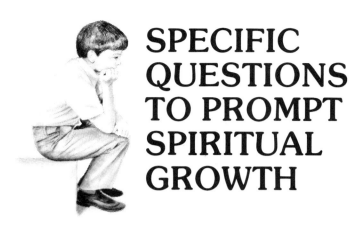

SPECIFIC QUESTIONS TO PROMPT SPIRITUAL GROWTH

The following questions have been effectively used by those who have an experiential understanding of the Seven Basic Principles of Life.

These questions go right to the heart of the key decisions that every Christian must make. When asked in a sincere, gentle manner by one whose life illustrates the answers, they will usually open up the listener to willingly hear and respond to Scriptural steps of action.

1. Assurance of Salvation
QUESTIONS:

☐ **What were the events that led up to your becoming a Christian?**
(Do not evaluate response.)

☐ **Since that time, have you had doubts about your salvation?**
(If the answer is yes, ask, "Would you like to get rid of your doubts?")

☐ Explain the Gospel.
☐ Lead the person in a prayer of salvation.

2. Acceptance of Self
QUESTION:

☐ **If you had the power to change anything about the way you look, what would you change?**

☐ Explain how unchangeable physical features are God's "marks of ownership" and motivations to build inward character.

☐ Lead the person to thank God for their unchangeables, especially those that have been most rejected.

3. Total Dedication
QUESTIONS:

☐ **Since the time that you became a Christian, have you ever totally dedicated your life to the Lord?**

☐ **Is there anything hindering you from doing it right now?**

☐ Explain Romans 12:1-2 and lead the person in a prayer of total commitment of his or her life to the Lord.

4. Obedience to Authority
QUESTION:

☐ **If I were to ask your parents, would they tell me that you are obedient to their authority?**

☐ Explain how an authority is an umbrella of protection and how devastating the consequences are of getting out from under it.

☐ Urge the person to tell God in prayer that from this moment forward they will get under the protection of God-given authority.

5. Clear Conscience
QUESTIONS:

☐ **Can you look every person in the eye and know that no one can point a finger at you and say, "You offended me and have never tried to make it right?"**

☐ **H**ow many people stand between you and a clear conscience?

☐ Help the person to list the offenses of those who have offended them, and then have them list their offenses toward others.

☐ Help the person to focus on their offenses and purpose to go back and ask forgiveness.

☐ Help the person to write out the wording ahead of time and together determine if it reflects genuine repentance.

6. Conquering Bitterness
QUESTIONS:

☐ **H**as anyone ever deeply offended you or hurt you?

☐ **H**ave you been able to respond to their hurts with a spirit of forgiveness and love?

☐ Explain the causes of persistent bitterness.

☐ Explain the steps to turn bitterness into forgiveness. Include the step which involves giving something of value to an offender.

☐ Lead the person in a prayer of thanking God for His purposes through the offense.

☐ Determine with the person what would be appropriate to bless and encourage in the life of the offender (words, prayer, assistance, praise, gift, etc.).

7. Anger—Yielding Rights
QUESTIONS:

☐ **D**o you feel that you have a problem from time to time with your temper?

☐ **W**ould you like to learn how to control your temper?

☐ Explain how anger is related to personal rights.

☐ Encourage the person to write out personal rights and to specifically give them to God. Prepare them to thank God for whatever He does with them.

☐ Distinguish between personal rights and personal responsibilities. Urge the person to fulfill responsibilities by the power of God's Spirit.

8. Moral Freedom
QUESTIONS:

☐ **E**ach of us faces battlefields in our moral life. First, there is the battlefield of impure thoughts. Then there is the battlefield of impure actions. If we lose on these battlefields, we have a third battlefield of impure habits. How many battlefields are you fighting in your own personal life?

☐ **W**ould you like to experience consistent victory over impurity?

☐ Explain the diagram on the development of concupiscence.

☐ Explain the seven steps that we must take to conquer moral impurity.

☐ Go over the further steps of walking in the Spirit.

9. Engrafting Scripture
QUESTIONS:

- [ ] **If** I were to ask you to quote Romans chapter 6 in the first person, could you do it?

- [ ] **How** much Scripture have you engrafted in your mind, will, and emotions?

- [ ] **What** Scripture did you use to put yourself to sleep last night?

- [ ] **The** last time you were tempted, did you effectively overcome it by quoting Scripture?

- [ ] **What** Scripture did you read this morning before you began your day?

- [ ] Explain the steps to engraft Scripture and the importance of establishing accountability for it.

10. Purpose in Life
QUESTIONS:

- [ ] **When** you get to the end of your life, what do you want to look back on and say, "This is what God was able to accomplish through me"?

- [ ] **What** do Christians do that irritates you or damages the cause of Christ, and what could you do through your life to resolve it?

- [ ] Explain the ways of God and the insights in finding God's will.

- [ ] Present the eight callings of God from II Peter 1:1–10.

- [ ] Help the person to focus on one area of need in the Body of Christ or on an opportunity of service to which they could dedicate their efforts.

- [ ] Explain that the goal is to bring every person to full spiritual maturity.

11. Right Friendships
QUESTIONS:

- [ ] **Do** you have good Christian friends who are working with you to reach your spiritual goals?

  What accountability do you have with each other?

- [ ] Explain the material on levels of friendship.

12. Dating/Marriage
QUESTIONS:

- [ ] **Do** you know what it means to be a one-woman man and a one-man woman?

- [ ] **Have** you purposed not to defraud the ones you date?

- [ ] **Do** you want God's best for your marriage?

- [ ] **Have** you purposed to get permission from the girl's father for the privilege of dating and for the freedom of discussing marriage?

- [ ] Explain the three aspects of a total marriage and the four decisions that a father should make with his daughter.

- [ ] Explain the six decisions necessary to help determine the right life partner and encourage them to make them before the Lord in prayer.

- [ ] Go over the engagement material prior to becoming engaged.

13. Witnessing
QUESTIONS:

☐ **W**hat friends or acquaintances do you have that you would like to see become Christians?

☐ **C**ould we pray together that God will give you an opportunity to witness to them?

☐ Have the person write out his or her own testimony.

☐ Explain how to lead another person to Christ and then design witnessing opportunities together.

ADDITIONAL QUESTIONS WHICH YOU CAN ASK YOUR SONS AND DAUGHTERS:

_____

_____

_____

_____

_____

_____

_____

_____

_____

_____

HOW CAN PARENTS COMMUNICATE TO THE MIND OF THEIR CHILD?

A. KNOW HIS MENTAL FRAME OF REFERENCE.

Words and expressions mean different things to different people, and to some people, certain words have no meaning at all. Communication requires that the one to whom we are speaking is able to mentally visualize or picture the meaning of our words.

It is, therefore, essential that parents learn what pictures come to the minds of their children when certain words are spoken. This knowledge can be gained by keeping the following questions in mind as time is spent with the child in listening to him and asking him questions:

1. What ideas influence his decisions?
2. What do certain words and phrases mean to him?
3. What does he think he needs?
4. What does he really need?

Being aware of a child's frame of reference will become increasingly important as he is exposed to more and more outside influence.

B. BUILD LARGER AND CLEARER PICTURES OF WORDS, AND RELATE THEM TO SPIRITUAL TRUTH.

When a father tells his son, "I want you to be wise," what pictures come to the son's mind for the word *wise*: an owl, an ancient man, or a crafty animal? The instruction for this word requires that it be defined as "looking at life from God's point of view."

Then the word *wise* should be associated with Jesus Christ, *"in whom are hid all the treasures of wisdom and knowledge" (Colossians 2:3).*

Similar definitions and associations are needed for such words as righteousness, faith, prayer, meekness, humility, etc.

BUILD CHARACTER

The goal of all learning should be to develop Godly character. The following pages define precise character qualities and explain how you can build them into the lives of your sons and daughters.

Additional information and resources about building character are available in the **Character Clues** game.

HOW TO DEVELOP CHARACTER QUALITIES

1 REALIZE THE IMPORTANCE OF LEARNING THIS CHARACTER QUALITY.

There are three major reasons why we must learn character. First, it reveals the true nature of Christ Who is the perfect fulfillment of each quality. Second, it is the basis for success in life. Lasting achievement is not possible without it. Third, it explains why things happen to us.

God's ultimate purpose in our lives is to conform us to the image of Christ. Only with this in mind can we understand how all things work together for good. (See Romans 8:28–29.)

2 MEMORIZE THE OPERATIONAL DEFINITION.

Definitions are found in the *Character Clues* game. They are also expanded in the *Character Sketches* books.

An operational definition goes beyond the dictionary to include the practical function of the term. For example, listening goes beyond hearing to the interpretation of ideas, and the evaluation of how they can be used in our lives. Nodding, smiling, taking notes, asking questions, or making comments are manifestations of listening.

3 IDENTIFY THE QUALITY IN SCRIPTURE.

By using a concordance, various aspects of a quality can be discovered. For example, researching attentiveness would include studying verses which deal with listening, hearing, giving ear, and being still.

In addition to verses, think of biographical illustrations that would illustrate both positive and negative aspects of the quality. Samuel listened to God's voice while Eli was inattentive to it.

4 EXPAND WITH SYNONYMS AND ANTONYMS.

Knowing what a quality is not is often as helpful as knowing what it is. Use the *Random House Thesaurus* to expand your understanding of the words which were found in the concordance.

322

5 BALANCE WITH RELATED QUALITIES.

No quality stands alone; it needs others to keep it from being used inappropriately or incompletely. **Attentiveness** must be balanced with **discernment** and combined with **obedience**.

6 LIST WHEN AND WHERE THE QUALITY IS TO BE USED.

Attentiveness is the first character quality to be learned. The ear is the first sensory organ to be developed in the womb. At least eighty percent of the communication in our lives depends upon attentiveness.

The degree of attentiveness will be demonstrated during times of prayer, listening to sermons, hearing the instruction of parents, conversing with others, receiving discipline, and reading books.

7 DESIGN GUIDELINES TO LEARN THE QUALITY.

After understanding the importance and scope of a quality, think through practical disciplines that would be necessary to make that quality a living part of each area of your life. To be attentive, learn to sit still for a given period of time; do not talk while others are speaking; lean forward when being spoken to; take notes during sermons or instruction; and maintain eye contact during conversations.

8 TURN PROBLEMS INTO CHARACTER CLASSES.

During the week that you are working on a particular character quality, expect God to give you specially designed situations in which the quality can be better understood and more deeply applied. Welcome trials and temptations as character-building friends rather than resented intruders.

9 EVALUATE PROGRESS.

At the end of the week have each family member draw the name of another family member and answer the following questions:

- ☐ How was the character quality of the week demonstrated by that family member?
  Attentiveness to each person during the week will be required in order to answer this question.
- ☐ How could that family member have demonstrated the quality?
  Give respectful suggestions about opportunities which were overlooked.
- ☐ How did I feel when that family member demonstrated the quality?
  Describe the emotion you experienced.
- ☐ How did I feel when that family member failed to demonstrate the quality?
  Explain your inward feelings and outward responses.
- ☐ What did God teach me through each situation?

Operational Definitions of Character Qualities

(As found in the Character Bookshelf Series game, Character Clues)

P	S	T	E	G	R	M
TRUTHFULNESS vs. Deception — Earning future trust by accurately reporting past facts — Ephesians 4:25 — P1	**ALERTNESS** vs. Unawareness — Being aware of that which is taking place around me so that I can have the right responses to them — Mark 14:38 — S1	**SELF-CONTROL** vs. Self-indulgence — Instant obedience to the initial promptings of God's Spirit — Galatians 5:24–25 — T1	**WISDOM** vs. Natural Inclinations — Seeing and responding to life situations from God's frame of reference — Proverbs 9:10 — E1	**RESOURCEFULNESS** vs. Wastefulness — Wise use of that which others would normally overlook or discard — Luke 16:10 — G1	**ORDERLINESS** vs. Disorganization — Preparing myself and my surroundings so that I will achieve the greatest efficiency — I Corinthians 14:40 — R1	**ATTENTIVENESS** vs. Unconcern — Showing the worth of a person by giving undivided attention to his words and emotions — Hebrews 2:1 — M1
OBEDIENCE vs. Willfulness — Freedom to be creative under the protection of divinely-appointed authority — II Corinthians 10:5 — P2	**HOSPITALITY** vs. Loneliness — Cheerfully sharing food, shelter, and spiritual refreshment with those God brings into my life — Hebrews 13:2 — S2	**REVERENCE** vs. Disrespect — Awareness of how God is working through the people and events in my life to produce the character of Christ in me — Proverbs 23:17–18 — T2	**DISCERNMENT** vs. Judgment — The God-given ability to understand why things happen — I Samuel 16:7 — E2	**THRIFTINESS** vs. Extravagance — Not letting myself or others spend that which is not necessary — Luke 16:11 — G2	**INITIATIVE** vs. Unresponsiveness — Recognizing and doing what needs to be done before I am asked to do it — Romans 12:21 — R2	**SENSITIVITY** vs. Callousness — Exercising my senses so that I can perceive the true spirit and emotions of those around me — Romans 12:15 — M2
SINCERITY vs. Hypocrisy — Eagerness to do what is right with transparent motives — I Peter 1:22 — P3	**GENEROSITY** vs. Stinginess — Realizing that all I have belongs to God and using it for His purposes — II Corinthians 9:6 — S3	**DILIGENCE** vs. Slothfulness — Visualizing each task as a special assignment from the Lord and using all my energies to accomplish it — Colossians 3:23 — T3	**FAITH** vs. Presumption — Visualizing what God intends for me to do in a given situation and acting in harmony with it — Hebrews 11:1 — E3	**CONTENTMENT** vs. Covetousness — Realizing God has provided everything that I need for my present happiness — I Timothy 6:8 — G3	**RESPONSIBILITY** vs. Unreliability — Knowing and doing what both God and others are expecting from me — Romans 14:12 — R3	**JUSTICE** vs. Fairness — Personal responsibility to God's unchanging laws — Micah 6:8 — M3
VIRTUE vs. Impurity — The moral excellence and purity of spirit that radiate from my life as I obey God's Word — II Peter 1:5 — P4	**JOYFULNESS** vs. Self-pity — The spontaneous enthusiasm of my spirit when my soul is in fellowship with the Lord — Psalm 16:11 — S4	**THOROUGHNESS** vs. Incompleteness — Knowing what factors will diminish the effectiveness of my work or words if neglected — Proverbs 18:15 — T4	**DISCRETION** vs. Simple-mindedness — The ability to avoid words, actions, and attitudes which could result in undesirable consequences — Proverbs 22:3 — E4	**PUNCTUALITY** vs. Tardiness — Showing high esteem for other people and their time — Ecclesiastes 3:1 — G4	**HUMILITY** vs. Pride — Recognizing that God and others are actually responsible for the achievements in my life — James 4:6 — R4	**COMPASSION** vs. Indifference — Investing whatever is necessary to heal the hurts of others — I John 3:17 — M4
BOLDNESS vs. Fearfulness — Confidence that what I have to say or do is true and right and just in the sight of God — Acts 4:29 — P5	**FLEXIBILITY** vs. Resistance — Not setting my affections on ideas or plans which could be changed by God or others — I Peter 1:5 — S5	**DEPENDABILITY** vs. Inconsistency — Fulfilling what I consented to do even if it means unexpected sacrifice — Psalm 15:4 — T5	**LOVE** vs. Selfishness — Giving to others' basic needs without having as my motive personal reward — I Corinthians 13:3 — E5	**TOLERANCE** vs. Prejudice — Acceptance of others as unique expressions of specific character qualities in varying degrees of maturity — Philippians 2:2 — G5	**DECISIVENESS** vs. Double-mindedness — The ability to finalize difficult decisions based on the will and ways of God — James 1:5 — R5	**GENTLENESS** vs. Harshness — Showing personal care and concern in meeting the needs of others — I Thessalonians 2:7 — M5
FORGIVENESS vs. Rejection — Clearing the record of those who have wronged me and allowing God to love them through me — Ephesians 4:32 — P6	**AVAILABILITY** vs. Self-centeredness — Making my own schedule and priorities secondary to the wishes of those I am serving — Philippians 2:20–21 — S6	**SECURITY** vs. Anxiety — Structuring my life around that which is eternal and cannot be destroyed or taken away — John 6:27 — T6	**CREATIVITY** vs. Under-achievement — Approaching a need, a task, an idea from a new perspective — Romans 12:2 — E6	**CAUTIOUSNESS** vs. Rashness — Knowing how important right timing is in accomplishing right actions — Proverbs 19:2 — G6	**DETERMINATION** vs. Faint-heartedness — Purposing to accomplish God's goals in God's time regardless of the opposition — II Timothy 4:7–8 — R6	**DEFERENCE** vs. Rudeness — Limiting my freedom in order not to offend the tastes of those God has called me to serve — Romans 14:21 — M6
PERSUASIVENESS vs. Contentiousness — Guiding vital truths around another's mental roadblocks — II Timothy 2:24 — P7	**ENDURANCE** vs. Giving up — The inward strength to withstand stress to accomplish God's best — Galatians 6:9 — S7	**PATIENCE** vs. Restlessness — Accepting a difficult situation from God without giving Him a deadline to remove it — Romans 5:3–4 — T7	**ENTHUSIASM** vs. Apathy — Expressing with my spirit the joy of my soul — I Thessalonians 5:16,19 — E7	**GRATEFULNESS** vs. Unthankfulness — Making known to God and others in what ways they have benefited my life — I Corinthians 4:7 — G7	**LOYALTY** vs. Unfaithfulness — Using difficult times to demonstrate my commitment to God and to those whom He has called me to serve — John 15:13 — R7	**MEEKNESS** vs. Anger — Yielding my personal rights and expectations to God — Psalm 62:5 — M7

EVALUATING YOUR CHILD'S CHARACTER

Name of child _____

Parents are the best qualified to point out the blind spots in a child's life. Using the chart below, place a *plus* sign (+) by the qualities which are strong in your child's life and a *minus* sign (—) by the qualities for which you see negative evidence. Please note that negative evidences are not opposites of the given character quality; they are behaviors observed when the positive quality is misused or carried to excess. The negative evidences are listed in parentheses following each character quality.

TRUTHFULNESS

____ Boldness (tactless, insensitive, undiplomatic, disrespectful, indiscreet)
____ Dependability (possessive, unable to include others, unable to delegate)
____ Expressiveness (wordy, glib, boisterous, melodramatic)
____ Honesty (outspoken, blunt, brutal, indiscreet)
____ Orderliness (over-meticulous, inflexible, possessive)
____ Persuasiveness (pushy, smooth-talking, high pressure tactics)
____ Purity (false piety, holier-than-thou, selective separation)
____ Sincerity (gullible, impulsive, over-serious)
____ Virtue (unwillingness to share defeats or inadequacies, cover of perfection, pride)

LOYALTY

____ Cooperativeness (compromising, conniving, lacking initiative)
____ Courage (reckless, brash, brazen, daring)
____ Dedication (over-conscientious, over-serious, nervous, meticulousness)
____ Determination (using people to achieve goals, rejecting cautions, rejecting God's death of a vision)
____ Devotion (possessive, blind obedience, undue attachment)
____ Endurance (disregarding health of self and others, neglecting other priorities)
____ Reverence (idol worship, debilitating subservience)

GRATEFULNESS

____ Contentment (apathetic, easy-going, resignation)
____ Enthusiasm (fanatical, over-bearing, over-wrought, aggressive)
____ Friendliness (gullible, status-seeking, spineless, socially preoccupied)
____ Generosity (extravagant, spend-thrift, wasteful, squandering)
____ Hospitality (ingratiating, social-climbing, cliquish)
____ Humility (self-abasing, extreme self-criticism, lack of self confidence)
____ Joyfulness (giddy, silly, inability to be serious)
____ Service (eye-service, pushy, presumptuous, forceful)

PATIENCE

____ Availability (intrusive, pushy)
____ Compassion (gushy sentimentalism, undiscerning empathy, taking up offenses)
____ Deference (self-conscious, superficial flattery, social stiffness)
____ Flexibility (wishy-washy, indecisive, spineless)
____ Forgiveness (irresponsible leniency, permissive, weak, compromising, covering sin)
____ Longsuffering (indifference, permissive, disinterested)
____ Meekness (docile, weak, too accomodating, spineless)
____ Persistence (stubborn, self-willed, headstrong, inflexible)
____ Tolerance (compromising, permissive, too accepting, undiscerning)

WISDOM

____ Decisiveness (inflexible, ruthless, domineering, close-minded)
____ Discernment (judgmental, critical, fault-finding, snoopy)
____ Discretion (secretive, timid, over-cautious)
____ Faith (presumptuous, visionary, over-active imagining, make believe)
____ Justice (indecisive, indiscriminate, undiscerning, unloving, insensitive, cold and calculating)
____ Thriftiness (stingy, miserly, penny-pinching)

ATTENTIVENESS

____ Alertness (jumpy, inquisitive, quick to criticize)
____ Cautiousness (fussy, petty, over-attention to detail)
____ Creativity (mischievous, crafty, devious, day-dreaming)
____ Initiative (intrusive, taking on the responsibilities of others, domineering)
____ Resourcefulness (manipulative, scheming, over-independent)
____ Sensitivity (touchy, easily offended, emotional)

OBEDIENCE

____ Consistency (inflexible, closed-minded, rigid)
____ Diligence (one-track minded, selfishly industrious, slavish)
____ Neatness (over-meticulous, stiff, perfectionistic, intolerant)
____ Punctuality (impatient with tardiness, inflexible, intolerant)
____ Responsibility (assuming the undone responsibilities of others, taking blame for things that are not his/her responsibility)
____ Self-control (rigid, harsh, overbearing, tyrannical, legalistic)
____ Thoroughness (perfectionistic, pedantic, insecure about task completion)

HOW TO STUDY A CHARACTER QUALITY

Ewing Galloway

- Examine the quality by learning its dictionary definition.

- Examine the quality by defining and illustrating its opposite.

- Conduct a detailed word study of the root word which names the quality. Examine its synonyms, antonyms, and related field of vocabulary.

- Examine the quality by discussing distortions (or excesses) of it.

- Memorize a key verse or passage of Scripture which gives direction concerning the character quality.

- Design projects which will bring about the practice of the quality.

ILLUSTRATIONS:

Alertness

Ability to anticipate right responses to that which is taking place around me

Dictionary definition: The practice or tendency of being watchful and prompt to meet danger or emergency.

Opposite: Unawareness

Synonyms of *alert*: Vigilant, circumspect, guarded, cautious, careful, heedful, observant, mindful, prompt, anticipating

Antonyms of *alert*: Unconscious, inattentive, heedless, unsuspecting, incognizant, unadvised, unwary, blinded, insensitive, unprepared, "off one's guard"

Related vocabulary: Cause and effect terminology, warnings, regulatory words, strategy terms for battle

Distortions: Jumpy, presumptuous, snoopy, nervous, reactionary, busybody, quick to criticize, inquisitive

Key verse: Mark 14:38

Projects/Assignments:
- Identify and chart the things in your "world" which are dangerous to you physically, mentally, and spiritually. On the chart, give one or two specific instructions for avoiding each danger.
- From a collection of news articles, identify the factor of unawareness which caused the defeat of the harmed person.
- Analyze the danger which motivated parents, teachers, police officers, etc. to make the particular rules they have made for you.

Availability

Making my own schedule and priorities secondary to the wishes of those I am serving

Dictionary definition: Accessible for use, at hand, usable, having the qualification or willingness to do something or to assume a responsibility

Opposite: Self-centeredness

Synonyms of *available*: Serviceable, helpful, practical, beneficial, functional, advantageous, ready, at hand, on call, commissioned, accessible, "at one's disposal"

Antonyms of *available*: Egocentric, (egotistical), vainglory, individualistic, selfish, self-seeking, self-indulgent, pretentious, unaccessible, unreachable, impenetrable

Related vocabulary: Terms relating to employment, qualifications, job description, preparation

Distortions: Aggressive, presumptuous, intrusive, officious, forward, obtrusive, self-assertive

Key verse: Philippians 2:20–21

Projects/Assignments:
- Volunteer to do some needed task at home. Keep a log for one month of parental response, changes in family relationships, and inner growth that result from each occasion.
- Volunteer to meet the need of someone outside your family while praying that God will use that service to open a door of witness for Him.
- Prepare a checklist of projects (diary) you start in one week's time. Evaluate the quality and

thoroughness of your work. Did you finish each project? Did you clean up without reminder as part of the project completion?

- Examine the qualifications of several life ministries (careers). Make a notebook which charts how the qualifications make that particular employee an asset to his employer.
- Write a job description for yourself as a Christian listing Jesus Christ as your "boss." For each qualification listed, write the steps needed to develop it in your life.
- Have your father write a job description for you as his son/daughter. Discuss steps necessary to develop each needed qualification.
- Keep a log of a week's activities in fifteen-minute segments. Tally the use of your time. Does its use match your priorities? Could you have found more time to be available by making some specific adjustments? What are they?

 **Attentiveness** Showing the worth of a person by giving sincere attention to his words

Projects/Assignments:
- Study the ear and the eye. Diagram the features of each. Relate the abilities of each to the science of sound and light. Notice how the Creator has planned for perceptiveness in listening and observing.
- Make a chart to log over a two-week period of time the contrast in your own experience of hearing vs. listening and seeing vs. observing. What were the results in each situation?
- Keep a notebook of ideas learned in Sunday School lessons and sermons. Practice giving the speaker "feedback" during a presentation by responding with facial expression, nodding your head, notetaking, etc.
- Describe something you saw or heard using as many adjectives and adverbs as possible.
- Practice keeping the conversational "ball" rolling by giving substantive answers rather than one-word responses to questions.
- Learn to analyze the form/design of a major work of music/art (e.g., outline of symphonic form, or symmetry, line, balance in a painting).
- Make a scrapbook of pictures of people's faces. Describe the message the person is conveying by analyzing his facial expression. Choose adjectives carefully.
- Construct a scale model (e.g., tabernacle, ark, your home or church) giving attention to accurate measurement and detail.
- Analyze the simple rules of everyday etiquette to describe how the exercise of those procedures illustrates your attentiveness to people around you.

 **Cautiousness** Knowing how important right timing is in accomplishing right actions

Projects/Assignments:
- Various types of weather demand certain cautions to be observed. Chart these in the four seasons with appropriate "warnings" for each based on the potential danger involved.
- Research a potential buying project for your family. Learn what questions to ask to evaluate the product; consult experts in the field; read appropriate periodicals; report the data you find and propose an appropriate action. (Consult *Men's Manual*, Volume II.)
- Analyze media advertising techniques. Make a scrapbook of examples to illustrate each technique. List on each page appropriate questions to diffuse the propaganda effects of that technique. (See *Men's Manual*, Volume II, chapter nine.)
- Keep a diary/log of warnings your parents have given you. List next to each warning an analysis of the danger from which you were to be protected. Notice that as you grew up the warnings were fewer and more generalized. This means that you increasingly had to learn to exercise the responsibility of caution for your own life.

Compassion Investing whatever is necessary to heal the hurts of others

Projects/Assignments:
- Make a list of your ten unchangeable features. Focus on a person who irritates you. List his unchangeable features as you can observe them. Which of these features make that person as he is? Begin to pray daily that God will change you so that you can have a ministry to them.
- Write a statement of life's purpose, destiny, hope, etc. from a lost person's point of view. Ask God to cause that vision to give you a burden to reach them with the message of salvation.
- Purpose in your heart that you will not make a joke at another's expense regarding the physical, mental, or family background characteristics that he cannot change. Analyze each evening for a month the conversational interchange between you and your friends to evaluate progress in keeping this resolution.
- Plan to give something dear to you to a person who needs special comfort. Give it as an expression of your heart's sympathy.

HOW CAN PARENTS KEEP THE ATTENTION OF THEIR SONS AND DAUGHTERS FOR INSTRUCTION?

● _____

_____

"Wisdom hath builded her house, she hath hewn out her seven pillars: She hath killed her beasts; she hath mingled her wine; she hath also furnished her table" (Proverbs 9:1–2).

DEVELOP THE ABILITY TO CREATE CURIOSITY FOR ESSENTIAL INFORMATION

One of the most effective methods which Jesus Christ used when teaching was to create curiosity through the use of stories, parables, and questions. In the same way parents should prepare their sons and daughters for essential information before they give it. *"The tongue of the wise makes knowledge attractive" (Proverbs 15:2).*

ORGANIZE AND INTERNALIZE INFORMATION

Instruction must be designed to achieve certain specific goals which must be clearly focused in the mind of the parent. Only then is he or she able to effectively organize and communicate information to help sons and daughters visualize, internalize, and achieve God's purpose for their lives. Some examples of these goals would be:

1. Personal character goals
2. Academic goals
3. Spiritual goals
4. Vocational goals
5. Marriage goals
6. Financial management goals

MAKE WISDOM YOUR GOAL

When finding the treasures of wisdom becomes our goal, we are brought to an intimate relationship with Jesus Christ, for in Him *"are hidden all the treasures of wisdom and knowledge" (Colossians 2:3).* Here are some of the significant qualities which will result from making wisdom our goal:

1 THROUGH WISDOM WE MAKE THE BEST USE OF OUR TIME.

"So teach us to number our days, that we may apply our hearts unto wisdom" (Psalm 90:12).

"Length of days is in her right hand; and in her left hand riches and honour" (Proverbs 3:16).

2 THROUGH WISDOM WE DISCOVER DIRECTION IN LIFE.

"Then shalt thou understand righteousness [doing what God requires], and judgment [right from wrong], and equity [fairness in difficult situations]; yea, every good path. When wisdom entereth into thine heart . . ." (Proverbs 2:9–10).

3 THROUGH WISDOM WE LEARN TO COMMUNICATE EFFECTIVELY.

"The heart of the wise teacheth his mouth, and addeth learning to his lips" (Proverbs 16:23).

"A wise man will hear, and will increase learning; and a man of understanding shall attain unto wise counsels" (Proverbs 1:5).

4 THROUGH WISDOM WE ARE ABLE TO DISCERN THE TRUE CHARACTER OF OTHERS.

"Say unto wisdom, Thou art my sister; and call understanding thy kinswoman: that they may keep thee from the strange woman . . . yea, many strong men have been slain by her" (Proverbs 7:4, 26).

5 THROUGH WISDOM WE BECOME CREATIVE.

"I wisdom dwell with prudence, and find out knowledge of witty inventions" (Proverbs 8:12).

6 THROUGH WISDOM WE GAIN TRUE HAPPINESS.

"Happy is the man that findeth wisdom, and the man that getteth understanding" (Proverbs 3:13).

7 THROUGH WISDOM WE GAIN TRUE RICHES AND HONOR.

"For the merchandise of it [wisdom] is better than the merchandise of silver, and the gain thereof than fine gold. She is more precious than rubies: and all the things thou canst desire are not to be compared unto her" (Proverbs 3:14–15).

8 THROUGH WISDOM WE DELIGHT THOSE WHO HAVE A GENUINE CONCERN FOR US.

"My son, if thine heart be wise, my heart shall rejoice, even mine" (Proverbs 23:15).

". . . A wise son maketh a glad father . . ." (Proverbs 10:1).

"Whoso loveth wisdom rejoiceth his father . . ." (Proverbs 29:3).

HOW A FATHER BUILT COMMUNICATION WITH HIS CHILDREN BY AN "ANSWER MAN" TIME

Ewing Galloway

The importance of a father being looked up to by his children as a man with answers cannot be overemphasized. Here is how one father established this relationship with his sons and daughters.

The father of three children, ages four, six, and nine became concerned that there was not the openness toward him that he desired. One evening he told his children that after they were ready for bed he would become "The Answer Man" and allow them to ask him any question they wanted.

It didn't take too many evenings before his children eagerly looked forward to these times with their father. The younger children would get ready for bed a lot quicker and then call out, "Time for the Answer Man."

There was no fear that they would ask him a question he could not answer. If he didn't know the answer, he would simply turn the question into an opportunity to look the answer up in an encyclopedia, concordance, dictionary, or some other source book. If he still was unable to find the answer, he or his wife would consult someone outside the family who might know.

He found that the children did not want to end. So, a time limit had to be set for the discussion. This made the children anticipate the evenings even more. Sometimes he would have special surprises for them in the form of stories, or interesting facts from history, biographies, or science.

SOME OF THE BENEFITS OF THIS PROJECT WERE AS FOLLOWS:

1. It brought out new anticipation for talking with their father each night.

2. It motivated both the father and the children to be more alert to life and learning.

3. It taught the children how to use resource books for finding answers.

4. It gave the father a regular opportunity to correlate knowledge with basic Scriptural principles.

5. It widened the concept of God as a concerned Father who is interested in giving answers to the questions of his children.

GUIDELINES FOR MAKING THIS PROJECT SUCCESSFUL:

1. Think through the clearest presentation of each answer before you give it.

2. Make sure each child is given an equal amount of time to ask questions.

3. Treat every question with equal interest and importance.

4. Show special pleasure when questions are asked about God and the Christian life.

5. Never demand the attention of the children—earn it. If discussion begins among the children, let it continue as long as it is profitable. Avoid any correction or discipline during these sessions.

6. Give your undivided attention to the children during this time. Do not allow yourself to be distracted. The mother should take care of phone calls and other interruptions during this time.

NOTES

DIAGRAMS

Wisdom Worksheet 1

"And seeing the multitudes, he went up into a mountain . . ." *(Matthew 5:1a).*

MORNING WISDOM SEARCHES

Gather as a family one-half hour before breakfast. Explore five Psalms and one chapter of Proverbs each morning. Begin with Psalm 1 and Proverbs 1. Read consecutively.

Search for words and ideas related to seeing, such as: □ eyes looking □ saw □ vision □ what God sees □ what we are to see □ what we are not to see.

After reading, share your insights and then individually ask God for wisdom to see as He sees.

CHARACTER FOCUS:

Alertness

□ How can we train our eyes to see what God wants us to see? □ How can we train our spiritual eyes to see what our physical eyes cannot see? □ What dims our spiritual eyesight?

MAJOR CONCEPT:
God sees differently than we see.

The key thinking skill needed to master this concept is **comparison vs. contrast**. Therefore, these questions can be asked.

- □ How much does God see?
- □ What does God see?
- □ Does anything stop God from seeing?
- □ How does God respond to what He sees?
- □ How much does man see?
- □ What does man see?
- □ Does anything stop man from seeing?
- □ How does man respond to what He sees?

INTRODUCTORY IDEAS:
A wise teacher makes learning fun!

Parents in one family helped their children see with understanding by designing a game of "What did you see?" They put several objects on a table and covered them with a towel. One child at a time was brought into the room and allowed to see the objects for five seconds. The objects were then recovered and the child tried to recall as many as he could.

Following this, they discussed how Jesus saw and comprehended all the needs of those in the multitude.

LEARNING ANALOGIES

Use mountains to illustrate the characteristics of God. This develops the thinking skill of **analogy**. An analogy shows how a specific aspect of one thing is related to a specific aspect of another thing. How do mountains picture: □ God's strength? □ God's protection? □ God's holiness? □ God's stability?

EVENING WISDOM SEARCHES

Principles and Concepts

The father leads the evening *Wisdom Searches* allowing family members to work on handcraft projects such as knitting or coloring pictures related to the reading. As family members identify a truth about alertness, they can stop the father to discuss it.

SUGGESTED SCHEDULE:

- □ **Monday**: Begin a program of reading through the Bible with Genesis 1–3. Look for evidences of what God sees and what man should see or not see.
- □ **Tuesday**: Read about alertness in *Character Sketches*, Volume II, pages 76–86.
- □ **Wednesday**: Read about Noah in *Character Sketches*, Volume II, pages 87–89.
- □ **Thursday**: Read Genesis 4–6.
- □ **Friday**: Discuss "Levels of Conflict" chart in Basic Seminar Textbook and Workbook.
- □ **Saturday**: Read Genesis 7–9.
- □ **Sunday**: Catch up and review what was learned during the week.

Linguistics

Languages, Grammar, Vocabulary, Communication

History

Archaeology, Geography, Prophecy, Music, Art, Literature

"AND SEEING THE MULTITUDES . . ."

- Estimate the number of people in this picture:
  Estimate _____ Actual _____

Do Project A.

☐ We tend to train our eyes to see what is important to us.

☐ Wisdom is training our eyes to see what is important to God.

Do Project B.

". . . HE WENT UP INTO A MOUNTAIN . . ."

The mountains of Palestine offered a place of quietness and privacy. Jesus frequented this wilderness for private prayer and undisturbed teaching.

SEEING
Greek: ἔιδω (ī-dō or ā-dō)
DEFINITION: To observe with understanding; to behold and consider; to perceive.

- When Jesus saw the multitudes, He saw more than just a crowd of people. He saw each individual and each personal need. He was moved with compassion.

Do Project C.

MULTITUDES
Greek: ὄχλος (**okh**-los)
DEFINITION: A great crowd; a throng; a huge assembly.

MOUNTAIN
Greek: ὄρος (**o**-ros)
DEFINITION: Rugged land elevated above the plain.

God chose the mountain of Zion to illustrate:

- His rule (See Psalm 2:6.)
- His protection (See Psalm 11:1.)
- His highness (See Psalm 24:3.)
- His holiness (See Psalm 48:1.)
- His beauty (See Psalm 48:2.)
- His peace (See Psalm 72:3.)
- His nearness (See Psalm 74:2.)
- His ownership (See Psalm 78:54.)
- His endurance (See Psalm 125:1.)
- His presence (See Psalm 125:2.)

A larger and clearer perspective is seen by those who are on a mountain. This was the spiritual objective which Jesus had when He gave the "Sermon on the Mount."

Do Project D.

What was the historical significance of Jesus' going into the mountain to preach?

Mount Sinai (Horeb)

Moses went up into Mount Sinai in 1491 B.C. to receive the Law of God.

Jesus went up into a mountain in 31 A.D. to clarify the meaning of the Law and to show His disciples how they could apply its teachings to their everyday lives.

Do Project E.

What personal sacrifices did the multitude make to hear Jesus teach?

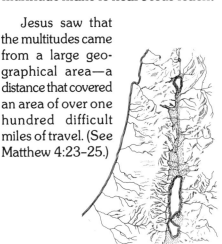

Jesus saw that the multitudes came from a large geographical area—a distance that covered an area of over one hundred difficult miles of travel. (See Matthew 4:23–25.)

The multitudes were composed primarily of men. Many demonstrated their willingness to sacrifice everything to follow Christ.

cience

When do we look at something without clearly seeing it?

Newborn babies "see," but have not yet learned to focus their eyes. Their vision is blurred.

SEEING REQUIRES TRAINING AND MATURITY

Muscles must learn to move the eye in the right direction, to focus on the object to be observed, and to regulate the amount of light which enters the eye. However, the real "seeing" comes as we train our minds to see things others overlook.

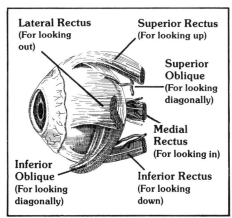

Lateral Rectus (For looking out)

Superior Rectus (For looking up)

Superior Oblique (For looking diagonally)

Medial Rectus (For looking in)

Inferior Oblique (For looking diagonally)

Inferior Rectus (For looking down)

The Six Eye Muscles

Even after training the eye muscles, errors of focusing can develop. **Myopia** results in distant objects being blurred (nearsightedness). **Hyperopia** results in near objects being blurred (farsightedness). **Amblyopia** is caused by one eye not cooperating with the other eye ("lazy" eye). **Presbyopia** is the loss of the ability to focus with age.

• *Can you apply each of these disorders to errors in spiritual perception?*

Do Project F.

aw

How do mountains illustrate characteristics of God's Law?

• The *permanency* of God's Law.

The mountains will pass away but God's Word will live forever. (See Luke 16:17.)

• The *protective limitations* of God's Law.

Mountains provide natural barriers in the same way that God's Law provides clear limitations for man's instruction. (See Psalm 125:2–3.)

• The *resources* of God's Law.

The precious metals that are found in mountains and the refreshing water from the mountain's snowcap clearly picture the riches and pure refreshment of God's Word. (See Psalm 19:7–11.)

How do multitudes illustrate the need for God's Law?

Jesus perceived that the multitudes had spiritual needs which were not being met by all the traditions of the scribes.

These religious leaders had taught the "letter of the Law," but had missed the "spirit of the Law."

Do Project G.

UNIVERSAL PRINCIPLES VERSUS RELIGIOUS TRADITIONS

When Jesus began to expound the underlying principles of the Law, the people were astonished at His teaching, *"For he taught them as one having authority, and not as the scribes"* (Matthew 7:29).

edicine

How do the things we see affect our physical strength?

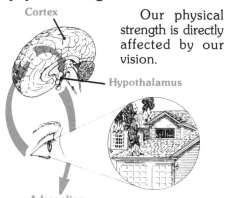

Cortex

Hypothalamus

Adrenaline

Our physical strength is directly affected by our vision.

If we saw a child in the window of a burning building, the hypothalamus in our brain would trigger the release of adrenaline (epinephrine) into our bloodstream.

Once in the bloodstream the adrenaline increases the body's rate of metabolism. This increase causes muscles to be stronger and to resist fatigue until the danger is resolved.

Do Project H.

How does living on a mountain increase physical vitality?

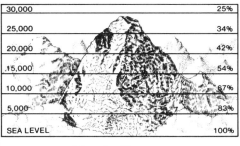

30,000	25%
25,000	34%
20,000	42%
15,000	54%
10,000	67%
5,000	83%
SEA LEVEL	100%

Alveolar Pressure

The alveoli are small air sacks in the lungs. Oxygen penetrates these thin membranes and enters the bloodstream.

Because there is less oxygen in the air at higher elevations, those who live in the mountains soon develop better circulation to compensate for the thinner oxygen level.

RESOURCE PROJECTS

For parents: Communicate to the spirit of your child by summarizing or completing each project.

A. DISCOVER THE PURPOSE OF MATH.

1 Have your children make a list of reasons for learning math. 2 Read the reasons given in the *Authority through Accuracy Resource* (exclude math problems). 3 Ask, "What math skills did the disciples need to know in order to carry out Christ's command to feed the five thousand?" 4 Read Mark 6:34–44. 5 Complete the math problems in the Resource.

B. TRAIN YOUR EYES TO "SEE."

1 Have each family member write at least three specific things the following people would see in a crowd that others might overlook: a policeman, a dentist, a mother, a shoe salesman. 2 Contact two of these to expand your answers. 3 Discuss what causes the answers to vary. 4 List three things a Christian should notice in a crowd. 5 Discuss how the things we notice reveal our values.

C. LEARN THE POWER OF THE PEN.

1 Discuss how the pen is mightier than the sword. 2 Read page 7. 3 Learn the precise definitions from the vocabulary cards. 4 Do Precision Project 1. 5 Distinguish between discernment and judgment (page 9). 6 Discuss "Levels of Conflict" (Friday evening *Wisdom Search*). 7 Do Precision Project 2.

Examples of clue cards:

antonym	homonym
clean clothes	flower
= dirty laundry	= flour

synonym	homonym
record player	sink(ing ship)
= stereo	= bathroom sink

Suggested Project:

To distinguish between synonyms, antonyms, and homonyms, plan a treasure hunt. Write clues (left) on 3 x 5 cards. Hide all clues as directed (except the starter clue). Have the family work as a team.

D. KNOW HOW LANGUAGES BEGAN.

1 Ask, "Why doesn't everyone speak the same language?" 2 Read Genesis 11:1–9. 3 Locate the ten major language families on a world map. 4 Ask, "Why did God write the Old Testament in Hebrew and the New Testament in Greek?" 5 Read the answer on page 12. 6 Explain how one third of the Greek alphabet can be learned from three words, and do Greek Investigation 1. 7 Learn Greek Sentence Analysis (page 14).

E. VISUALIZE THE LAND OF PALESTINE.

1 Use the captions in the History Resource as a quiz (pages 16–19). 2 Pinpoint the locations on a map as you read the answers. 3 Use the scale of miles to answer the distance questions on page 20. 4 Match the locations with the corresponding descriptions on pages 21–22.

F. RELATE SIGHT TO SPIRITUAL VISION.

1 Draw the six cartoon faces from the Science Resource on a marker board. 2 List the six vision irregularities. 3 Have the children try to match them. 4 Read the resource, and apply the insights to your lives.

G. KNOW THE LAW BEHIND THE SERMON.

1 Draw Mount Sinai and Mount Gerizim side by side on top of the marker board. 2 Read Matthew 5–7. 3 List the topics covered under Mount Gerizim. 4 Read Exodus 20. 5 List the topics covered under Mount Sinai. 6 Draw lines connecting similar topics.

H. RELATE SIGHT TO STRENGTH.

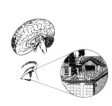

1 Ask, "How could a man with a weak heart lift 1,800 pounds?" 2 Read the account in the Medicine Resource (page 27). 3 Recall situations of fright and describe physical changes that occurred. 4 Learn what adrenaline does (pages 27–29). 5 Complete the quiz about David (page 29). 6 Discuss the value of adrenaline in fleeing evil or standing against it (page 30).

Wisdom Worksheet (Matthew 5:1a)

How can parents motivate disinterested sons and daughters?

- _____

- _____

- _____

One day an argument erupted between a father and his eighteen-year-old son. It occurred when the father asked the son to paint his room. The son said, "no," and the father became angry and harsh with him. The son, in turn, became angry, packed his bags, and left home.

This father was not aware that when he asked his son to paint his room, the son consciously or unconsciously asked himself the following two questions:

- **What will I gain if I do it?**
- **What will I lose if I don't do it?**

The fact that he asked these questions was revealed later when the son explained: "I didn't want to do it because I knew I would be leaving for college in a few weeks anyway, and I wouldn't be able to use it." In other words, his decision not to paint his room was based on the immature reason that he would not gain anything if he did it.

An entirely different response could have been gained from the son if the father would have answered these two motivational questions in his own mind and from the viewpoint of his son's mind **before** he asked the son to paint the room.

For example:

What will my son gain if he paints the room?

A. Skill in painting?
B. Financial reward?
C. Parental approval?
D. A cleaner room to return to during college breaks?
E. A pleasant reminder to the parents of the son's achievement when guests use his room?

What losses will my son experience if he doesn't paint his room?

A. Parental disapproval?
B. Financial loss?
C. Poor example?
D. Opportunity of expressing appreciation to the parents?

If none of these reasons would have been meaningful to the son, then it would have been necessary to relate the reward or losses of the painting to something which would have been meaningful to him, such as offering to paint the room with him so that the father and son would be able to enjoy fellowship.

What should parents do when a child disobeys instructions?

2 _____

_____

- _____

- _____

- _____

EFFECTIVE WARNING APPEALS TO THE CONSCIENCE

WHAT IS THE CONSCIENCE?

The conscience is the inward sensitivity to right and wrong. It is referred to in John 1:9 as "*. . . the true Light, which lighteth every man that cometh into the world.*" This "light of conscience" is sensitive to the qualities of God's nature as well as to the lack of them.

Whenever the child behaves contrary to any one of these qualities, a sense of conviction results. This conviction is "felt" in the conscience.

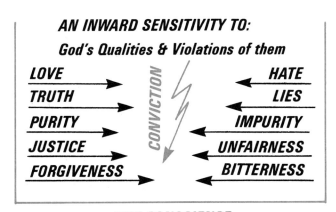

AN INWARD SENSITIVITY TO:
God's Qualities & Violations of them

	CONVICTION	
LOVE →		← HATE
TRUTH →		← LIES
PURITY →		← IMPURITY
JUSTICE →		← UNFAIRNESS
FORGIVENESS →		← BITTERNESS

THE CONSCIENCE

HOW CAN PARENTS REINFORCE THE CONSCIENCE OF THEIR CHILD?

There are two primary ways in which parents can strengthen the conscience of a son or daughter. Each should be used consistently.

1 Use God's Word to reinforce the moral law which He has already written in the heart of each child. *"Which shew the work of the law written in their hearts, their conscience also bearing witness, and their thoughts the meanwhile accusing or else excusing one another" (Romans 2:15).*

God's moral law causes a child to be aware when he is demonstrating love, truthfulness, purity, justice, forgiveness, etc. or the opposite of these qualities.

2 Use the reproofs of life to help the child learn how violating his conscience results in broken relationships. Help the child understand that God uses mental and physical pain to reprove those who violate the principles of His Word.

CONSCIENCE — THE REPROOFS OF LIFE

CONSCIENCE	THE REPROOFS OF LIFE
HATE	Parents
LIES	Brothers and sisters
IMPURITY	Friends
	Government
	Enemies
INJUSTICE	Instructors, employers
BITTERNESS	Circumstances
	Health
	Life partner

Cooperate with the inward working of the Holy Spirit in the child as He convicts of sin, righteousness, and judgment. (See John 16:8.)

CAN WE "KILL" THE CONSCIENCE?

A son or daughter can never "kill his conscience," but he can "sear it," "defile it," "weaken it," and "quench" the promptings of God's Spirit in it. When the conscience is weakened, it is possible for the child to rationalize every single offense toward God and toward man.

HOW IS A WEAKENED CONSCIENCE REVIVED?

The conscience is revived in the same way it is initially reinforced: on the one hand through the living and written Word of God and on the other hand through the reproofs of instruction which occur in a damaged relationship or circumstance.

HOW DOES A PARENT DETERMINE WHETHER OR NOT HE IS APPEALING TO THE CONSCIENCE OF HIS CHILD?

Notice how the following statements differ in their primary appeal to the child:
1. You will stay in if you disobey. (Physical)
2. You'll really hurt me by doing that. (Emotions)
3. Promise me you won't do that again. (Will)
4. Was that a smart thing to do? (Intellect)
5. Did you tell me the truth? (Conscience)

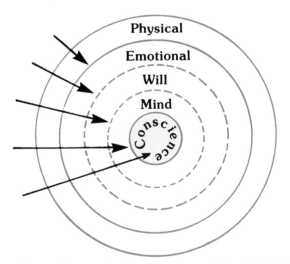

Appealing to the conscience of the child is to cooperate with the Spirit of God. It is measuring the child's behavior against the holy standard of God rather than the examples of his friends or even his parents.

The Apostle Paul appealed directly to the conscience of those with whom he worked and gained lasting results when he told them that he was speaking the plain truth to them and thus, commending himself to every man's conscience in the sight of God. (See II Corinthians 4:2.)

What should parents do if a child continues to disobey after being properly instructed and warned?

3 _____

_____

BASIC STEPS OF CORRECTION

Effective discipline can be measured by the principles which God uses in disciplining His sons and daughters.

"My son, despise not the chastening of the Lord; neither be weary of his correction: For whom the Lord loveth he correcteth; even as a father the son in whom he delighteth" (Proverbs 3:11–12).

What should every parent do before approaching a son or daughter who needs to be disciplined?

☐ _____

_____

"No man can enter into a strong man's house, and spoil his goods, except he will first bind the strong man; and then he will spoil his house" (Mark 3:27).

What is the first goal in the discipline process?

☐ _____

_____

"If we confess our sins, he is faithful and just to forgive us our sins, and to cleanse us from all unrighteousness" (I John 1:9).

When a child disobeys after instruction and warning, then it is necessary for the parent to direct a question to the child which will cause the child to assume the responsibility for his disobedience. It is important that you ask that question in a non-accusing manner. Ask the child, **"What did you do?"**

The purpose of this question is to clarify the offense in the mind of the child, as well as to encourage him to repent of the offense. Do not ask, "Why did you do it?" because the child will then tend to blame others or his circumstances. Also, do not ask, "Did you do it?" This question only motivates the child to deny the implied accusation.

Where should discipline take place?

☐ _____

_____

"As ye know how we exhorted and comforted and charged every one of you, as a father doth his children" (I Thessalonians 2:11).

A child should be corrected alone whenever possible, especially if his offense did not occur in public. When a parent brings up a previous offense in front of his child's friends and attempts to correct the child, the child will tend to be more concerned for his own reputation than remorseful about the offense he committed.

A publicly embarrassing correction not only demoralizes the child, but also produces a wounded spirit, which will affect future communication between the parent and the child. It also motivates him to figure out ways to justify his actions to those who saw him punished, so that they will side with him.

The child's need of self-justification could also motivate him to look for faults in his parents so that these could be shared with those who saw him punished, thus strengthening his side of the conflict.

The spirit of private correction is emphasized in Matthew 18:15: *"Moreover if thy brother shall trespass against thee, go and tell him his fault between thee and him alone: if he shall hear thee, thou hast gained thy brother."*

What attitude should a parent display when administering discipline?

☐ _____

_____

"And when I heard this thing, I rent my garment and my mantle, and plucked off the hair of my head and of my beard, and sat down astonied" (Ezra 9:3).

A parent should sit down in silence with the offending child and communicate grief over the offense through facial expressions. The purpose of this time is to allow both parent and child to reflect upon what has been done.

This reflection allows the parent to translate any anger into genuine grief which the child should be able to view. It also allows the parent time to carefully and prayerfully determine the most effective means of correction and decide which parent should administer it.

The ultimate goal of the reflection time is to bring the child to sincere repentance. The parent should pray inwardly that the child's will will be broken, but not his spirit. A vivid picture of this step of correction was given to us by God when He caused the prophets to rend their clothes and sit down in sackcloth and ashes as a demonstration of God's grief over their sin. The sight of His grieving prophet produced a sense of conviction and repentance. (See Ezra 9–10.)

The length of this time of reflection would depend upon the seriousness of the offense and the responsiveness of the child. Many teenagers have testified of the effectiveness of this type of corrective action. It produced repentance and emphasized their parents' deep concern for them.

How can a parent bring about true repentance?

☐ _____

_____

"Which shew the work of the law written in their hearts, their conscience also bearing witness, and their thoughts the mean while accusing or else excusing one another" (Romans 2:15).
(See previous pages.)

What should a parent explain before chastening?

☐ _____

_____

"He that spareth his rod hateth his son: but he that loveth him chasteneth him betimes" (Proverbs 13:24).

"For whom the Lord loveth he chasteneth, and scourgeth every son whom he receiveth" (Hebrews 12:6).

If a parent loves his child, his chief concern will involve the development of those qualities which are essential for the success and happiness of the child. Correction using "the rod" must be translated to the child as a necessary means of reinforcing the development of these positive qualities.

The child must understand that the absence of these positive qualities in his life will lead to harmful and damaging consequences. He should also know that the absence of correction means the absence of love from the parent.

One of the most effective ways to communicate this point to a child is to explain that just as God loves you (the parent) and proves that love by chastening you when you have done wrong, so you must prove your love and concern to your child by correcting him when he has done wrong. Never correct your child out of personal irritation, wounded pride, or the motivation of "getting even" with him for what he has done. (See Hebrews 12:6–7.)

What caution must the parent observe in discipline?

☐ _____

_____

"Looking diligently lest any man fail of the grace of God; lest any root of bitterness springing up trouble you, and thereby many be defiled" (Hebrews 12:15).

It is important that a parent establish God as the final authority in the discipline process. When a child feels that the parent is the final authority, the child feels safe from punishment any time the parent is unable to watch him or he is able to deceive the parent.

The need for correction provides a significant opportunity to emphasize to the child God's chain of command. Explain that you as a parent are responsible under God to develop Godly character and attitudes in the child.

Emphasize that if you are unable to accomplish these qualities, God will use more severe means of discipline in his life. These include a guilty conscience which brings destruction to health; reproofs and rejection from other people; arrest and punishment by law officers; or even accidents, sickness, and death. (See I Corinthians 11:31.)

Let your child know that even if he deceives you, he still must contend with God's all-seeing eye. "... Thou God seest me" (Genesis 16:13).

Scripture speaks of "a rod of reproof" in giving correction. This should not be an object which will damage the child. The value of a neutral object is seen in that a child will usually associate pain and punishment with whatever inflicts it. Thus, even the very act of getting "the rod" from the closet or drawer will produce a marked improvement in the behavior of a stubborn child. (See Proverbs 10:13, 13:24, 14:3, 22:15, 23:13–14, and 26:3.)

The will of the child can be expressed in his response to the spanking. He can stubbornly refuse to cry or he can scream so loudly that you become embarrassed by his outburst. If a child's will is not soon brought under subjection, the parent should stop the discipline process and evaluate his own life. It is often true that some major failure in the parent's life is being reflected by the willfulness in the son or daughter.

It is not necessary that a child cry; however, crying is one way by which a child cleanses his conscience. One day a small boy asked his mother to spank him. Further questions revealed that he had stolen something from the store, and he wanted some relief from his guilt.

The least amount of correction needed to bring the will into submission should be used. If the parent overcorrects the child, the child will grow up feeling inferior and frustrated. (See Ephesians 6:4.) Tears are not always an expression of a broken will, however, and the parent must be sensitive to the actual spirit of the child. *Chasten thy son while there is hope, and let not thy soul spare for his crying* (Proverbs 19:18).

What will destroy the potential of discipline?

☐ _____

_____

"And, ye fathers, provoke not your children to wrath: but bring them up in the nurture and admonition of the Lord" (Ephesians 6:4).

A. PORNOGRAPHY = DESTROYS SPIRITUAL PROTECTION

THE NO. 1 CONTRIBUTING CAUSE OF CHILD ABUSE IN AMERICA IS PORNOGRAPHY

1. **It destroys a man's love for God, his wife, and his children.** "And because iniquity shall abound, the love of many shall wax cold" (Matthew 24:12).

2. **It damages a man's marriage through mental adultery.** "... Whosoever looketh on a woman to lust after her hath committed adultery with her already in his heart" (Matthew 5:28).

3. **It distorts a man's view of love and binds him with lust.** "... Why wilt thou, my son, be ravished with a strange woman ... His own iniquities shall take the wicked himself, and he shall be holden with the cords of his sins" (Proverbs 5:20, 22).

4. It exposes a man's family to Satan's destruction. "No man can enter into a strong man's house, and spoil his goods, except he will first bind the strong man [the father]; and then he will spoil his house" (Mark 3:27).

5. It produces insensitivity and conflicts which arouse a man's anger and cause overcorrection. "He that soweth iniquity shall reap vanity: and the rod of his anger shall fail [kalah: to consume, to destroy]" (Proverbs 22:8).

6. It corrupts a man's nation with wickedness. "Do not prostitute thy daughter, to cause her to be a whore; lest the land fall to whoredom, and the land become full of wickedness" (Leviticus 19:29).

B. ALCOHOL = LOSE CONTROL

"Wine is a mocker, strong drink is raging: and whosoever is deceived thereby is not wise" (Proverbs 20:1).

THE SIN OF DRUNKENNESS BEGINS BY VIOLATING GOD'S COMMAND:

"Look not thou upon the wine when it is red, when it giveth his colour in the cup, when it moveth itself aright. At the last it biteth like a serpent, and stingeth like an adder" (Proverbs 23:31–32).

THE PHYSICAL EFFECTS OF DRINKING:

Alcohol is an antibacterial agent. It temporarily lowers or stops the bacterial action in the upper bowel. It also temporarily blocks the damaging effects of toxins on the nervous system.

However, when drinking stops the bacterial action increases, and greater toxin affects the nervous system. This beneficial, yet harmful effect, is the deception of alcohol and causes a "can't drink, can't quit" dilemma. (Information obtained from *Journal of the International Academy or Preventive Medicine*, Vol. IV, No. 2, Winter 1977, p. 43.)

"Who hath woe? who hath sorrow? who hath contentions? who hath babbling? who hath wounds without cause? who hath redness of eyes? They that tarry long at the wine; they that go to seek mixed wine" (Proverbs 23:29–30).

What parents allow in moderation, their children will excuse in excess.

C. DIVORCE = TWO MASTERS = HATE

"No man can serve two masters: for either he will hate the one, and love the other; or else he will hold to the one, and despise the other . . ." (Matthew 6:24).

The rapid and complete disintegration of the family is the most devastating symptom of a dying nation.

- **DIVORCE RATES** in the United States are now the highest in the world. Five out of every nine marriages (55%) end in divorce. Forty-seven states now have "no-fault," mail-order divorces to make divorce even easier.[1]

- **ABORTION** was legalized in 1970. During that year, 193,000 abortions were performed. In 1979, there were over 1,200,000 abortions.[2] God requires justice for the blood of every human being that is murdered. If we do not do something about this, God will.[3]

- **REBELLIOUS YOUTH** are the tragic product of our godless society. They are being trained without character or moral restraint. In 1972, 10,000 young people were running away from home each week. Government agencies set up houses of refuge. The next year a million young people ran away from home!

Seventy thousand teachers are attacked each year in public schools, and vandalism costs taxpayers $500,000,000 every year![4]

- **DRUG ABUSE AND DRUNKENNESS** have now reached epidemic proportions in America. There are 1,200 new alcoholics every day. One million, three hundred thousand young people between twelve and seventeen years of age have a "serious" drinking problem.[5]

It is estimated that 43,000,000 Americans have experimented with marijuana. Some 10,000,000 U.S. citizens have tried cocaine. In 1960, there were 55,000 heroine addicts in America; now there are over 500,000.

- **VIOLENT CRIMES** in most categories have risen as much as 100 or 200 percent during the last two decades.[6]

1. *U.S. News and World Report*, October 27, 1975.
2. Tabulated by the U.S. Government's Center for Disease Control (1979).
3. Deuteronomy 19:10; Joel 3:19, etc.
4. *Reader's Digest*, January 1974.
5. ACAP, 119 Constitution Avenue, N.E., Washington, D.C.
6. *U.S. News and World Report*, November 24, 1975.

What should be done if parents have failed in major areas?

☐ _____

_____

"*Let him that stole steal no more: but rather let him labour, working with his hands the thing which is good, that he may have to give to him that needeth*" (Ephesians 4:28).

"*Therefore if thou bring thy gift to the altar, and there rememberest that thy brother hath aught against thee; Leave there thy gift before the altar, and go thy way; first be reconciled to thy brother, and then come and offer thy gift*" (Matthew 5:23-24).

If others were offended, discuss the need to ask their forgiveness and make any necessary restitution. Full correction not only involves bringing the child's will into submission, it also involves assuming responsibility for his action. Any consequences involving hurt or loss to others must be made right with them directly.

What steps should follow chastening?

☐ _____

"*Now no chastening for the present seemeth to be joyous, but grievous: nevertheless afterward it yieldeth the peaceable fruit of righteousness unto them which are exercised thereby*" (Hebrews 12:11).

Very often when the child is corrected properly, he will seek reassurance of the parent's love. It is not wise to send him up to his room after punishment since this would indicate a rejection by the parent and also double punishment.

A child may be comforted by the very presence and attention of the parent after discipline by words and hugs. The parent giving correction should be the one to give the comfort. A child who delays in seeking comfort should be sought for it.

What should be done about damages to others?

☐ _____

"*Or how wilt thou say to thy brother, Let me pull out the mote out of thine eye; and, behold, a beam is in thine own eye? Thou hypocrite, first cast out the beam out of thine own eye; and then shalt thou see clearly to cast out the mote out of thy brother's eye*" (Matthew 7:4-5).

If you wronged the child in any way through falsely accusing him, being angry with him, attacking him as a person rather than his wrong behavior, embarrassing him, or demonstrating a vindictive spirit, then go to him and ask him to forgive you.

A child has a keen sense of fairness and will be highly sensitive to his parents' offenses as well as his own. One of the most common accusations children have against their parents is that they rarely admit when they are wrong. This pride on the parents' part makes a right response to future discipline more difficult.

NOTES

DIAGRAMS

GOD'S PRESUPPOSITIONS FOR SUCCESSFUL EDUCATION

Christ astonishing the teachers at age twelve

The Lord Jesus Christ could have entered the world as a mature adult, but He came instead through all the stages of human development.

When Jesus was twelve years of age, *"all that heard him were astonished at his understanding and answers" (Luke 2:47)*.

When Jesus was thirty years of age, *". . . the people were astonished at his doctrine: For he taught them as one having authority, and not as the scribes" (Matthew 7:28–29)*.

It would be easy for us to attribute these kinds of responses to the fact that Jesus was the Son of God, except for two verses. First, we are told that Jesus grew *". . . in wisdom . . ." (Luke 2:52)*. Second, we are informed that as Christians *". . . we have the mind of Christ" (I Corinthians 2:16)*.

The principles behind the teaching of Christ must, therefore, become the presuppositions for successful education.

GOD'S PRESUPPOSITIONS FOR SUCCESSFUL EDUCATION

At what point can a person say that he is educated? When he has completed a prescribed course of study at a school? When he has read a certain number of books? When he has a college degree? Or a post graduate degree? When he can pass a standard achievement test?

The tragedy is that a person can have all of these things and be totally unprepared for the basic responsibilities he will face in life. Therefore, to rethink the essence of education, we need to consider the following points.

1 _____

_____

_____

• Raise the foundations of many generations—

"And they that shall be of thee shall build the old waste places: thou shalt raise up the foundations of many generations; and thou shalt be called, The repairer of the breach, The restorer of paths to dwell in" (Isaiah 58:12).

• "That the generation to come might know them, even the children which should be born; who should arise and declare them to their children" (Psalm 78:6).

• "His seed shall be mighty upon earth . . ."

"Praise ye the Lord. Blessed is the man that feareth the Lord, that delighteth greatly in His commandments. His seed shall be mighty upon earth: the generation of the upright shall be blessed" (Psalm 112:1-2).

2 _____

_____

_____

_____

_____

• Training until the time appointed by the father—

"Now I say, That the heir, as long as he is a child, differeth nothing from a servant, though he be lord of all; But is under tutors and governors until the time appointed of the father" (Galatians 4:1-2).

• Teach to children and children's children—

"And thou shalt teach them diligently unto thy children, and shalt talk of them when thou sittest in thine house, and when thou walkest by the way, and when thou liest down, and when thou risest up" (Deuteronomy 6:7).

"Children's children are the crown of old men; and the glory of children are their fathers" (Proverbs 17:6).

• Responsible for faithful children—

"If any be blameless, the husband of one wife, having faithful children not accused of riot or unruly" (Titus 1:6).

3 GOD ESTABLISHED THE HOME, NOT THE SCHOOL, AS THE PRIMARY LEARNING CENTER, AND THE SCHOOL AND CHURCH MUST BE RECOGNIZED AS EXTENSIONS OF IT.

"And thou shalt teach them diligently unto thy children, and shalt talk of them when thou sittest in thine house, and when thou walkest by the way, and when thou risest up" (Deuteronomy 6:7).

- **Managing home required to manage church -**

  "For if a man know not how to rule his own house, how shall he take care of the church of God?" (I Timothy 3:5).

- **Relating to church members comes by relating to family**

  "Rebuke not an elder, but entreat him as a father; and the younger men as brethren; The elder women as mothers; the younger as sisters, with all purity" (I Timothy 5:1-2).

4 _____
_____
_____
_____
_____

- **Initial counsel to sons in Proverbs 1:10-19**

  "My son, if sinners entice thee, consent thou not. If they say, Come with us, let us lay wait for blood, let us lurk privily for the innocent without cause: Let us swallow them up alive as the grave; and whole, as those that go down into the pit:

  "We shall find all precious substance, we shall fill our houses with spoil: Cast in thy lot among us; let us all have one purse:

  "My son, walk not thou in the way with them; refrain thy foot from their path: For their feet run to evil, and make haste to shed blood.

  "Surely in vain the net is spread in the sight of any bird. And they lay wait for their own blood; they lurk privily for their own lives.

  "So are the ways of every one that is greedy of gain; which taketh away the life of the owners thereof" (Proverbs 1:10-19).

- **Children are commanded to obey parents, not peers -**

  "Children, obey your parents in all things: for this is well pleasing unto the Lord" (Colossians 3:20).

- **A companion of fools will be destroyed -**

  "He that walketh with wise men shall be wise: but a companion of fools shall be destroyed" (Proverbs 13:20).

5 GOD WANTS THE PRIORITIES OF EVERY FAMILY BUILT AROUND DAILY ENGRAFTING OF SCRIPTURE, RATHER THAN JUST ACCUMULATING MAN'S KNOWLEDGE.

- **Ways which seem right end in death -**

  "There is a way which seemeth right unto a man, but the end thereof are the ways of death" (Proverbs 14:12).

- **Engrafting Scripture saves the soul -**

  "Wherefore lay apart all filthiness and superfluity of naughtiness, and receive with meekness the engrafted word, which is able to save your souls" (James 1:21).

- **Meditation is basis for success -**

  "This book of the law shall not depart out of thy mouth; but thou shalt meditate therein day and night, that thou mayest observe to do according to all that is written therein: for then thou shalt make thy way prosperous, and then thou shalt have good success" (Joshua 1:8).

  "But his delight is in the law of the Lord; and in his law doth he meditate day and night" (Psalm 1:2).

  "Meditate upon these things; give thyself wholly to them; that thy profiting may appear to all" (I Timothy 4:15).

6 _____

_____

_____

_____

_____

- ## Precepts give understanding to hate every false way

"Through thy precepts I get understanding: therefore I hate every false way" (Psalm 119:104).

- ## God's laws produce health, wealth, and wisdom -

"And he will love thee, and bless thee, and multiply thee: he will also bless the fruit of thy womb, and the fruit of thy land, thy corn, and thy wine, and thine oil, the increase of thy kine, and the flocks of thy sheep, in the land which he sware unto thy fathers to give thee.

"Thou shalt be blessed above all people: there shall not be male or female barren among you, or among your cattle.

"And the Lord will take away from thee all sickness, and will put none of the evil diseases of Egypt, which thou knowest, upon thee; but will lay them upon all them that hate thee." (Deuteronomy 7:13-26).

- ## God's wisdom makes us wiser than teachers -

"Thou through thy commandments hast made me wiser than mine enemies: for they are ever with me" (Psalm 119:98).

7 WHEN KNOWLEDGE IS LEARNED BEFORE GODLY CHARACTER, IT PRODUCES ARROGANCE.

- ## True knowledge grows out of virtue -

"And beside this, giving all diligence, add to your faith virtue; and to virtue knowledge" (II Peter 1:5).

- ## Knowledge tends to puff up -

"Now as touching things offered unto idols, we know that we all have knowledge. Knowledge puffeth up, but charity edifieth" (I Corinthians 8:1).

- ## All knowledge is centered in Christ -

"In whom are hid all the treasures of wisdom and knowledge" (Colossians 2:3).

8 _____

_____

_____

_____

_____

- ## Church leaders must give an account -

"Remember them which have the rule over you, who have spoken unto you the word of God: whose faith follow, considering the end of their conversation" (Hebrews 13:7).

- ## The authorities that be are ordained of God -

"Let every soul be subject unto the higher powers. For there is no power but of God: the powers that be are ordained of God. Whosoever therefore resisteth the power, resisteth the ordinance of God: and they that resist shall receive to themselves damnation" (Romans 13:1-2).

- ## Let all men be subject to higher authority -

"Likewise, ye younger, submit yourselves unto the elder. Yea, all of you be subject one to another, and be clothed with humility: for God resisteth the proud, and giveth grace to the humble" (I Peter 5:5).

History provides a vivid illustration of why Christians who rise up against government authority are not working in harmony with the will and program of God.

THE REVOLT OF THE MACCABEES

Mattathias appealed to his fellow countrymen: "Now therefore, my sons, be ye zealous for the law . . ."

Doré Bible Illustrations

A strange silence paralyzed the tiny Jewish village of Modin. Houses, streets, and alleyways were deserted. The normally busy vineyards and olive groves were abandoned and still. A visitor would surely have been convinced that it was the Sabbath day.

All of the villagers had gathered in the marketplace, but there were no fruits or vegetables for sale, and no one dared to speak a word. They were dressed, as they had been ordered, in their Sabbath clothing. Their somber faces reluctantly focused on a pagan altar in the town square.

A sacrificial pig squealed nervously as a Syrian soldier secured it to the altar. Looking on from his golden litter, Apelles (ə-**pel**-ēz) contemptuously surveyed the crowd of Jews.

The royal emissary quickly realized that this was to be no simple ceremony. His eyes concentrated on Mattathias (**mat**-ə-thī-əs). Mattathias tried to control his anger and disgust as he glanced at the pig, an animal of abomination to his people.

The old priest quietly prepared himself for the battle of wills that was about to take place. He knew that Apelles would order him to take part in the sacrifice and eat the pork that would symbolically bind the village to the pagan worship of the Seleucids (sə-**lü**-sidz).

The armed guards snapped to attention as Apelles rose to address the crowd. Antiochus Epiphanes (an-**ti**-ə-kəs ē-**pi**-fə-nēz), imperial ruler of the Seleucid Empire, had commissioned him to establish the worship of Zeus (züs) in Palestine. This was the king's will, and the king's will would be done.

Whatever Apelles saw in the eyes of the old priest, it was not submission. His words to Mattathias were recorded by a contemporary historian.

"You are a leader here, a man of mark and influence in the village and firmly supported by your sons and brothers. Be the first to come forward and carry out the order of the king.

"All the other people have done so, as have the leading men in Judea and the people left in Jerusalem. Do this, and you and your sons will be counted among the Friends of the King; you will receive high honor, rich rewards of silver and gold, and many further benefits."

The determined, war-hardened general motioned to Mattathias to approach the altar. The Jewish priest stood firm, surrounded by his five sons. His reply would dramatically influence the course of Jewish history.

"Though all nations within the king's dominion obey him and forsake their faith, though they have chosen to submit to his commands, yet I and my sons and my brothers will follow the covenant of our fathers.

"Heaven forbid we should ever abandon the Law and its statutes. We will not obey the command of the king, nor will we deviate one step from our worship."

Dore Bible Illustrations

The marketplace was engulfed with tension. Suddenly, a Jew stepped forward out of the crowd. He calmly walked past the rigid troops that surrounded the altar. The lone figure approached Apelles and announced, to the amazement of the multitude, that he was willing to carry out the sacrifice.

The Jew was handed the sacrificial knife as he ascended the altar and approached the statue of Zeus. Mattathias frantically lunged at the betrayer and stabbed him. He then turned on the unsuspecting Apelles and killed him with the same sword. Before the soldiers could react, they were slain by the angry mob.

In the village of Modin the banner of rebellion had been raised against the mighty Antiochus.

Doré Bible Illustrations

Villagers quickly gathered their belongings. The pagan altar was triumphantly torn down. For the rest of their lives, they would be hunted down as outlaws and rebels.

Antiochus Epiphanes had attempted to unite his faltering empire through emperor worship and Greek humanism. His title, *theos Epiphanes* (god-manifest), suggests that he tried to imitate his powerful predecessor, Alexander the Great. All of his subjects would adopt the Greek way of life. He would allow no exceptions.

The Jews, however, refused to reject their faith in Jehovah. Their belief in one God became an insult to the powerful emperor.

Thousands of Jews were put to death for reading and studying the Law of Moses. Those who refused to eat pork were also killed. Others were murdered for refusing to bow down to pagan idols.

Royal decree prohibited the worship of Jehovah. A Jew could either comply or face death.

Enraged by his failure to destroy the Jewish culture, Antiochus desecrated the Temple at Jerusalem. Seleucid troops entered the Temple in 167 B.C. They destroyed or removed everything that was sacred to the Jewish faith.

The Temple was rededicated to Zeus, and a large image of the Greek god was erected above the Jewish altar. The dedication became official

Statue of Zeus (Jupiter) found at Caesarea. Throughout Judea, Syrian overlords pressed the Jews to worship before such idols at public altars.

when a pig was sacrificed to the pagan image. Its blood was sprinkled in the Holy of Holies to complete the horrible sacrilege.

Historians agree that Antiochus Epiphanes was a wicked and merciless dictator. But did his cruel and cold-blooded actions justify a rebellion against his authority by Mattathias and his five Maccabee sons?

• *Pause for Discussion*

HOW DID OTHER JEWS RESPOND TO WICKED RULERS?

Other Jews suffered similar oppression and persecution at the hands of some of history's most brutal despots. Their reaction to governmental authority differed greatly from the organized revolt of the Maccabees.

Shadrach, Meshach, and Abednego refused to bow to the golden image of King Nebuchadnezzar. Threatened with death in the fiery furnace, they chose to accept the consequences of their decision and trust God for the results. (See Daniel 3:17–18.)

The three young Jewish men were miraculously protected from the flames, and Nebuchadnezzar later praised their God after being harshly judged for his cruelty and pride.

Facing the consequences of a wicked law, Daniel trusted God and responded correctly. His decision insured continued protection and blessing from the Lord through the king. (See Daniel 6:22–28.)

The prophet Daniel also purposed in his heart that he would not violate Scriptural commands. Jealous Persian princes conspired against him, but they could not devise any personal or political scandal. Frustrated by Daniel's excellent spirit and servant's heart, they tricked the king into establishing a law that would condemn the Jewish prophet to certain death for praying to anyone but the king. (See Daniel 6:7.)

Daniel continued to pray and thank the Lord three times a day. (See Daniel 6:10.) Trapped by his own foolish decree, the king sadly sent his faithful friend to the lions. After a sleepless night, Darius hurried to the den, hoping to find Daniel alive.

"And when he came to the den, he cried with a lamentable voice unto Daniel: and the king spake and said to Daniel, O Daniel, servant of the living God, is thy God, whom thou servest continually, able to deliver thee from the lions?" (Daniel 6:20).

Daniel replied, *"My God hath sent his angel, and hath shut the lions' mouths, that they have not hurt me: forasmuch as before him innocency was found in me; and also before thee, O king, have I done no hurt"* (Daniel 6:22).

Because Daniel trusted God, his enemies were destroyed, and the wicked law was revoked. Darius issued a new proclamation that throughout his kingdom men should fear the God of Daniel. (See Daniel 6:25–28.)

Doré Bible Illustrations

The Apostle Paul's ministry flourished under the shadow of a wicked and sadistic ruler. The emperor Nero brutally murdered thousands of innocent people, including his own wife and mother. However, at the height of Nero's domination in Rome, Paul penned the words of the thirteenth chapter of Romans.

"Let every soul be subject unto the higher powers. For there is no power but of God: the powers that be are ordained of God. Whosoever therefore resisteth the power, resisteth the ordinance of God: and they that resist shall receive to themselves damnation" (Romans 13:1–2). Paul went to his execution a loyal citizen of Rome and a faithful servant of God.

WHY WAS THE REVOLT OF THE MACCABEES A TRAGIC MISTAKE?

The Maccabees succeeded in their attempt to overthrow Seleucid tyranny. What consequences occurred as a result of their rebellion?

First, all five of Mattathias' sons were killed. Judas was defeated and slain at the Battle of Elasa.

Doré Bible Illustrations

John was captured and tortured to death. Eleazar was crushed by an elephant during the Battle of Beth Zur. Jonathan was treacherously murdered by Tryphon, a Syrian prince. Simon was assassinated by Ptolemy, his son-in-law.

Secondly, an unwise alliance with Rome secured military aid against Antiochus but later led to bondage. The Roman general Pompey officially made Judea a Roman province in 63 B.C., bringing down the curtain on the Maccabean period.

The final result of the Revolt of the Maccabees proved to be the most tragic. Because the Maccabees were honored and admired as liberating heroes, the Jewish concept of the Messiah became warped and twisted. The Jews eagerly anticipated a great military leader who would free them from the humiliating bondage of Rome.

When Christ presented the kingdom of God and all of its spiritual facets, His teachings were rejected by many because they did not fit the Maccabean mold.

Quotations taken from Moshe Pearlman, *The Maccabees* (New York: Macmillan Publishing Co., 1973), pages 11, 69.

9 SONS AND DAUGHTERS THRIVE WITH APPROPRIATE RESPONSIBILITY, AND IT IS GOD'S GOAL THAT THEY BE MATURE IN THEIR YOUTH.

• Sons like plants; daughters like cornerstones in palace -

"That our sons may be as plants grown up in their youth; that our daughters may be as corner stones, polished after the similitude of a palace" (Psalm 144:12).

• Christ was mature at age 12 -

"And the child grew, and waxed strong in spirit, filled with wisdom: and the grace of God was upon him. . . .

"And Jesus increased in wisdom and stature, and in favour with God and man" (Luke 2:40, 52).

"For who hath known the mind of the Lord, that he may instruct him? But we have the mind of Christ" (I Corinthians 2:16).

• Hebrew boys over twelve were treated as men -

Bar mitz-vah (bär **mits**-və). Also **bar miz-vah.** *Judaism.* 1. A thirteen-year-old Jewish male, considered an adult and thenceforth responsible for his moral and religious duties.

10 _____

_____
_____
_____
_____

• Teach your sons and your son's sons -

"Only take heed to thyself, and keep thy soul diligently, lest thou forget the things which thine *eyes have seen, and lest they depart from thy heart all the days of thy life: but teach them thy sons, and thy sons' sons"* (Deuteronomy 4:9).

- **Fathers and sons were to meet three times a year -**

"Three times in a year shall all thy males appear before the Lord thy God in the place which he shall choose; in the feast of unleavened bread, and in the feast of weeks, and in the feast of tabernacles: and they shall not appear before the Lord empty" (Deuteronomy 16:16).

- **God taught Adam before Eve-**

"For Adam was first formed, then Eve" (I Timothy 2:13).

"And the Lord God commanded the man, saying, Of every tree of the garden thou mayest freely eat: But of the tree of the knowledge of good and evil, thou shalt not eat of it: for in the day that thou eatest thereof thou shalt surely die" (Genesis 2:16-17).

11 WHEN SCHOOLS GROUP CHILDREN BY AGES, OLDER EXAMPLES ARE CUT OFF AND REBELS USUALLY RISE TO LEADERSHIP.

- **God designed families with various ages**

- **First-born was given special responsibilities -**

"And they sat before him, the firstborn according to his birthright, and the youngest according to his youth: and the men marvelled one at another" (Genesis 43:33).

- **Older children can greatly influence younger children -**

"Likewise, ye younger, submit yourselves unto the elder . . ." (I Peter 5:5).

12 _____

_____

_____

_____

- **All Scripture is profitable for life -**

"All scripture is given by inspiration of God, and is profitable for doctrine, for reproof, for correction, for instruction in righteousness: That the man of God may be perfect, throughly furnished unto all good works" (II Timothy 3:16-17).

- **The Bible is the textbook on all subjects -**

"For my thoughts are not your thoughts, neither are your ways my ways, saith the Lord. For as the heavens are higher than the earth, so are my ways higher than your ways, and my thoughts than your thoughts" (Isaiah 55:8-9).

- **Courses without God's knowledge are vain -**

"Beware lest any man spoil you through philosophy and vain deceit, after the tradition of men, after the rudiments of the world, and not after Christ" (Colossians 2:8).

13 TRUE SOCIALIZING DOES NOT TAKE PLACE IN THE ARBITRARY GROUPINGS OF SCHOOL, BUT IN THE REAL WORLD OF CHILDREN-TO-ADULT RELATIONSHIPS.

- **Peer pressure brings self-rejection -**

"For we dare not make ourselves of the number, or compare ourselves with some that commend themselves: but they measuring themselves by themselves, and comparing themselves among themselves, are not wise" (II Corinthians 10:12).

- **Success requires relating to authority -**

"And whatsoever ye do, do it heartily, as to the Lord, and not unto men; Knowing that of the Lord ye shall receive the reward of the inheritance: for ye serve the Lord Christ" (Colossians 3:23–24).

- **God wants leadership, not conformity -**

"Let no man despise thy youth; but be thou an example of the believers, in word, in conversation, in charity, in spirit, in faith, in purity" (I Timothy 4:12).

14 _____

_____
_____
_____
_____

- **We must make the best use of our time -**

"Walk in wisdom toward them that are without, redeeming the time" (Colossians 4:5).

- **The greatest learning readiness times come at home -**

". . . And shalt talk of them when thou sittest in thine house . . ." (Deuteronomy 6:7).

- **We are to apply our hearts to wisdom -**

"So teach us to number our days, that we may apply our hearts unto wisdom" (Psalm 90:12).

15 THE KEY TO EFFECTIVE EDUCATION IS NOT JUST A TRAINED TEACHER AND A PROFESSIONAL CURRICULUM BUT A CONCERNED PARENT AND A MOTIVATED CHILD.

- **Parent involvement increases student interest -**

"Honour thy father and mother; which is the first commandment with promise" (Ephesians 6:2).

- **Lack of parent involvement will result in judgment -**

"And he shall turn the heart of the fathers to the children, and the heart of the children to their fathers, lest I come and smite the earth with a curse" (Malachi 4:6).

- **A motivated child goes beyond the teacher -**

"I have more understanding than all my teachers: for thy testimonies are my meditation" (Psalm 119:99).

16 _____

_____
_____
_____
_____

- **God wants us to discern evil with our spirit -**

"Beloved, believe not every spirit, but try the spirits whether they are of God: because many false prophets are gone out into the world" (I John 4:1).

- **God wants us to be naive regarding evil -**

". . . But yet I would have you wise unto that which is good, and simple concerning evil" (Romans 16:19).

- **Learning evil will corrupt right living -**

"Cease, my son, to hear the instruction that causeth to err from the words of knowledge" (Proverbs 19:27).

HOW JESUS MATURED IN HIS YOUTH -
Luke 2:40–52

- **Physical growth -**
  ". . . The child grew. . . ."

- **Personal vigor -**
  He ". . . waxed strong. . . ."

- **Spiritual perception -**
  He was ". . . filled with wisdom. . . ."

- **Inward motivation -** ". . . The grace of God was upon him. . . ."

- **Hunger for God -**
  He was ". . . in the temple. . . ."

- **Related to adults -** He was ". . . sitting in the midst of the doctors. . . ."

- **Attentiveness -** He was ". . . hearing them. . . ."

- **Perceptive inquiry -** He was ". . . asking them questions."

- **Recognition -** ". . . All that heard him were astonished at his understanding and answers."

- **Fulfillment of Scripture -** "I have more understanding than all my teachers." (Psalm 119:99)

- **Life purpose -** ". . . I must be about my Father's business."

- **Submission -** He ". . . was subject unto them [his parents]."

- **Discernment -**
  He ". . . increased in wisdom. . . ."

- **Maturity -**
  He ". . . increased . . . in stature. . . ."

- **Approval -**
  He was ". . . in favour with God. . . ."

- **Acceptance -**
  He was ". . . in favour with . . . man."

NOTES

DIAGRAMS

OPERATIONAL DEFINITIONS

1. ACHIEVEMENT — Helping a person find out what he needs, then helping him find the best way to get it. (I Thess. 2:11)

2. ADULTERY — Violation of God's moral law after marriage. (Matt. 5:32)

3. ANGER — An inward alarm system revealing personal rights which we have either not given to God or have taken back from Him. (Eph. 4:26, 31)

4. AVERAGE CHRISTIAN — Best of the worst, worst of the best. Nauseating to God. (Rev. 3:16)

5. BITTERNESS — The inward evidence that we are more concerned with things that will be destroyed with time than inward character that is important for eternity. (Heb. 10:32-34)

6. BOREDOM — Failure to develop and integrate spiritual, psychological and physical aptitudes, interest and capacities into our life purpose. (John 10:10)

7. CHRISTIAN — One in whom Christ lives. (Phil. 1:21)

8. CLEAR CONSCIENCE — Being able to look every person in the eye without any of them pointing a finger and saying, "You offended me and you never tried to make it right." (Matt. 5:23, 24)

9. COMMUNICATION — Guiding important ideas around another person's mental roadblocks. (Prov. 15:2)

10. COMMUNION — A specific time to thoroughly examine each past word, thought, action and attitude in the light of Christ's way of life. (I Cor. 11:28)

11. COMPLETE REPENTANCE — Agreeing and grieving with God about my willfulness. Giving Him His rightful place at the center of my life and being sensitive and obedient to the promptings of His Holy Spirit. (Rom. 10:9; 8:4)

12. CONCUPISCENCE — Possessing stronger sensual drives than spiritual desires. (I Thess. 4:3-5)

13. DEFERENCE — Showing respect for the tastes of those in authority over me by restricting my freedom to be in harmony with them. (Heb. 13:17)

14. DEFRAUDING — Arousing sensual desires in others which can not be righteously satisfied. (I Thess. 4:6)

15. DENIAL OF SELF — Dying to the natural impulses of fulfilling our rights and expectations. (Gal. 5:13)

16.	DILIGENCE	Full concentration of energy and creativity on assigned projects. (Col. 3:23, 24)
17.	DISCIPLE	A disciplined one living within the limitations of God's Spirit. (Gal. 5:17)
18.	DISCRETION	Knowing precisely how to apply Scriptural principles in a difficult situation. (Prov. 2:11)
19.	DISSOLVING EXPECTATIONS	Putting our heart in such a state that we have no will of our own by finding as many reasons why we should not get what we want as reasons why we should get what we want. (I Tim. 6:6-10)
20.	EQUITY	Constructing a solution to a difficult situation from existing Scriptural revelation. (Prov. 2:3,4,9)
21.	ENVY	A feeling of displeasure because of the gain of others but a desire to have the same thing. (Prov. 23:17,18)
22.	FAITH	Visualizing what God intends to do. (Heb. 11:1)
23.	"FALSE GUILT"	Attaching conviction from real offenses to offenses which others will assure us aren't so bad. (Rom. 2:15)
24.	FLATTERY	Expressing envy by praising features in others which they had no control in developing. (Prov. 26:28)
25.	FORNICATION	Violation of God's moral law before marriage. (Matt. 5:32)
26.	FREEDOM	Not the right to do what we want but the power to do what we should. (Gal. 5:13)
27.	FRUSTRATION	Failing to define our responsibilities or our priorities or failing to put our whole heart into achieving them. (Gal. 6:4)
28.	GODLINESS	A Godward focus which manifests itself in Christ-like words, thoughts, actions and attitudes. (II Peter 1:6,7)
29.	GOD'S WILL	The ever-expanding development of our life message on how to achieve spiritual maturity. (I Thess. 2:11,12)
30.	GOSSIP	Sharing private information about others with those that are not part of the problem or part of the solution. (Matt. 18:15,16)
31.	GRACE	An active force within us giving us the desire and the power to do things God's way. (Phil 2:13; Heb. 12:15)

356

32.	GRACE OF GOD	The desire and power to reproduce ourselves spiritually. (Rom. 12:5,6)
33.	GRACE OF LIFE	The desire and power to reproduce ourselves physically. (I Pet. 3:7)
34.	IDOLATRY	Terminating our delight in a person or object rather than using them as a springboard to converse with and delight in God. (Ps. 37:4)
35.	INCOMPLETE REPENTANCE	Being more grieved about the conflicts in my life than about the fact that they were caused by me being the boss of my life. (Ps. 51:4)
36.	INFERIORITY	Comparing our appearance, abilities, parentage or social heritage with that of others. (II Cor. 10:12)
37.	INSECURITY	Building our life and affections around someone or something we know can be taken away from us. (Matt. 6:33)
38.	INSIGHT	The ability to detect principles of life in Scripture and apply them to daily living. (Prov. 1:5,6)
39.	JEALOUSY	The desire to deprive another of pleasures which draw him away from you. (Prov. 6:34; II Cor. 11:2)
40.	LASCIVIOUSNESS	Stirring up lustful desires. (I Peter 4:13)
41.	LEADERSHIP	Seeing the consequences of our actions further in the future than those around us can. (I Thess. 5:12-14)
42.	LIBERATION (SUBMISSION)	Freedom to be creative under the protection of divinely appointed authority. (I Tim. 2:1,2)
43.	LOVE	Giving to the basic needs of others without motive of personal reward. Love does not depend upon the response of the one being loved for its continuance. (John 3:16) Love can always wait to give; lust can never wait to get. (Gen 29:20)
44.	MEEKNESS	Yielding personal rights and possessions to God and giving Him the option of returning them as privileges. (Job 1:21)
45.	PATIENCE	The freedom to respond in a situation so that the qualities of Christ can be displayed. (Romans 5:3-5)
46.	PRIDE	Avoiding necessary character change by expecting others to fit their ideas and feelings around mine. (Prov. 13:10)
47.	QUIET SPIRIT	The confidence that God will use even the mistakes of those in authority over us to achieve His ultimate will. (I Peter 3:4)
48.	REPROBATE	Believing a philosophy of immorality through the motivation of personal impurity. (Rom. 1:28)

49.	SECURITY	Building our life and affections around someone who can never be taken away from us. (Col. 3:1)
50.	SENSUALITY	Planned appeal to the physical senses for personal gratification. (I Peter 2:11)
51.	SERVANT'S HEART	Becoming excited about making someone else successful. (John 15:12, 13)
52.	SLANDER	Telling the truth with a design to hurt. (Prov. 17:9)
53.	SOUND DOCTRINE	Teachings which are based on Christ's own words and that which leads to Christ-like living. (I Tim. 6:3)
54.	SPIRITUAL MATURITY	Forming the characteristics of Christ in us and reproducing them in the lives of others. Indicated by the length of time we can wait between achievement and reward. (Gal. 4:19)
55.	SUCCESS	Measuring what we are by what we could be, and what we have done by what we could have done - achieving the full potential God planned for us. (Col. 1:28, 29)
56.	"SUPERIORITY COMPLEX"	Being motivated by feelings of inferiority to narrow our field of comparison. (Gal. 6:3)
57.	TEMPTATIONS	Situations designed by Satan to draw us away from God. (James 1:13)
58.	TRIALS	Situations designed by God to draw us to Him. (I Cor. 10:13)
59.	UNDERSTANDING	Responding to life situations from God's point of view. (Prov. 3:13)
60.	WAY OF GOD	The foundation of life from which basic principles are discovered. (Isaiah 55:8,9)
61.	WISDOM	Seeing life from God's point of view. (Col. 1:9,10)
62.	WORRY	Assuming responsibilities God never intended us to have. (Phil. 4:6,7)

HOW TO TRANSFORM CRITICISM INTO STRENGTH

©Providence Lithograph Co.

Stephen's face shone with God's glory when he was reviled.

When a Christian purposes to live by God's standards, reaction and criticism will come. Christ assured His disciples that persecution for doing right was not only normal, but necessary if Christians are going to have significant impact upon the world in which they live.

The rewards of properly responding to unjust criticism are significant enough to merit our rejoicing. *"Blessed are ye, when men shall revile you, and persecute you, and shall say all manner of evil against you falsely, for my sake. Rejoice, and be exceeding glad" (Matthew 5:11–12).*

The secret we are given to transform critism is to *"... consider Him that endured such contradiction of sinners against himself, lest ye be wearied and faint in your minds" (Hebrews 12:3).*

NOTES

DIAGRAMS

HOW GOD USES REACTION TO BRING REVIVAL

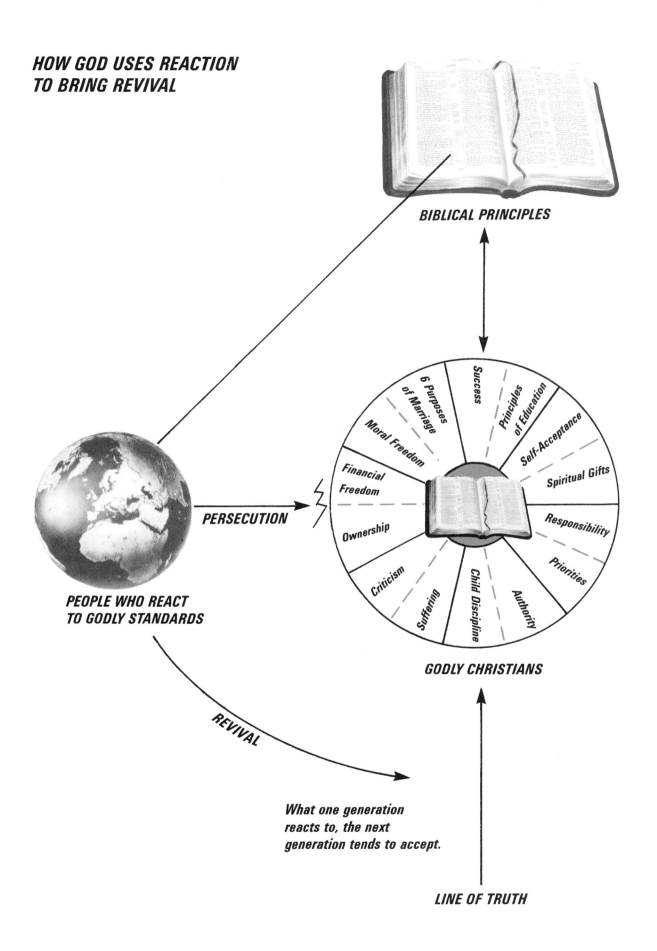

BIBLICAL PRINCIPLES

Success
Principles of Education
Self-Acceptance
Spiritual Gifts
Responsibility
Priorities
Authority
Child Discipline
Suffering
Criticism
Ownership
Financial Freedom
Moral Freedom
6 Purposes of Marriage

PERSECUTION

PEOPLE WHO REACT TO GODLY STANDARDS

GODLY CHRISTIANS

REVIVAL

What one generation reacts to, the next generation tends to accept.

LINE OF TRUTH

SEVEN IMPORTANT STEPS TO TAKE WHEN YOU RECEIVE CRITICISM

An important part of Christ's teaching to His disciples was that they would receive hateful reaction when they lived by His principles. Jesus prayed for His disciples and us in the garden when He said:

"I have given them thy word; and the world hath hated them, because they are not of the world, even as I am not of the world...Neither pray I for these alone, but for them also which shall believe on me through their word" (John 17:14, 20).

Paul became an example of how to respond to persecution and assured us, *"Yea, and all that will live godly in Christ Jesus shall suffer persecution" (II Timothy 3:12).*

Peter became the third witness when he instructed, *"Beloved, think it not strange concerning the fiery trial which is to try you, as though some strange thing happened unto you: but rejoice, inasmuch as ye are partakers of Christ's sufferings..." (I Peter 4:12–13).*

We will not be able to rejoice in tribulation unless we respond to it in the proper way.

To what Old Testament trial can we compare the experience of receiving criticism for doing right?

1 _____

_____

If a wife was accused by her husband of being unfaithful to him, he was to bring her before the priest and the priest was to "set her before the Lord" he was then to take water in a cup and some dust from the tabernacle floor, mix it together, and give it to the woman to drink.

She was told, *"... if no man have lain with thee, and if thou hast not gone aside to uncleanness with another instead of thy husband, be thou free from this bitter water that causeth the curse: but if thou hast gone aside to another... The Lord make thee a curse and an oath among thy people,* when the Lord doth make thy thigh to rot, and thy belly to swell" (Numbers 5:19–21).

What should be our first step when we receive criticism?

● _____

_____

_____

"In everything give thanks: for this is the will of God in Christ Jesus concerning you" (I Thessalonians 5:18).

How do close friends often respond when we are accused?

● _____

_____

"My lovers and my friends stand aloof from my sore; and my kinsmen stand afar off" (Psalm 38:11)

What response proves that you have failed the test?

● _____

_____

"As the bird by wandering, as the swallow by flying, so the curse causeless shall not come" (Proverbs 26:2).

Who suffers when you become bitter?

● _____

_____

"Looking diligently lest any man fail of the grace of God; lest any root of bitterness springing up trouble you, and thereby many be defiled" (Hebrews 12:15).

What are the rewards of "passing the test"?

● _____

_____

_____

"And if the woman be not defiled, but be clean; then she shall be free, and shall conceive seed" (Numbers 5:28).

Having God pronounce us "clean" is far more effective than pronouncing ourselves "clean." When we go through the disillusionment of public criticism and rejection, we experience a new freedom from the disabling desire for the praise of man.

Then because of the humbling experience, God is able to give us an abundance of new grace. This grace gives us the desire and power to forgive our offenders to receive rich comfort and council from Scripture, to see where we have been wrong and to have more of Christ formed in us.

What response tells others that you have passed the "trial of bitter water"?

●_____

_____

"Rejoice, and be exceeding glad: for great is your reward in heaven: for so persecuted they the prophets which were before you" (Matthew 5:12).

After thanking God for criticism, what should our next step of action be?

2 _____

_____

"The simple believeth every word: but the prudent man looketh well to his going" (Proverbs 14:15).

Why is it not effective to react to those who speak out against us?

●_____

_____

_____

"A froward man soweth strife: and a whisperer separateth chief friends" (Proverbs 16:28).

Why is it difficult to detect our silent critics?

●_____

_____

_____

"I behaved myself as though he had been my friend or brother: I bowed down heavily, as one that mourneth for his mother.

"But in mine adversity they rejoiced, and gathered themselves together: yea, the abjects gathered themselves together against me, and I knew it not; they did tear me, and ceased not:

With hypocritical mockers in feasts, they gnashed upon me with their teeth" (Psalm 35:14-16).

"Yea, mine own familiar friend, in whom I trusted, which did eat of my bread, hath lifted up his heel against me" (Psalm 41:9).

"For it was not an enemy that reproached me; then I could have borne it: neither was it he that hated me that did magnify himself against me; then I would have hid myself from him: but it was thou, a man mine equal, my guide, and mine acquaintance. We took sweet counsel together, and walked unto the house of God in company" (Psalm 55:12-14).

What should our steps of action be when falsely accused?

●_____

_____

"Moreover if thy brother shall trespass against thee, go and tell him his fault between thee and him alone: if he shall hear thee, thou hast gained thy brother.

"But if he will not hear thee, then take with thee one or two more, that in the mouth of two or three witnesses every word may be established" (Matthew 18:15-16).

Because criticism is compared to venom, fire, and poison, when is the proper time to deal with it?

3 _____

"Even so the tongue is a little member, and boasteth great things. Behold, how great a matter a little fire kindleth!" (James 3:5).

How do we demonstrate proper humility to our critics?

● _____

_____

"A fool despiseth his father's instruction: but he that regardeth reproof is prudent" (Proverbs 15:5).

What if we are partly right and partly wrong?

● _____

_____

"Holding faith, and a good conscience; which some having put away concerning faith have made shipwreck" (I Timothy 1:19).

What is God's way to "condemn" those who criticize?

● _____

_____

"No weapon that is formed against thee shall prosper; and every tongue that shall rise against thee in judgment thou shalt condemn. This is the heritage of the servants of the Lord, and their righteousness is of me, saith the Lord" (Isaiah 54:17).

American Museum of Photography (Philadelphia)

"By faith Noah, being warned of God of things not seen as yet, moved with fear, prepared an ark to the saving of his house; by the which he condemned the world, and became heir of the righteousness which is by faith"* (Hebrews 11:7).

How can we protect our family from some of the hurtful consequences of unjust criticism?

● _____

_____

"And make straight paths for your feet, lest that which is lame be turned out of the way; but let it rather be healed. Follow peace with all men, and holiness, without which no man shall see the Lord: Looking diligently lest any man fail of the grace of God; lest any root of bitterness springing up trouble you, and thereby many be defiled" (Hebrews 12:13-15).

If we expect God to silence our critics, what does God require us to do for our critics?

● _____

_____

"Bless them which persecute you: bless, and curse not" (Romans 12:14).

HOW A PASTOR TRANSFORMED CRITICISM INTO A MORE EFFECTIVE MINISTRY

"As pastor of a church, I had been faithfully preaching and teaching God's Word. During this time, I developed a close relationship with several Godly men in the church whom God has raised up as spiritual leaders. One day a group of men (several spiritual leaders included) approached me about certain blind spots in my life and ministry. It was a very humbling experience. Although my natural inclination was to leave the church, God gave me the grace to stay and work on the blind spots mentioned.

"Soon after this experience, while I was visiting one of these men, a conflict developed between us over an issue before the church. The problem was simple: I was right and he was wrong—or so I thought. The conversation got a bit heated and I left his house. This man had a heart condition, and it flared up immediately after I left. I felt terrible! I knew I had to do something to reconcile the relationship. Having attended the Basic Seminar many times, I knew that I must go to him and ask his forgiveness. I did so, and he said he forgave me.

"After a couple of years, I began to notice how this same leader was reacting against my ministry. It seemed as though everything that I was for, he was against. Although God was blessing in other areas, the tension between us increased to such a degree that others close to us began to notice it. I knew that something must be done, but I also felt that my conscience was clear concerning the situation three years before. Of course we had had our disagreements since then, but they were nothing major—I thought! Finally I decided that the logical thing to do was to get together with him and discuss it.

"One evening after a board meeting I asked if I could see him for a minute in my office. I said, 'You know my relationship with you is very important, but I feel like there is a barrier between my spirit and your spirit. I would like to discuss it with you.' His response surprised me. He said he did not want to discuss it! I told him if I had offended him in any way, I wanted to clear it up. He said he did not have time to go into it, and after admitting he had a bad attitude toward me, he left. Here I had tried to reconcile the relationship, yet he was unwilling to meet with me and discuss it.

"My next response was to seek counsel from two close friends in positions of spiritual leadership. They recommended that two elders should go and approach this deacon about his bad attitude, following the steps given in Matthew 18. I agreed. There was, however, one minor complication in this plan—nobody would go and talk with him about the matter. After two weeks with the situation still unresolved, the tension continued to mount. This man and his wife quit coming to church on Sunday nights. Their conspicuous absence was enough to let the whole church know something was wrong.

"I remembered the material, 'Steps a Pastor Must Take When Members React Against His Ministry.' In looking at the title I thought, 'This is exactly what I need—whatever it says, I'll do it!' I did not know what I was getting into."

1. THANK GOD FOR THE OPPOSITION.

"This step came fairly easily for me. I was used to thanking God for my trials, and this was a real tribulation. As I thanked God, I began to see this as a new opportunity for personal spiritual growth. This freed me up emotionally to follow the next step.

2. SEE THE COMPLAINT FROM THE OTHER'S POINT OF VIEW.

"The flesh doesn't die easily, and this was much more difficult for me. God showed me that my responsibility was not to convict the opposition. Instead, I was to become an example to the flock by following the procedures that they all must take when they receive reproofs in their lives. I saw that I must become an example of humility, a learner, and a servant.

"I must confess I was not used to eating 'humble pie.' Becoming an example of humility was not an easy procedure. The first step toward humility was to concede the fact that there must be some valid reasons for the man's criticism. That was a hard pill to swallow, but God gave me the grace to do it. I knew that I had blind spots that possibly only he could see, so I purposed to confess and remove anything in my life or ministry that conflicted with the message of Scripture or the character of Christ."

3. FIND OUT THE AREAS THAT CAUSED THE CONFLICT AND PRAYERFULLY WORK OUT EXACTLY WHAT TO SAY.

"I was having a hard time discerning the root cause of our conflict, so I decided to have a day of prayer and fasting. That afternoon, after reflecting on my relationship with this brother in Christ, I listed no less than nine conflicts we had had over the past six years. Then God really convicted me about my wrong attitudes. I realized that in trying to reconcile our relationship, I had only been dealing with surface problems. I had never dealt with my wrong attitudes of pride, selfishness, and an independent spirit which had led to disrespect and insensitivity toward this brother. God also showed me that I had approached him in the wrong way that last time I had tried to get together with him."

4. ASK FOR FORGIVENESS.

"After determining the right words to say when asking his forgiveness, I called to make an appointment with him and his wife. Using the sample given in the material I said, 'God has been prompting me to do a lot of personal re-evaluation, and I now see that I need your counsel in certain matters. Could I meet with you and your wife for this?' His response again surprised me—he said that he would! We then arranged a meeting for two days later.

"I approached the appointment with much fear and trembling. I knew that I needed not only to humble myself by asking his forgiveness for my wrong attitudes, but that I also needed to become a learner by asking him to share further areas of my life and ministry that needed improvement. When we got together, I shared about my attitudes and asked his forgiveness. He forgave me."

5. ASK COUNSEL FOR IMPROVEMENT.

"The next step was even more humbling. I asked him, 'Would you please share with me any areas in my life that you see need improving?' Tears rolled down my face as he explained how my wrong attitudes had caused him to lose respect for me as his pastor and had prevented him from responding to my preaching and teaching. As he shared these things in love (not to hurt me), I knew that God had chosen him to help me work on these areas. I then asked if we could meet together on a regular basis to see that these areas were improved. He agreed. After reconfirming our love and commitment to one another, I left his house really encouraged with deep joy in my heart.

"I can now say this brother is a close friend once again. The relationship has been restored and we have a new love and devotion for one another I never thought possible. I am still in this process of becoming an example of a servant and God is continuing to show me many new areas to work on. How I praise the Lord for teaching me that the principles of Scripture really work when properly appled!"

A Pastor

WHAT GIVES US THE CONFIDENCE TO FACE CRITICISM?

4 _____

_____

"But let every man prove his own work, and then shall he have rejoicing in himself alone, and not in another" (Galatians 6:4).

How can we confirm that we are in God's will?

• _____

"The steps of a good man are ordered by the Lord: and he delighteth in his way" (Psalm 37:23).

Why should criticism not surprise us?

• _____

_____

"Beloved, think it not strange concerning the fiery trial which is to try you, as though some strange thing happened unto you" (I Peter 4:12).

Why is it essential to humble ourselves when criticism comes?

• _____

"But he giveth more grace. Wherefore he saith, God resisteth the proud, but giveth grace unto the humble" (James 4:6).

How can criticism benefit our life message?

• _____

_____

"It is good for me that I have been afflicted; that I might learn thy statutes" (Psalm 119:71).

When we are overwhelmed with criticism, how can we follow David's example in responding to it?

5 _____

_____

"And David was greatly distressed; for the people spake of stoning him, because the soul of all the people was grieved, every man for his sons and for his daughters: but David encouraged himself in the Lord his God" (I Samuel 30:6).

How can we overcome discouragement in the morning?

• _____

_____

How can we remove the pressure of criticism at night so that we can get a good night's sleep?

* _____

_____

"My soul shall be satisfied as with marrow and fatness; and my mouth shall praise thee with joyful lips: When I remember thee upon my bed, and meditate on thee in the night watches" (Psalm 63:5-6).

How can we find courageous people to strengthen our hearts?

* _____

_____

MARTIN LUTHER
1483-1546

JOHN WESLEY
1703-1791

HUDSON TAYLOR
1832-1905

FANNY CROSBY
1820-1915

A list of biographies in Scripture is given in Hebrews, Chapter 11.

Why is it always too soon to quit?

* _____

_____

_____

"Therefore, my beloved brethren, be ye steadfast, unmoveable, always abounding in the work of the Lord, forasmuch as ye know that your labour is not in vain in the Lord" (I Corinthians 15:58).

"And let us not be weary in well-doing: for in due season we shall reap, if we faint not" (Galatians 6:9).

Why is fear so destructive to a Christian?

6 _____

_____

"For God hath not given us the spirit of fear; but of power, and of love, and of a sound mind" (II Timothy 1:7).

What will happen if we allow fear to lodge in our hearts?

* _____

_____

"For the thing which I greatly feared is come upon me, and that which I was afraid of is come unto me. I was not in safety, neither had I rest, neither was I quiet; yet trouble came" (Job 3:25-26).

How often does God warn us not to fear?

* _____

"The fear of man bringeth a snare: but whoso putteth his trust in the Lord shall be safe" (Proverbs 29:25).

How do we conquer and remove fear?

* _____

_____

☐ *Darkness -*

"I will both lay me down in peace, and sleep: for thou, Lord, only makest me dwell in safety" (Psalm 4:8).

☐ *Loss of reputation -*

"Looking unto Jesus the author and finisher of our faith; who for the joy that was set before him

NOTES

DIAGRAMS

endured the cross, depising the shame, and is set down at the right hand of the throne of God" (Hebrews 12:2).

☐ *Loss of job -*

"I have been young, and now am old; yet have I not seen the righteous forsaken, nor his seed begging bread" (Psalm 37:25).

How can we avoid the trap of using carnal efforts to prove that we are right?

7 _____

_____

"But the God of all grace, who hath called us unto his eternal glory by Christ Jesus, after that ye have suffered a while, make you perfect, stablish, strengthen, settle you. To him be glory and dominion for ever and ever. Amen" (I Peter 5:10–11).

How can we expect God to confirm our message?

• _____

_____

"Wherefore lift up the hands which hang down, and the feeble knees; And make straight paths for your feet, lest that which is lame be turned out of the way; but let it rather be healed" (Hebrews 12:12–13).

What is God's method of putting critics to shame?

• _____

_____

"Having your conversation honest among the Gentiles: that, whereas they speak against you as evildoers, they may by your good works, which they shall behold, glorify God in the day of visitation" (I Peter 2:12).

Why must we have patience in responding to unjust criticism?

• _____

_____

"He that goeth forth and weepeth, bearing precious seed, shall doubtless come again with rejoicing, bringing his sheaves with him" (Psalm 126:6).

HOW TO DEAL WITH DISCOURAGEMENT

Discouragement is one of Satan's most effective weapons against Christians.

Firey Dart

Faith

WHAT IS DISCOURAGEMENT?

> "Discourage: To deprive of confidence, hope, or spirit; dishearten;

THREE STAGES OF DISCOURAGMENT

1 MILD

Minor problems or pressures which affect our emotions.

2 STRONG

Major problems or pressures which affect our spirit so that others will notice.

Note: Those closest to you may think that they caused your discouragement unless you assure them otherwise.

3 DISABLING

Overwhelming problems or pressures which drain us of spiritual, mental, emotional, and physical strength. Our heart melts within us, and we have no desire, energy, or ability to go on.

THE CAUSES OF DISCOURAGEMENT

• At the base of every discouragement is a lie from Satan. Fear, unbelief, bitterness, self-pity, or condemnation are all based on Satan's lies.

• The root cause—putting down the shield of faith. (See Ephesians 6:16.)

When we lose sight of God's ways or our resources in Christ, we remove the spiritual protection which Christ provided for us in the shield of faith.

STEPS TO CONQUER DISCOURAGEMENT

There are several basic steps which must be followed in order to have victory over discouragement. Here is a suggested list of these steps:

1 REMOVE ANY GUILT

Guilt is removed by repentance and confession. (See I John 1:8–9.)

Satan will try to use past failures to keep us from removing guilt and dealing with discouragement. David faced this difficulty with Absalom. Because of his past failure with Bathsheba, it was difficult for David to discipline Absalom.

2 TAKE UP THE SHIELD OF FAITH

"Above all, taking the shield of faith . . . to quench all the fiery darts of the wicked [one]" (Ephesians 6:16).

HOW DO WE TAKE UP THE "SHIELD OF FAITH"?

By quoting God's truth when we recognize Satan's lies, we take up the shield of faith. (See II Corinthians 10:5.)

The following are some of Satan's fiery darts which we must verbally respond to with God's truth:

LIES	GOD'S TRUTH
• God has left us.	*". . . I will never leave . . ."* (Hebrews 13:5).
• No good will come from this.	*". . . All things work together . . ."* (Romans 8:28–29).
• People hurt us.	*". . . We wrestle not . . ."* (Ephesians 6:12).
• God is punishing us.	*"For whom the Lord loveth . . ."* (Hebrews 12:6–11).
• We are weak.	*". . . My strength is made . . ."* (II Corinthians 12:9).

3 ENCOURAGE OUR HEART IN THE LORD

David's greatest calamity came just a few days before he was established as the king. (See I Samuel 30:6.) Satan often brings to us the greatest discouragements just before God fulfills our expectation. It is for this reason that He warns us not to give up. *". . . We shall reap, if we faint not"* (Galatians 6:9).

HOW DO WE ENCOURAGE OUR HEART IN THE LORD?

• We let God's Spirit commune with our spirit through the Psalms.

We must not allow our mind, will, or emotions (soul) to communicate with our spirit, but rather take every effort to have God's Spirit (through His Word) communicate to our spirit.

DISCOURAGED BY	QUOTE
• Failure and sin	Psalm 32, 51
• Rejection by friends	Psalm 35, 55
• Slander against us	Psalm 38, 59

• We meditate on God's truth every night as we go to sleep.

It is at night that we are usually faced with the most intense discouragement.

4 ESTABLISH A PLACE TO BE ALONE WITH GOD

We need to establish a "Bethel" for personal times to be with the Lord. (See Luke 6:12.) It must be away from the telephone, work, or other pressures.

5 REMOVE OURSELF FROM FEARFUL PEOPLE AS MUCH AS POSSIBLE

One of God's requirements for service in the army of Israel was not to be fearful. (See Deuteronomy 20:8; Judges 7:3.) A fearful person will spread his fear among others and make them fearful.

6 READ BIOGRAPHIES OF GREAT CHRISTIANS

We will discover that every person whom God used mightily went through times of great discouragement. God's work in their lives provides an important overview for us. We are able to see our trouble from a bigger perspective and discover God's purposes, comfort, and direction. (See II Corinthians 1:4.)

7 AVOID MAKING MAJOR DECISIONS DURING TIMES OF DISCOURAGEMENT

It is so easy for Satan to get us to make major decisions during times when we are not thinking clearly or responding by faith. Never doubt in the darkness what God has shown you in the light.

"And let us not be weary in well doing: for in due season we shall reap, if we faint not" (Galatians 6:9).

8 OVERCOME THE PRIDE OF NOT TELLING OUR AUTHORITIES, FAMILY, OR FRIENDS THAT WE ARE DISCOURAGED AND NEED THEIR PRAYERS

Sometimes we feel reluctant to tell others that we are discouraged. We want others to believe that we are strong and able to quickly overcome setbacks. However, this can be pride in our life. Our honesty in sharing needs will help others to realize that they are not the only ones who experience discouragement. As we humble ourself, God will give us more grace, and our response will be a living example to those who are praying for us.

9 FOCUS ON GOD'S REPUTATION

When we are discouraged, it is very important to evaluate whose reputation will suffer—ours or God's. (See Matthew 6:9.) If our reputation suffers, it means that our concerns are for our program or that we are in charge. If we can assure God that He led us to do what we are doing and it is His reputation and Word that will be blasphemed, we can then confidently expect Him to show Himself strong on our behalf. We need to always make sure that we are doing God's work in God's way.

10 FOCUS ON OUR POSITION IN CHRIST

· Consider what Christ endured in order to glorify God and to secure our salvation. (See Hebrews 12:1-17.)

• Know your resources.

Because we are in Christ, we are able to enter into His victory over Satan. We can accomplish this victory by quoting Romans 6:1-11 and using the word *discouragement* for the sin: "What shall we say then, shall we continue *to be discouraged* that grace may abound? God forbid. How shall we who are dead to *Satan's discouragement* live any longer therein?"

11 OFFER THE SACRIFICE OF THANKSGIVING AND PRAISE TO GOD

It is important for us to recall God's blessings to us and thank Him for what He has done. (See I Thessalonians 5:18.) When King Jehoshaphat and the army sang and praised the Lord, God set an ambush against their enemy. (See II Chronicles 20:21-22.) There is spiritual power over Satan in audibly praising God.

12 REMEMBER THE PRINCIPLE OF THE BIRTH, DEATH, AND FULFILLMENT OF A VISION

• God will give us a vision of how we can be effectively used by Him.

• God will then allow us to experience the death of a vision to build character in our life.

• God will then fulfill His vision through us in a supernatural way.

13 DISCERN HOW GOD CAN USE OUR PROBLEMS OR PRESSURES FOR HIS GOOD

Further insights on how to deal with discouragement are contained in the next section of material which deals with adversity. Listed are sixteen benefits that we receive when God takes us through adversity to bring about His purpose in our lives. (See Romans 8:28-29.)

IDENTIFY AND AVOID DISCOURAGEMENT WHICH COMES BECAUSE OF "BLIND SPOTS"

One day I listened as a young couple argued. The wife was accusing her husband of flirting with other girls. He was vigorously denying it. After talking with the husband, I could see what the problem was. He had a "blindspot" and was not aware of it.

1. God has a "norm" or standard of behavior for each one of us in every area of our life.

NORM OF BEHAVIOR

- In morality
- In obedience
- In gratefulness
- In humility

Violating God's Norm

"BLINDSPOT"

He could not see it because his focus was on what he used to be rather than on what he should be.

Seeing God's Norm

Seeing Husband's Norm

Wife

Husband

"Great Improvement"

2. When the husband mentioned above was in high school, he greatly violated God's norm in his moral life.

LOWERED NORM OF MORALITY

3. Following his schooling, he repented of his immoral way of life and purposed to live a Godly life. He looked back on what he used to be and was encouraged with his improvement.

- Every one of us has blind spots, and it is essential that we have various intimate friends who have the freedom to tell us what they are. *"Faithful are the wounds of a friend . . ."* (Proverbs 27:6). *"Iron sharpeneth iron; so a man sharpeneth the countenance of his friend"* (Proverbs 27:17).

HOW TO UNDERSTAND ADVERSITY

> *Our first response to adversity should not be to try to remove it, but to allow it to reveal our true weakness.*

WHAT ARE GOD'S PURPOSES FOR ALLOWING ADVERSITY?

Adversity can be our greatest motivation for spiritual growth or our deadliest means of discouragement. The difference depends on our understanding of God's purposes through adversity.

1 ADVERSITY IS GOD'S WAY OF GETTING OUR ATTENTION

The "cares of this world" are God's stiffest competition for our time, attention, and affections. They choke out the Word of God and drown out the voice of His Holy Spirit. (See Matthew 13:18–23.)

While we are busy with our plans, goals, projects, and friendships, God patiently reminds us: *". . . I have spoken unto you, rising early and speaking; but ye hearkened not unto me"* (Jeremiah 35:14).

When adversity comes, we are suddenly faced with problems and pressures that are too big for us to resolve. Our inward response should be, *"Unto thee, O Lord, do I lift up my soul. O my God, I trust in thee: let me not be ashamed, let not mine enemies triumph over me"* (Psalm 25:1–2).

As adversity continues and our human strength is drained, Christ's invitation becomes more and more attractive. *"Come unto me, all ye that labour and are heavy laden, and I will give you rest"* (Matthew 11:28).

God's ultimate purpose in getting our attention is to conform us to the image of Christ. On the basis of this purpose, all adversity works together for our good. (See Romans 8:28–29.) Through it we learn of Christ, Who is meek and lowly and Whose burden is light.

2 ADVERSITY IS OUR ASSURANCE THAT GOD LOVES US

"For whom the Lord loveth he chasteneth, and scourgeth every son whom he receiveth. If ye endure chastening, God dealeth with you as with sons; for what son is he whom the father chasteneth not" (Hebrews 12:6–7).

"For they verily for a few days chastened us after their own pleasure; but he for our profit, that we might be partakers of his holiness. Now no chastening for the present seemeth to be joyous, but grievous: nevertheless afterward it yieldeth the peaceable fruit of righteousness unto them which are exercised thereby" (Hebrews 12:10–11).

When we recognize God's love in adversity, we are able to *". . . lift up the hands which hang down, and the feeble knees; And make straight paths for your feet, lest that which is lame be turned out of the way; but let it rather be healed"* (Hebrews 12:12–13).

3 ADVERSITY IS GOD'S CALL FOR SELF-EXAMINATION

"For if we would judge ourselves, we should not be judged. But when we are judged, we are chastened of the Lord, that we should not be condemned with the world" (I Corinthians 11:31–32).

"As many as I love, I rebuke and chasten: be zealous therefore, and repent" (Revelation 3:19).

God requires that we search out, confess, and forsake every sin. *"He that covereth his sins shall not prosper: but whoso confesseth and forsaketh them shall have mercy"* (Proverbs 28:13).

God established the regular observance of the Lord's table as the time and place for self-examination. When this is neglected or abused, God may give physical adversity as a further motivation for self-examination. *"But let a man examine himself, and so let him eat of that bread, and drink of that cup. For he that eateth and drinketh unworthily, eateth and drinketh damnation to himself, not discerning the Lord's body. For this cause many are weak and sickly among you, and many sleep"* (I Corinthians 11:28–30).

Self-examination must take place in God's Word. For example, if things are not going well for us, the reason may be that we dishonored our parents. *"Honour thy father and mother . . . That it may be well with thee, and thou mayest live long on the earth"* (Ephesians 6:2–3).

If it seems that evil will not depart from our household, it is possibly because we have rewarded evil to those who did good to us: *"Whoso rewardeth evil for good, evil shall not depart from his house"* (Proverbs 17:13).

4 ADVERSITY IS GOD'S WAY OF CONQUERING OUR PRIDE

The adversity of contention reveals pride. *"Only by pride cometh contention . . ."* (Proverbs 13:10).

The adversity of destruction is the consequence of pride. *"Pride goeth before destruction, and an haughty spirit before a fall"* (Proverbs 16:18).

The adversity of shame is God's means of humbling us. *"When pride cometh, then cometh shame: but with the lowly is wisdom"* (Proverbs 11:2).

"For whosoever exalteth himself shall be abased; and he that humbleth himself shall be exalted" (Luke 14:11).

". . . God resisteth the proud, but giveth grace unto the humble. Submit yourselves therefore to God. Resist the devil, and he will flee from you" (James 4:6–7).

The ultimate event of history will be when every knee shall bow before the Holy God of the universe. (See Philippians 2:10.) The recurring scene in heaven will be of all the redeemed on their faces before the throne of God. (See Revelation 4:10–11.) God wants us to have that attitude of heart now.

5 ADVERSITY IS A REMINDER OF OUR WEAKNESSES

Only as we learn how to glory in our unchangeable features will we be able to experience the power of Christ resting upon us. *". . . There was given to me a thorn in the flesh, the messenger of Satan to buffet me, lest I should be exalted above measure. For this thing I besought the Lord thrice, that it might depart from me. And he said unto me, My grace is sufficient for thee: for my strength is made perfect in weakness. Most gladly therefore will I rather glory in my infirmities, that the power of Christ may rest upon me. Therefore I take pleasure in infirmities,*
in reproaches, in necessities, in persecutions, in distresses for Christ's sake: for when I am weak, then am I strong" (II Corinthians 12:7–10).

"Like as a father pitieth his children, so the Lord pitieth them that fear him. For he knoweth our frame; he remembereth that we are dust" (Psalm 103:13–14).

6 ADVERSITY IS OUR MOTIVATION TO CRY OUT TO GOD

God responds to the cry of His children when they are in adversity. *"The righteous cry, and the Lord heareth, and delivereth them out of all their troubles"* (Psalm 34:17).

Adversity should motivate us to cry out in the right ways:

- We are to cry out to God with our voice. *"I cried unto the Lord with my voice, and he heard me out of his holy hill"* (Psalm 3:4).
- We are to cry out to God daily during adversity. *"Be merciful unto me, O Lord: for I cry unto thee daily"* (Psalm 86:3).
- We are to cry out to God in humility. *". . . He forgetteth not the cry of the humble"* (Psalm 9:12).
- We are to cry out to God with a pure heart. *"If I regard iniquity in my heart, the Lord will not hear me"* (Psalm 66:18).

Our second response to adversity should not be to focus on outward circumstances but to realize that we are dealing with unseen spiritual powers.

7 ADVERSITY IS EVIDENCE OF SPIRITUAL WARFARE

If we do not recognize when adversity is spiritual warfare, we will be overwhelmed and tempted to give up.

When adversity takes the form of confusion, suspicion, and division, spiritual warfare is on.

Paul encouraged Timothy to be strong, courageous, and prepared to be a good soldier.

"Put on the whole armour of God, that ye may be able to stand against the wiles of the devil. For we wrestle not against flesh and blood, but against principalities, against powers, against the rulers of the darkness of this world, against

spiritual wickedness in high places. Wherefore take unto you the whole armour of God, that ye may be able to withstand in the evil day, and having done all, to stand. Stand therefore, having your loins girt about with truth, and having on the breastplate of righteousness; And your feet shod with the preparation of the gospel of peace; Above all, taking the shield of faith, wherewith ye shall be able to quench all the fiery darts of the wicked. And take the helmet of salvation, and the sword of the Spirit, which is the word of God: Praying always with all prayer and supplication in the Spirit, and watching thereunto with all perseverance and supplication for all saints" (Ephesians 6:11–18).

8 ADVERSITY IS GOD'S METHOD OF PURIFYING OUR FAITH

"But without faith it is impossible to please him . . ." (Hebrews 11:6). Faith, however, may need to be tested in the fires of adversity.

". . . Now for a season, if need be, ye are in heaviness through manifold temptations: That the trial of your faith, being much more precious than of gold that perisheth, though it be tried with fire, might be found unto praise and honour and glory at the appearing of Jesus Christ" (I Peter 1:6–7).

Faith is essential for living the Christian life because the ways of God are opposite to the natural inclinations of man. Because of this dichotomy, adversity may come from those who mock God's principles; or it may come because we violate God's principles. In either case, adversity will strengthen our faith.

Patience is another benefit of having our faith purified by the fire of adversity. "Knowing this, that the trying of your faith worketh patience" (James 1:3).

With this kind of faith and patience we can obtain the promises of God. Be ". . . followers of them who through faith and patience inherit the promises" (Hebrews 6:12).

9 ADVERSITY INCREASES OUR HATRED FOR EVIL

When God exposes secret sin, He allows others to see its devastating consequences. In this way, the simple are warned not to be fooled by Satan's focus on ". . . the pleasures of sin [which last] for a season" (Hebrews 11:25).

God wants to focus on the fact that He will not be mocked with our sin. ". . . For whatsoever a man soweth, that shall he also reap. For he that soweth to his flesh shall of the flesh reap corruption; but he that soweth to the Spirit shall of the Spirit reap life everlasting" (Galatians 6:7–8).

Our hatred of evil should increase as we realize how sin robs us of our potential for achieving and enjoying what God had planned for us.

Our hatred of evil should also increase as we see how our sins damage the lives of those whom we love.

Perhaps one of the biggest reasons why we fail to hate evil is that we cannot comprehend its final cost. Adam and Eve might have had second thoughts about disobeying God if they had seen a glimpse of the untold miseries that have resulted from their sin.

10 ADVERSITY IS A REMINDER TO PRAY FOR OUR AUTHORITIES

God teaches that a quiet and peaceable life is related to intercessory prayer for those in authority over us. "I exhort therefore, that, first of all, supplications, prayers, intercessions, and giving of thanks, be made for all men; For kings, and for all that are in authority; that we may lead a quiet and peaceable life in all godliness and honesty" (I Timothy 2:1–2).

Those who are in positions of responsibility provide spiritual protection for those under their care. When there are failures in the life of a leader, the "umbrella of protection" develops "leaks," and Satan is given greater freedom to defeat those who are under that authority.

Even a little leak in a roof can let in a lot of water. For this reason, spiritual leaders are judged by a higher standard. (See James 3:1.)

When we experience the pressures of temptation, we should realize that those who are in authority over us are also undergoing temptations and are in need of our intercessory prayer.

11 ADVERSITY IS A SIGNAL TO RE-EVALUATE PRIORITIES

Wrong priorities may result in much painful adversity, not only for us but also for those who are affected by our lives.

When we fail to spend proper time with the Lord in memorizing His Word, meditating, and praying, we rob others of necessary spiritual encouragement and direction. Instead, we become vulnerable to transgression.

"Fools because of their transgression, and because of their iniquities, are afflicted ... Then they cry unto the Lord in their trouble, and he saveth them out of their distresses" (Psalm 107:17–19).

The means which God uses to save us out of our distresses is His Word. *"He sent his word, and healed them, and delivered them from their destructions"* (Psalm 107:20).

Adversity which comes as a result of having wrong priorities may be the consequence of trying to do more than God intended for us to do. *"It is vain for you to rise up early, to sit up late, to eat the bread of sorrows: for so he giveth his beloved sleep"* (Psalm 127:2).

If we have more projects than we can manage to do in six days, we have assumed more work than God intended. *"Six days shalt thou labour, and do all thy work"* (Exodus 20:9).

12 ADVERSITY IS GOD'S MEANS OF TESTING OUR WORK

Every spiritual house must be tested in order to confirm that it is founded on truth.

"Therefore whosoever heareth these sayings of mine, and doeth them, I will liken him unto a wise man, which built his house upon a rock: And the rain descended [to test the roof], and the floods came [to test the foundation], and the winds blew [to test the structure], and beat upon that house; and it fell not: for it was founded upon a rock. And every one that heareth these sayings of mine, and doeth them not, shall be likened unto a foolish man, which built his house upon the sand: And the rain descended, and the floods came, and the winds blew, and beat upon that house; and it fell: and great was the fall of it" (Matthew 7:24–27).

"... The fire shall try every man's work of what sort it is. If any man's work abide which he hath built thereupon, he shall receive a reward. If any man's work shall be burned, he shall suffer loss: but he himself shall be saved; yet so as by fire" (I Corinthians 3:13–15).

13 ADVERSITY IS GOD'S WAY OF SIFTING OUR FRIENDSHIPS

Adversity will always test friendships. It will reveal which friends are concerned about getting and which friends are concerned about giving.

A true friend loves at all times—especially during a time of adversity. (See Proverbs 17:17.) Jesus explained this kind of friendship in His parable of the good Samaritan. The Samaritan's commitment to his neighbor, who had fallen among thieves, continued until all of the neighbor's needs were met. (See Luke 10:30–37.)

In contrast to this parable is the account of the prodigal son. As long as he was spending his inheritance, the son had many friends. However, when the money ran out and the hardships came, he found himself without friends. (See Luke 15:12–16.)

A true friendship is richly illustrated in the story of David and Jonathan. Their hearts were knit together in love, but then adversity came to David. Jonathan could have chosen many valid reasons for rejecting David, but instead he stood by him right up to the end of his life. Jonathan warned and protected David. He encouraged and befriended him, he risked his life for him, and he accepted him as the one who would be king in his place.

The depth of love between David and Jonathan was expressed in David's anguish at Jonathan's death. *"I am distressed for thee, my brother Jonathan: very pleasant hast thou been unto me: thy love to me was wonderful, passing the love of women"* (II Samuel 1:26).

> **Our third response to adversity should not be to live for Christ in our own efforts, but to realize that Christ must live in us through the power of His Holy Spirit.**

14 ADVERSITY IS GOD'S CALL TO IDENTIFY WITH CHRIST

One of the ultimate purposes of adversity is to cause us to desire more of Christ's power.

Paul suffered the loss of all things in order that he might win more of Christ and experience the power of Christ's resurrection. *"That I may know him, and the power of his resurrection, and the fellowship of his sufferings, being made conformable unto his death"* (Philippians 3:10).

This power is available to every Christian through *". . . the spirit of wisdom and revelation in the knowledge of him"* (Ephesians 1:17).

The "knowledge" referred to here is further explained in Romans 6, 7, and 8. At first, this knowledge appears to be unrealistic because it does not match our experience. However, as we accept it by faith and begin to live in its truth, the spiritual eyes of our understanding become enlightened and we begin to experience *". . . the exceeding greatness of his power to us-ward who believe, according to the working of his mighty power, Which he wrought in Christ, when he raised him from the dead, and set him at his own right hand in the heavenly places"* (Ephesians 1:19–20).

God's power becomes a reality within our lives when we enter into the truths of Romans 6, 7, and 8.

In Romans 6, we learn how to *know* that we are crucified with Christ, how to *reckon* ourselves dead unto sin and alive unto God, and how to *yield* ourselves to God and our members as instruments of righteousness to Him. (See Romans 6:6, 11, 13.)

In Romans 7, we discover a new problem: We are still overcome by the demands of the law. We try to live according to God's principles, but we find that we cannot do it. We learn that our death in Christ also caused us to die to the law so that we are free to be controlled by God's Spirit in order to bring forth spiritual fruit. (See Romans 7:4, 6.)

In Romans 8, we learn our source of power over sin: the indwelling Spirit of God based on our position in Christ. We see that by walking in God's Spirit rather than in our own flesh, God is able to fulfill the righteousness of the law in us. (See Romans 8:2–4.)

15 ADVERSITY IS MOTIVATION FOR OPEN ACCOUNTABILITY

God's key to life, peace, wisdom, and lasting achievement is a moment-by-moment awareness of our accountability for all of our words, thoughts, actions, attitudes, and motives.

This continuing awareness is actually the fear of the Lord. It is the beginning of wisdom and the fountain of life. (See Proverbs 9:10; 14:27.)

When we lose our awareness of God, we become vulnerable to thinking and acting as if God did not exist. In response, God raises up painful reminders on a human level. He illustrates this with His nation, Israel.

". . . Because that this people hath transgressed my covenant which I commanded their fathers, and have not hearkened unto my voice; I also will not henceforth drive out any from before them of the nations which Joshua left when he died: That through them I may prove Israel, whether they will keep the way of the Lord to walk therein, as their fathers did keep it, or not" (Judges 2:20–22).

16 ADVERSITY IS OUR PREPARATION TO COMFORT OTHERS

"Blessed be God, even the Father of our Lord Jesus Christ, the Father of mercies, and the God of all comfort; Who comforteth us in all our tribulation, that we may be able to comfort them which are in any trouble, by the comfort wherewith we ourselves are comforted of God. For as the sufferings of Christ abound in us, so our consolation also aboundeth by Christ" (II Corinthians 1:3–5).

"We are troubled on every side, yet not distressed; we are perplexed, but not in despair; Persecuted, but not forsaken; cast down, but not destroyed; Always bearing about in the body the dying of the Lord Jesus, that the life also of Jesus might be made manifest in our body" (II Corinthians 4:8–10).

"So then death worketh in us, but life in you. . . . For which cause we faint not; but though our outward man perish, yet the inward man is renewed day by day" (II Corinthians 4:12–16).

NOTES

DIAGRAMS

NOTES   **DIAGRAMS**

NOTES

DIAGRAMS

NOTES

DIAGRAMS

NOTES

DIAGRAMS

NOTES

DIAGRAMS